Table of Contents

My Name

first

middle

last

Draw yourself here.

a to z

Start at **a** and go to **z**.
You must go in alphabetical order.

start

a	b	c	n	r	t	o	s
q	u	d	e	f	p	l	v
h	p	o	w	g	h	m	k
b	q	n	m	x	i	f	j
g	r	y	l	k	j	d	e
c	s	t	u	b	a	m	r
o	e	a	v	w	x	y	z

stop

Now write the letters in order.

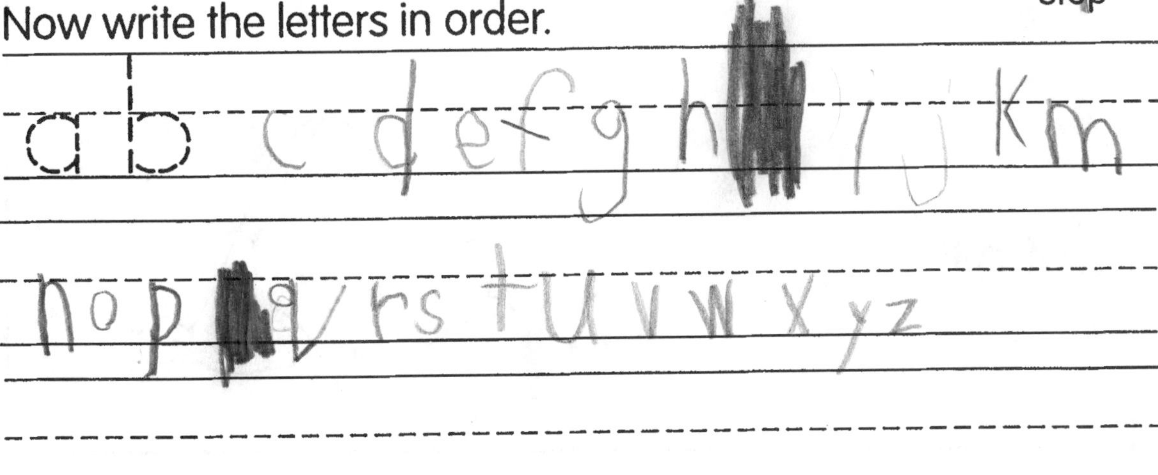

Read.
Match.

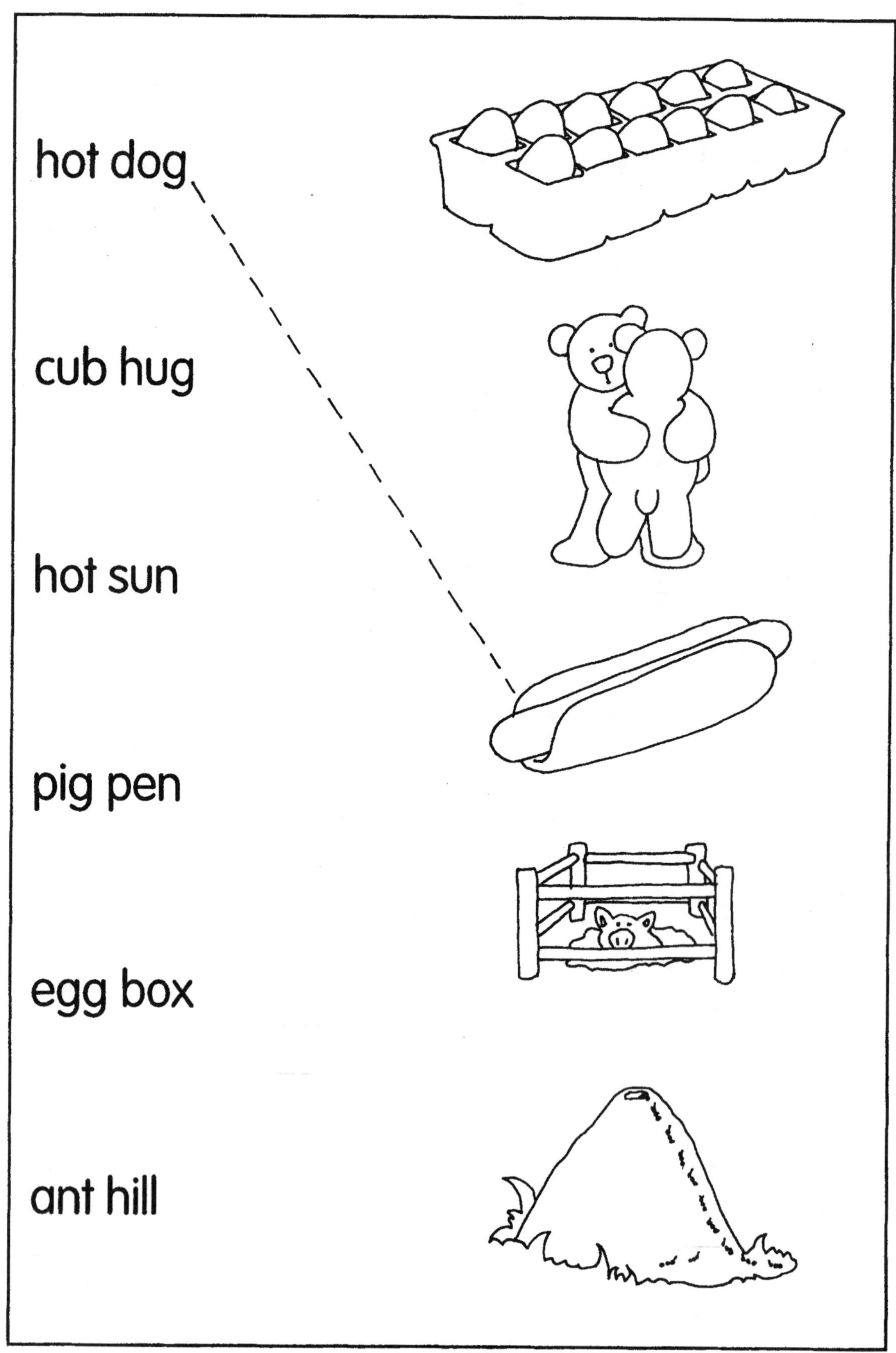

hot dog
cub hug
hot sun
pig pen
egg box
ant hill

Copy this Poem

Fuzzy Wuzzy was a bear.
Fuzzy Wuzzy had no hair.
Fuzzy wasn't very fuzzy.
Was he?

Find the Words

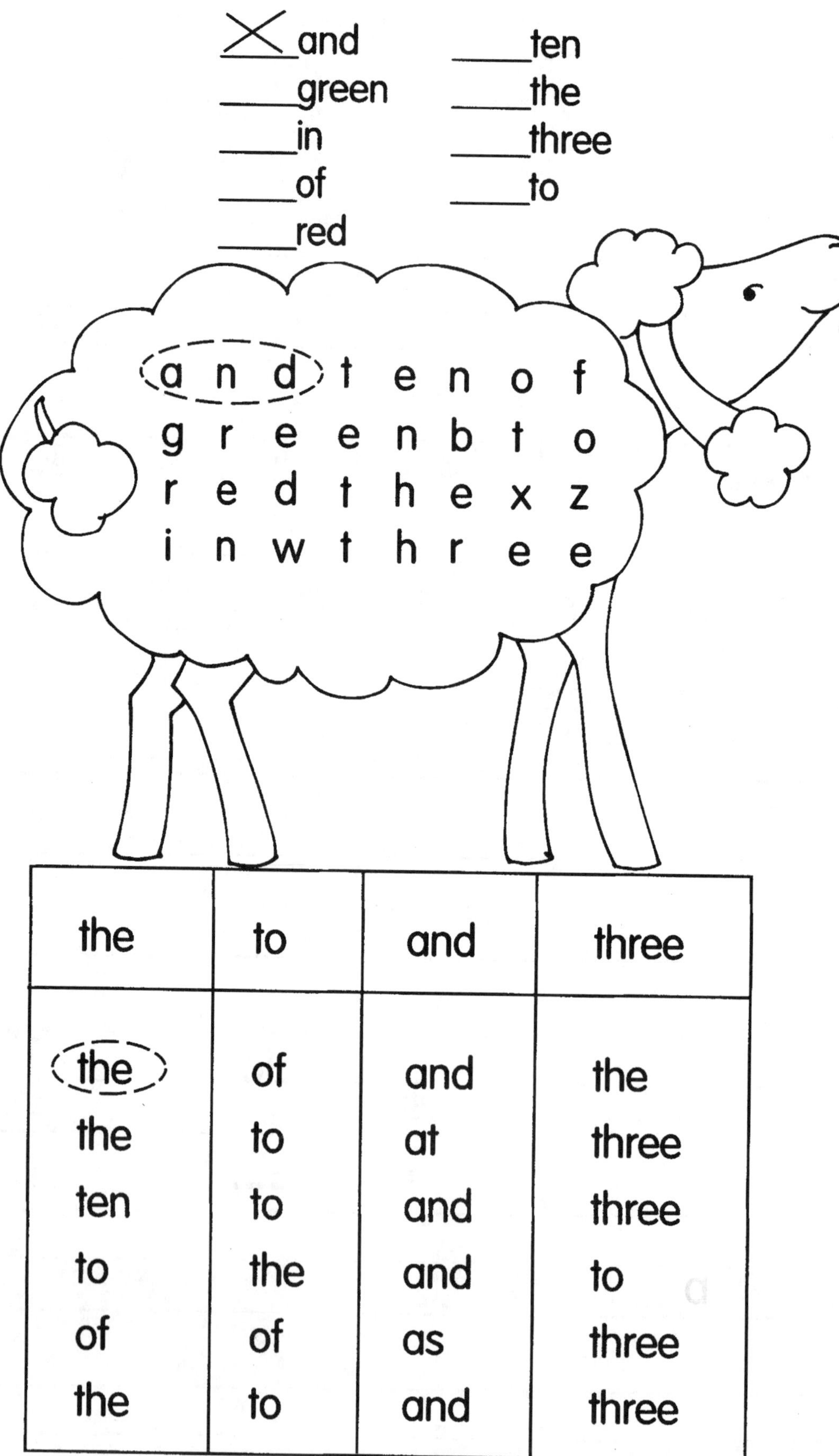

X and ___ ten
___ green ___ the
___ in ___ three
___ of ___ to
___ red

a n d	t e n o f		
g r e e n b t o			
r e d t h e x z			
i n w t h r e e

the	to	and	three
the	of	and	the
the	to	at	three
ten	to	and	three
to	the	and	to
of	of	as	three
the	to	and	three

Identifying key vocabulary words

How to Eat Pizza

1. Read 2. Cut 3. Paste in order

	1
	2
	3
	4

Bite into the pizza.	Lick your lips!
Pick up the biggest part.	Cut the pizza into parts.

What do you like on your pizza?

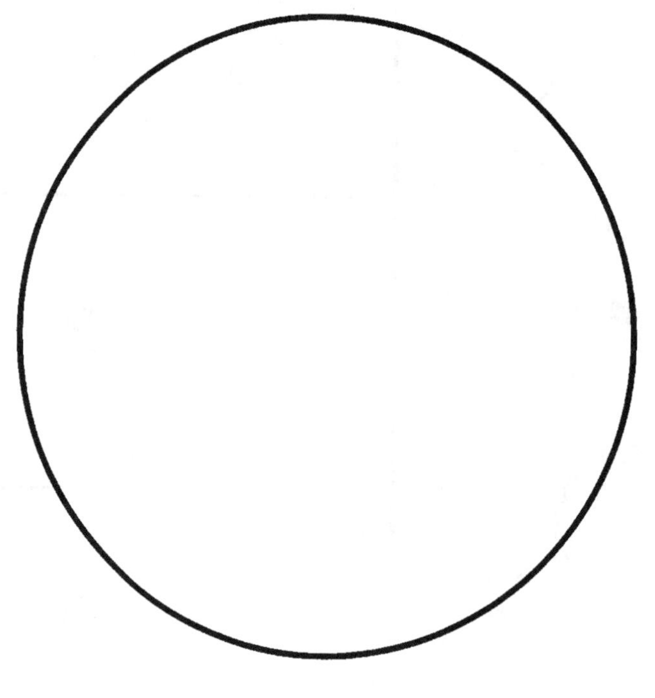

Parents: Point to each word and say it for your child. Have him/her repeat the word back to you.

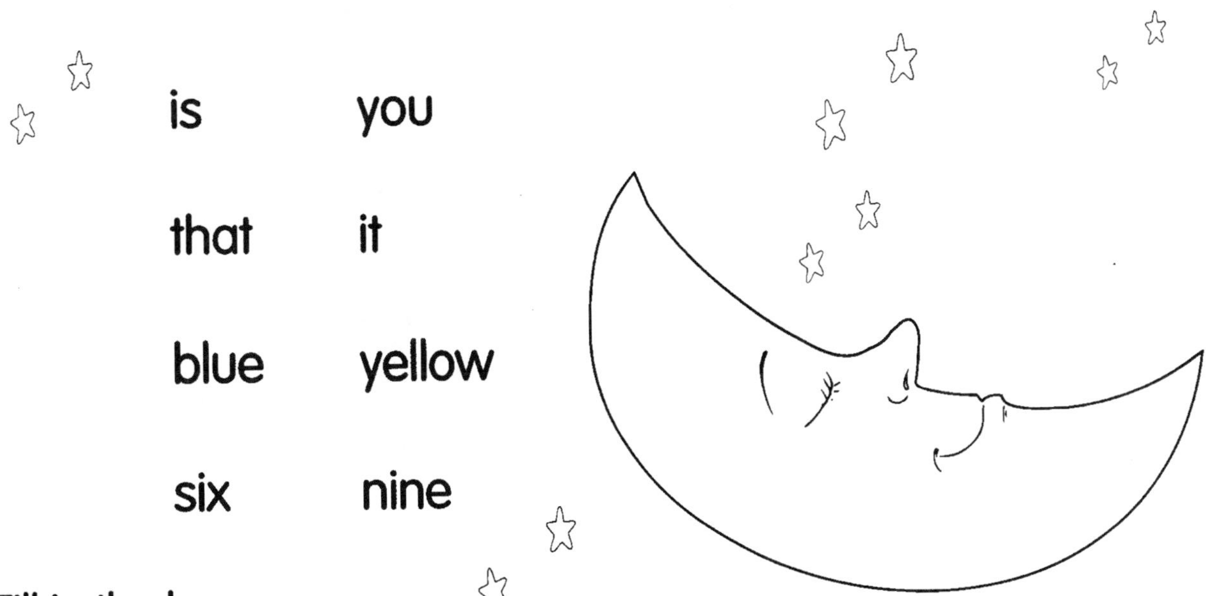

is you

that it

blue yellow

six nine

Fill in the boxes:

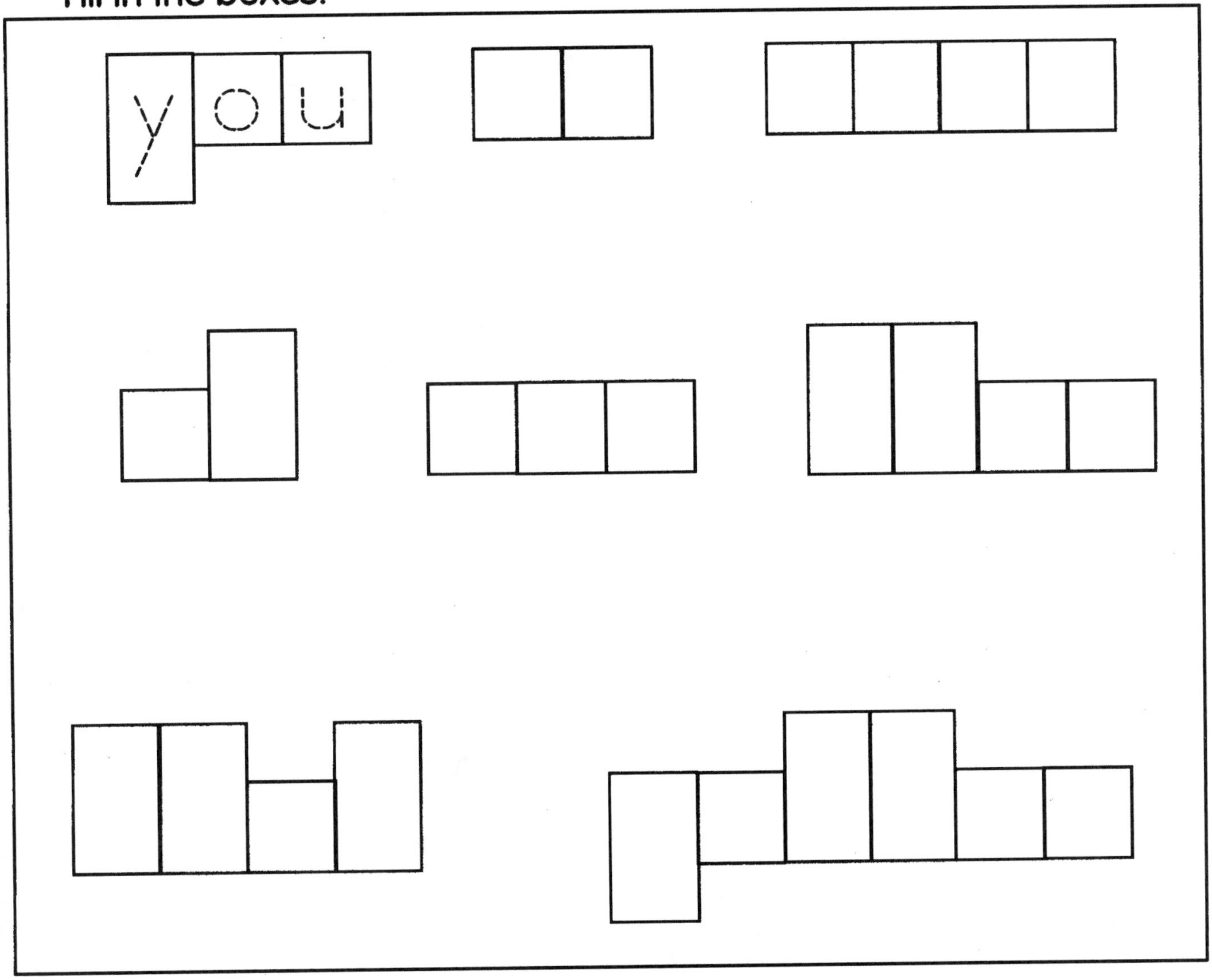

y o u

Trace.
Match.

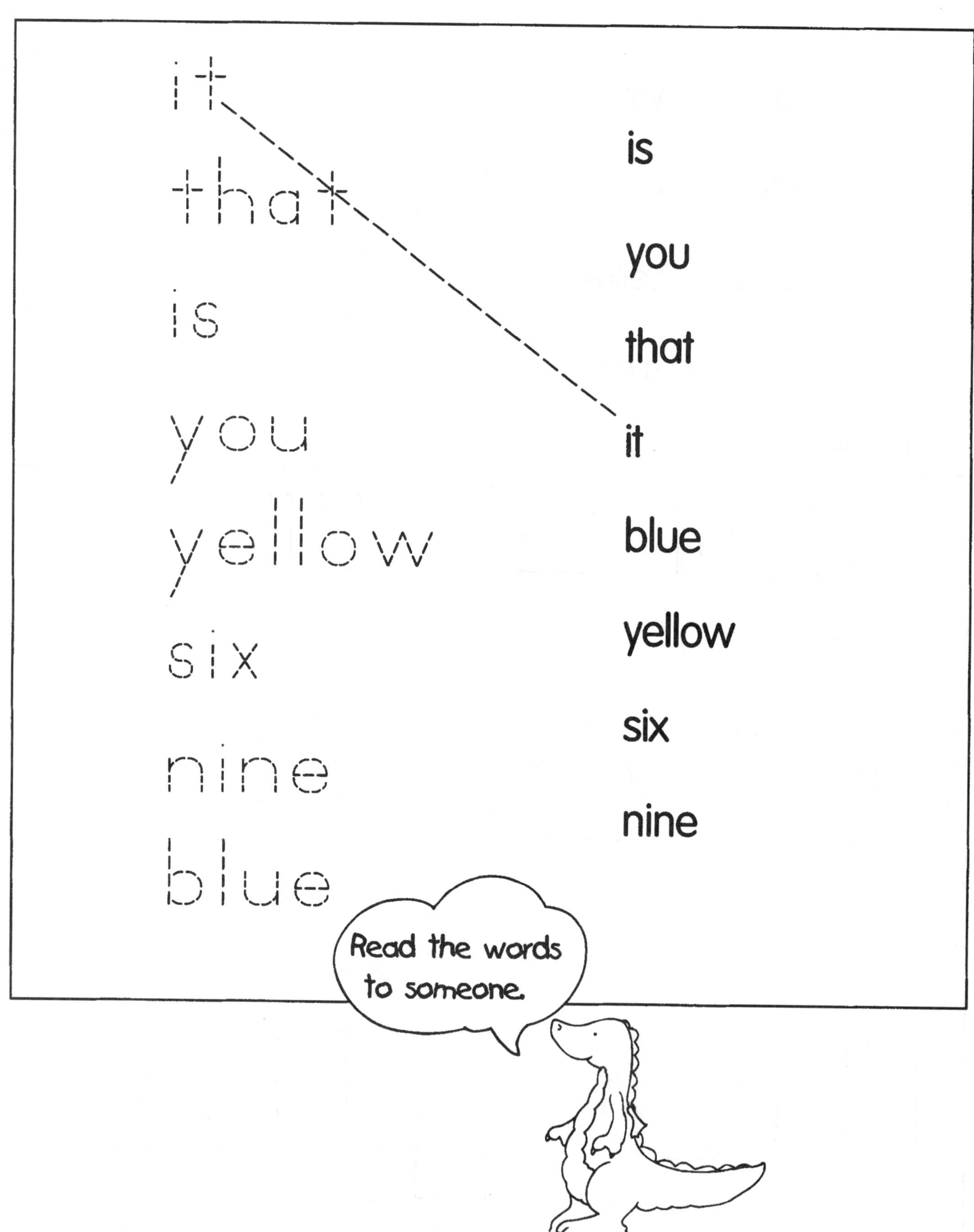

Identifying key vocabulary words

Unscramble the words.

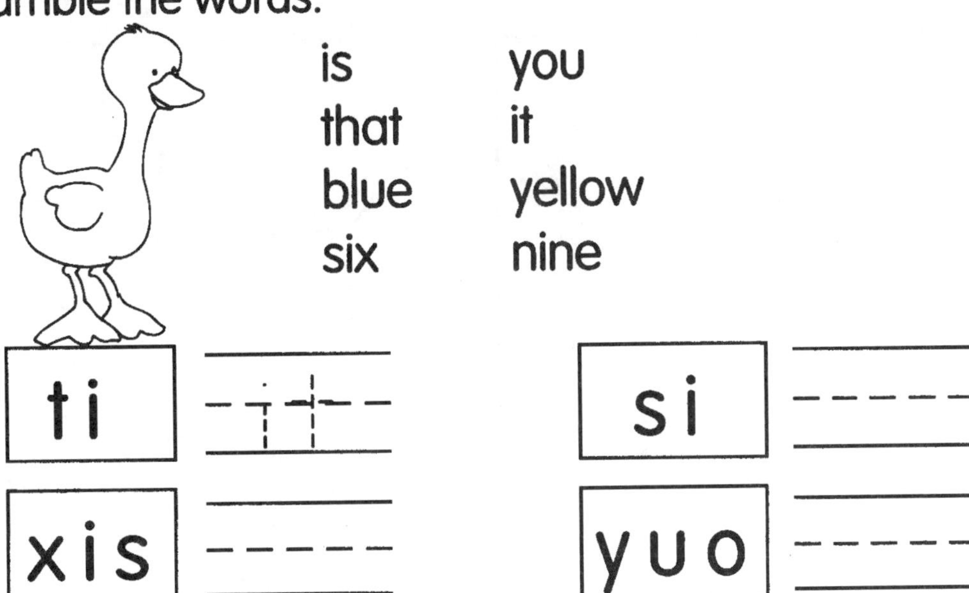

is that blue six

you it yellow nine

Match.

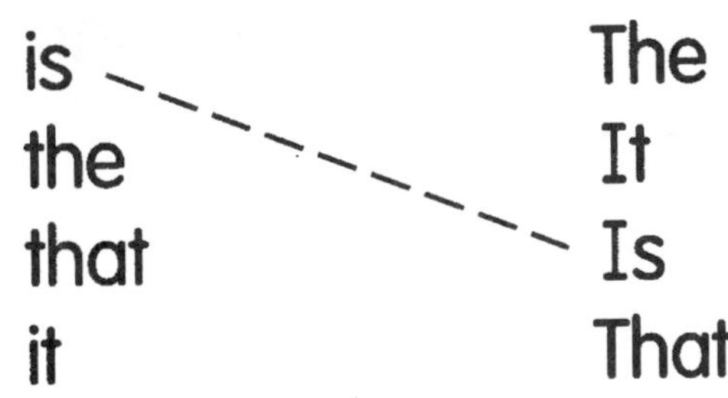

Draw.

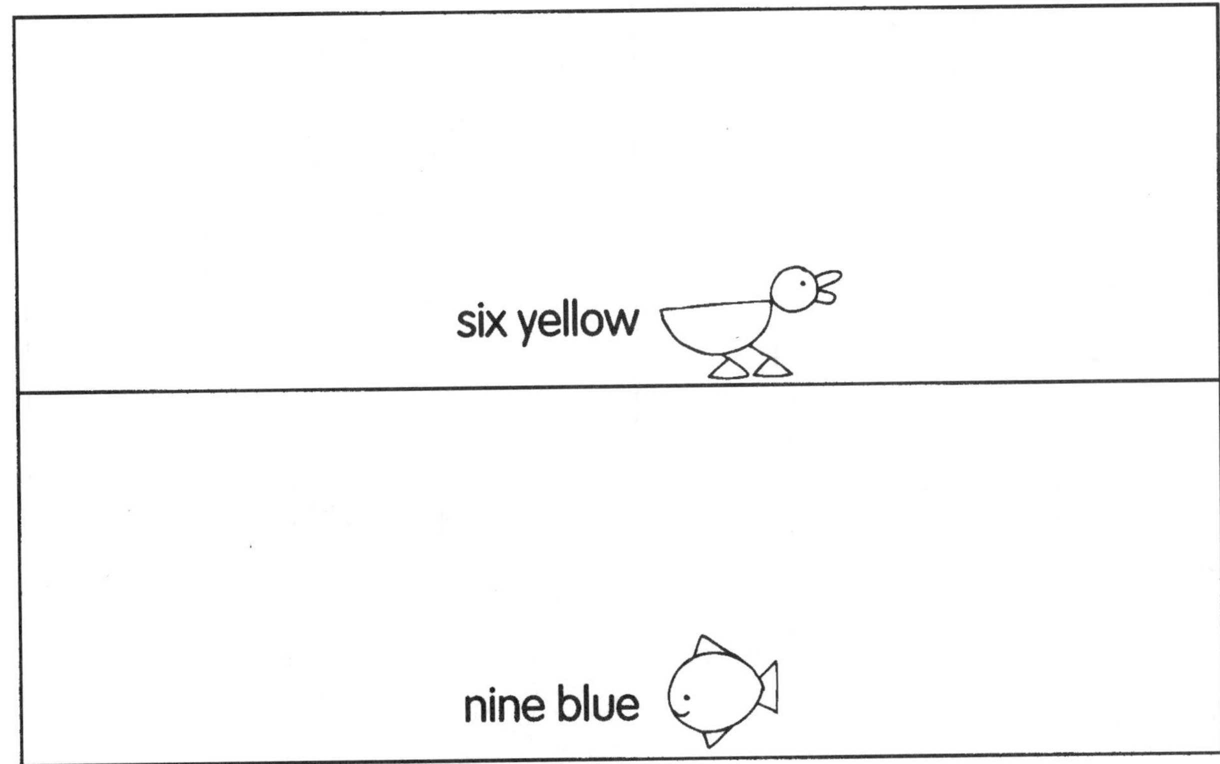

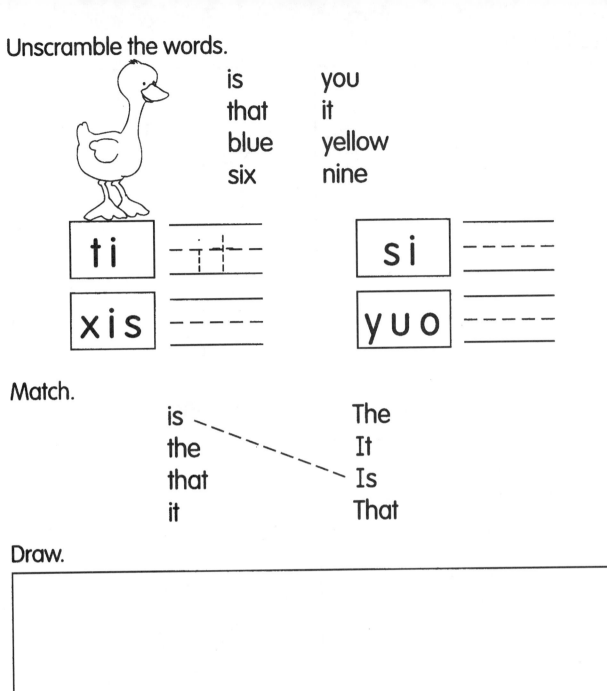

Read and color.

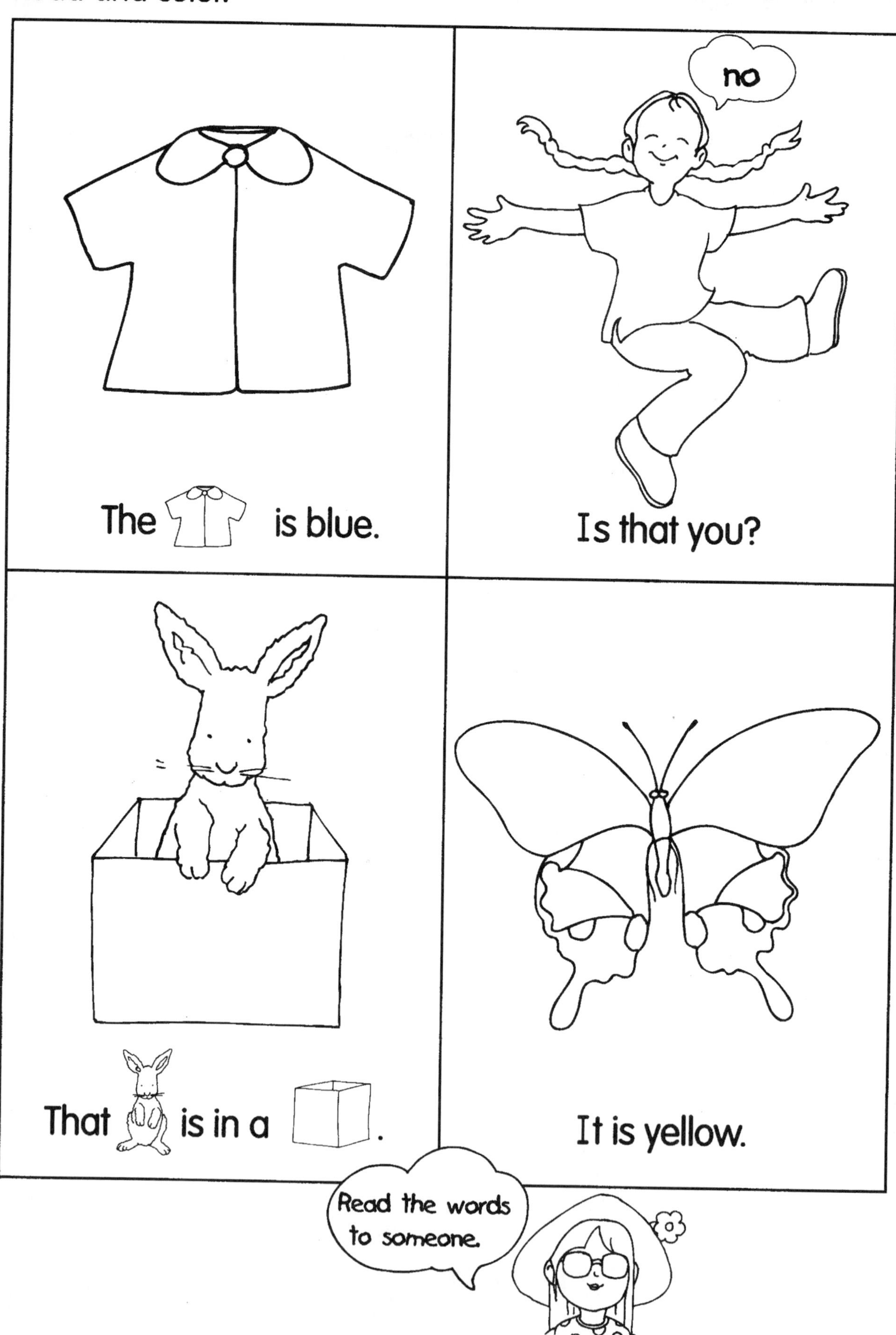

no
The is blue.
Is that you?
That is in a .
It is yellow.
Read the words to someone.

Parents: Explain to your child that words at the beginning of a sentence start with a capital letter.

a - A the - The it - It

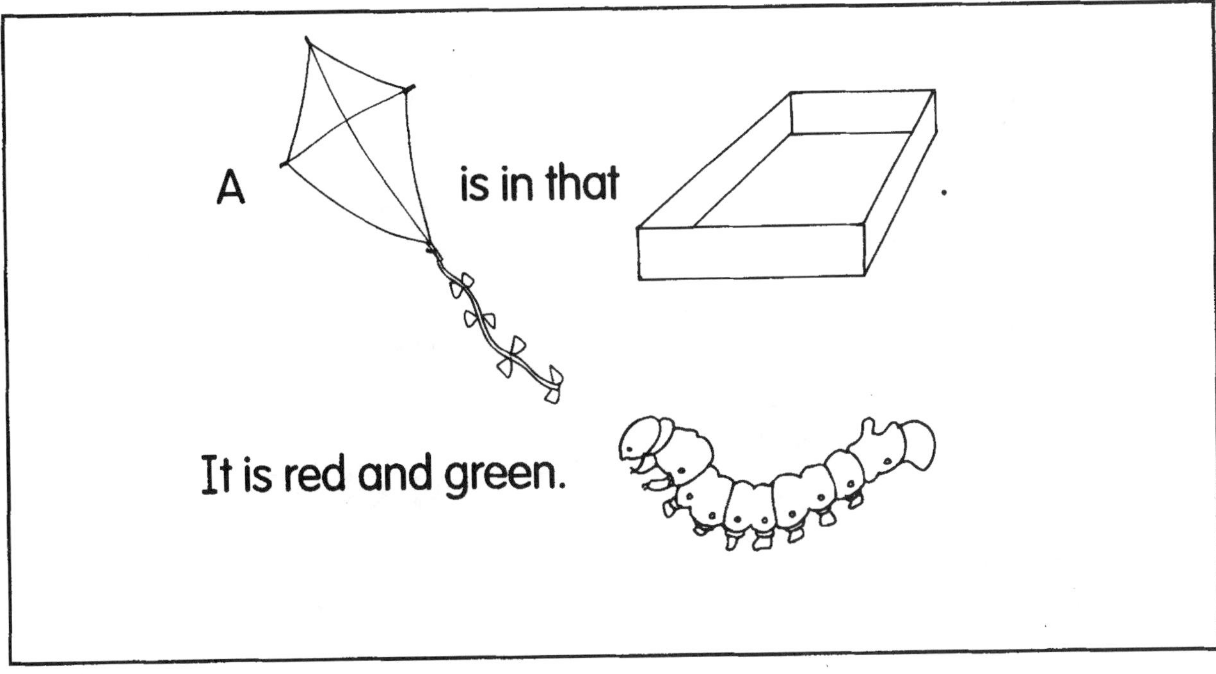

A is in that .
It is red and green.

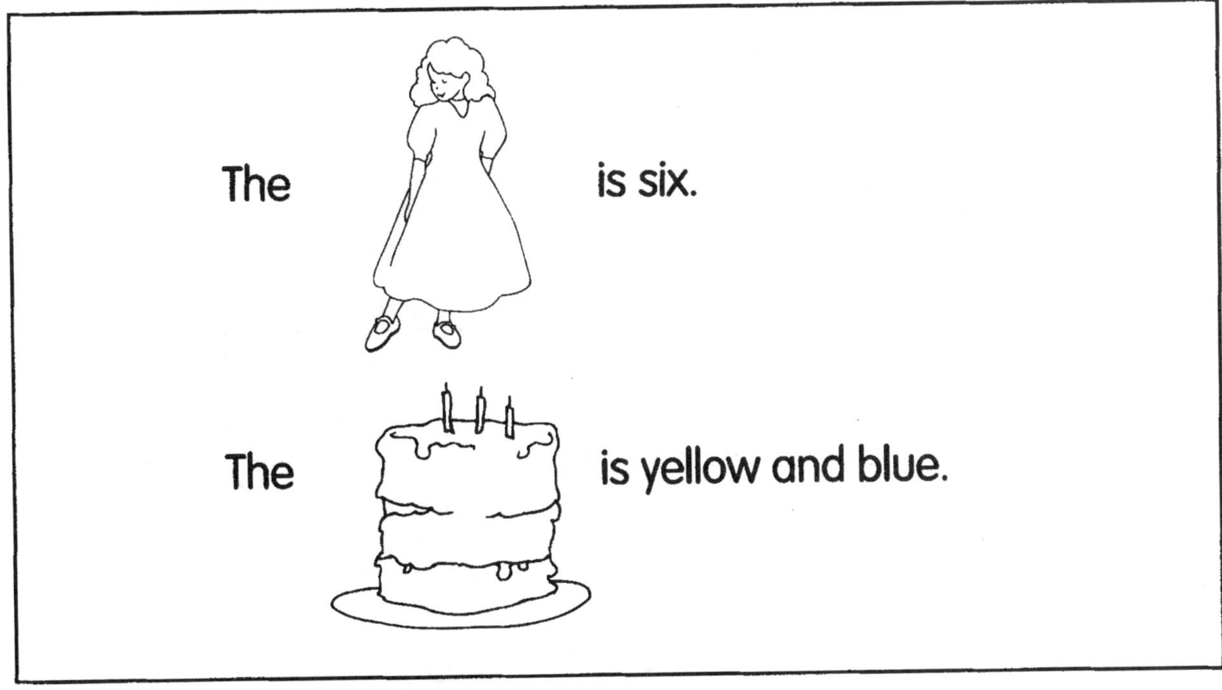

Trace.
Match.

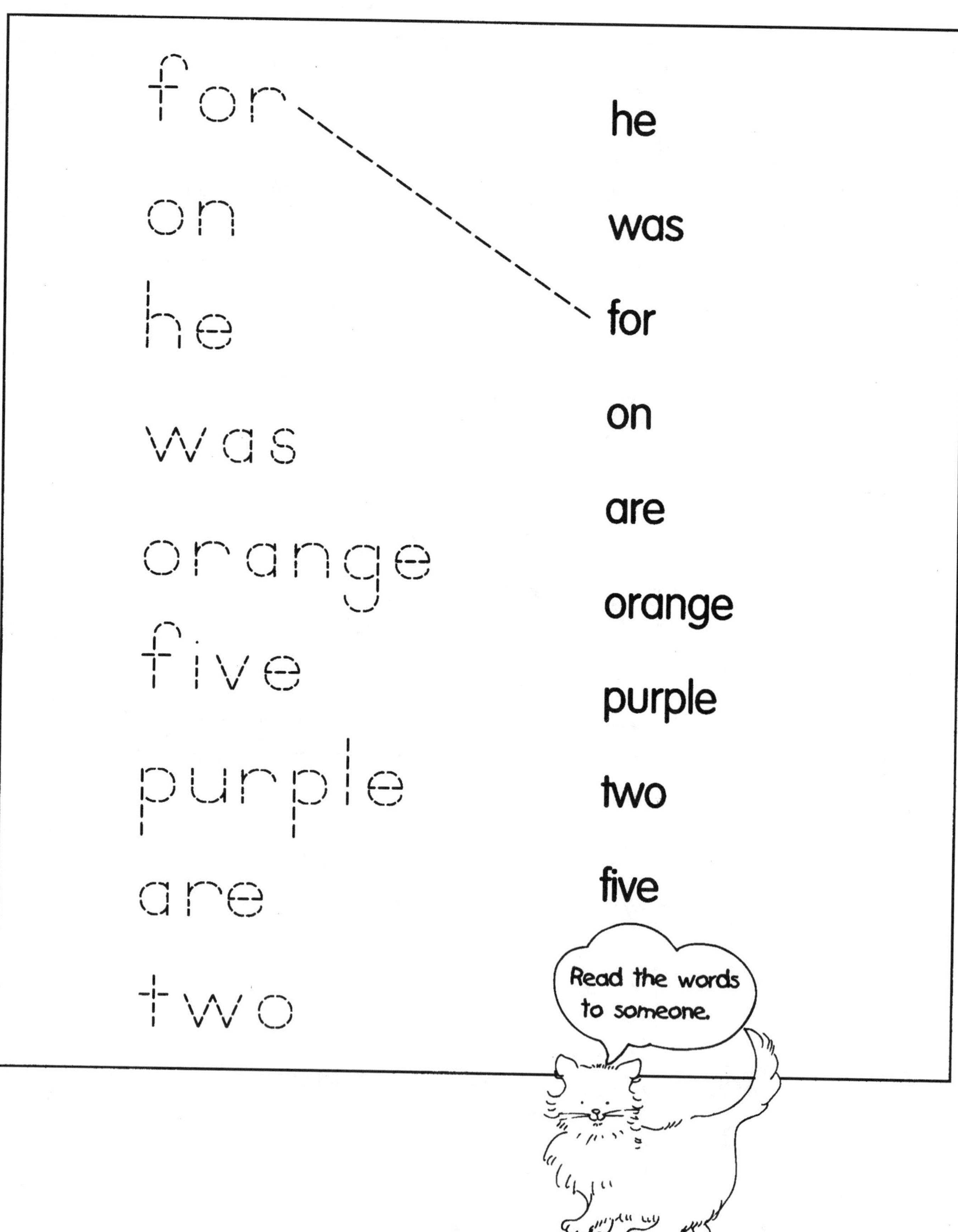

for
on
he
was
orange
five
purple
are
two
he
was
for
on
are
orange
purple
two
five
Read the words to someone.

How to Make an Ice Cream Cone

1. Read 2. Cut 3. Paste in order

	1
	2
	3
	4

Take a big lick and gobble it down.	Then get the ice cream from the freezer.
First get a scoop and a cone.	Take a big scoop of ice cream and put it on the cone.

Fill this ice cream cone.

How many scoops do you have?

What flavors do you have?

Read and color.

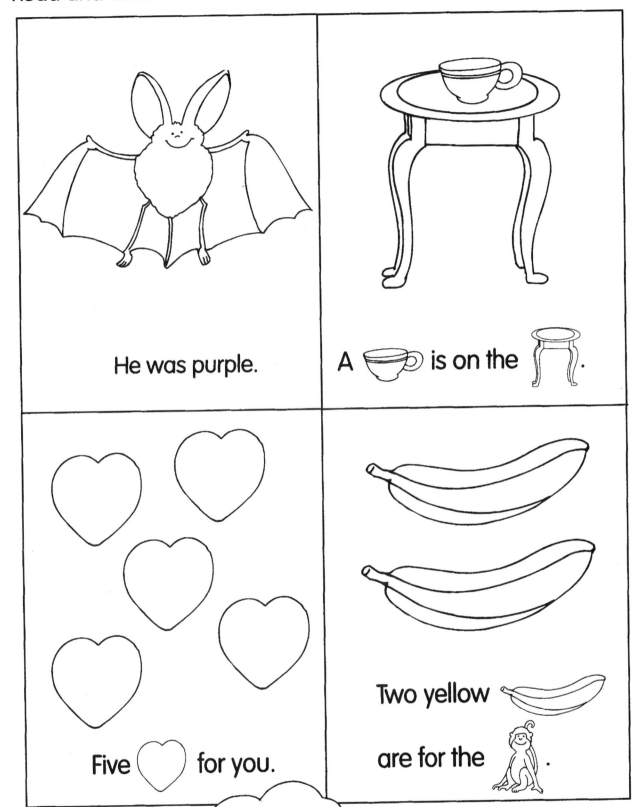

He was purple.

A cup is on the table.

Five hearts for you.

Two yellow bananas are for the monkey.

Find the Words

____ he	____ was	____ for
____ on	____ are	____ orange
____ purple	____ two	____ five

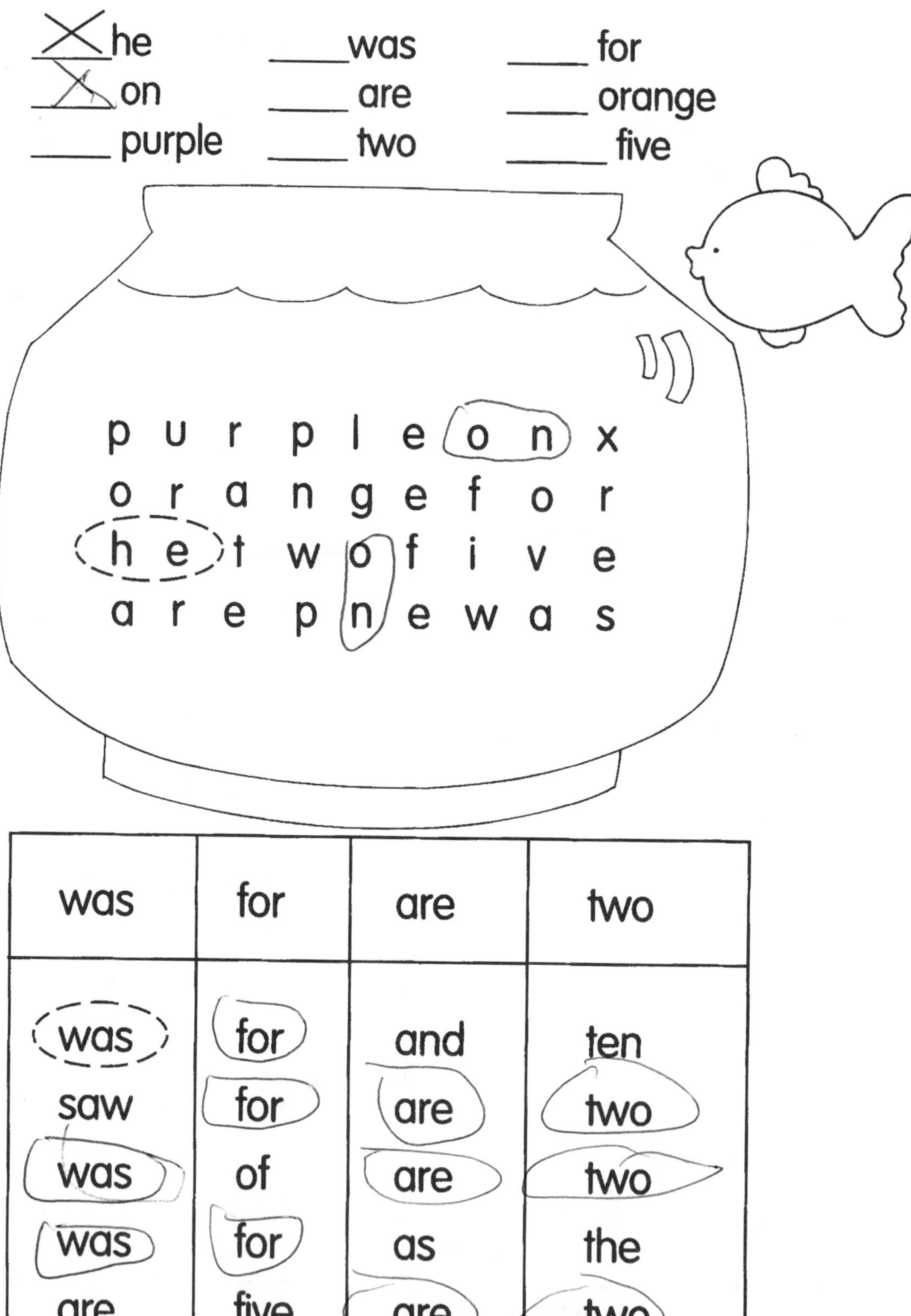

was	for	are	two
was	for	and	ten
saw	for	are	two
was	of	are	two
was	for	as	the
are	five	are	two
was	for	are	two

Parents: Point to each word and say it for your child. Have him/her repeat the word back to you.

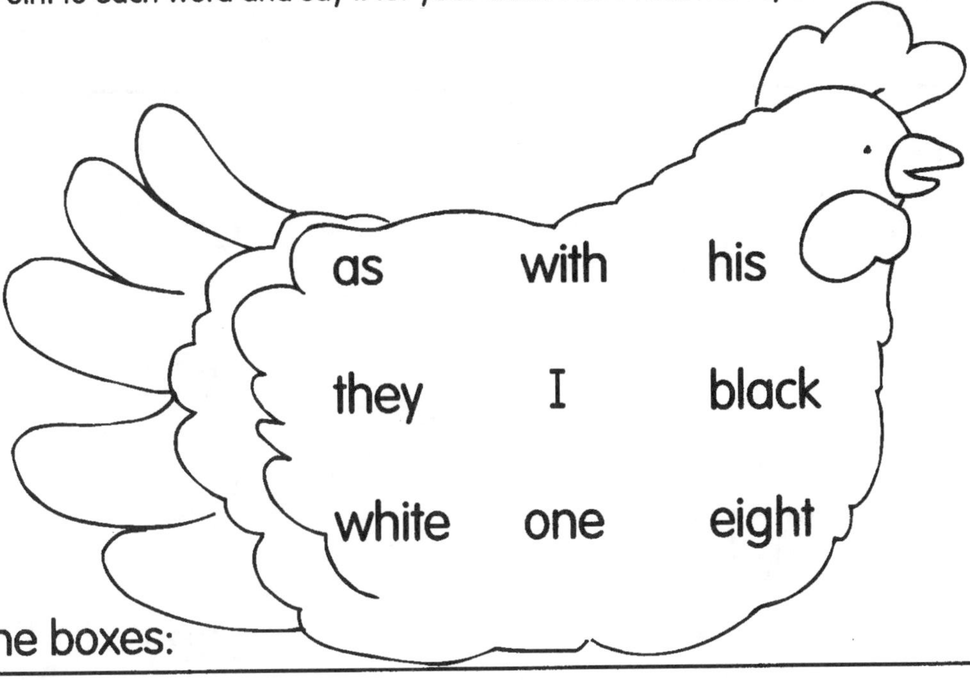

as with his

they I black

white one eight

Fill in the boxes:

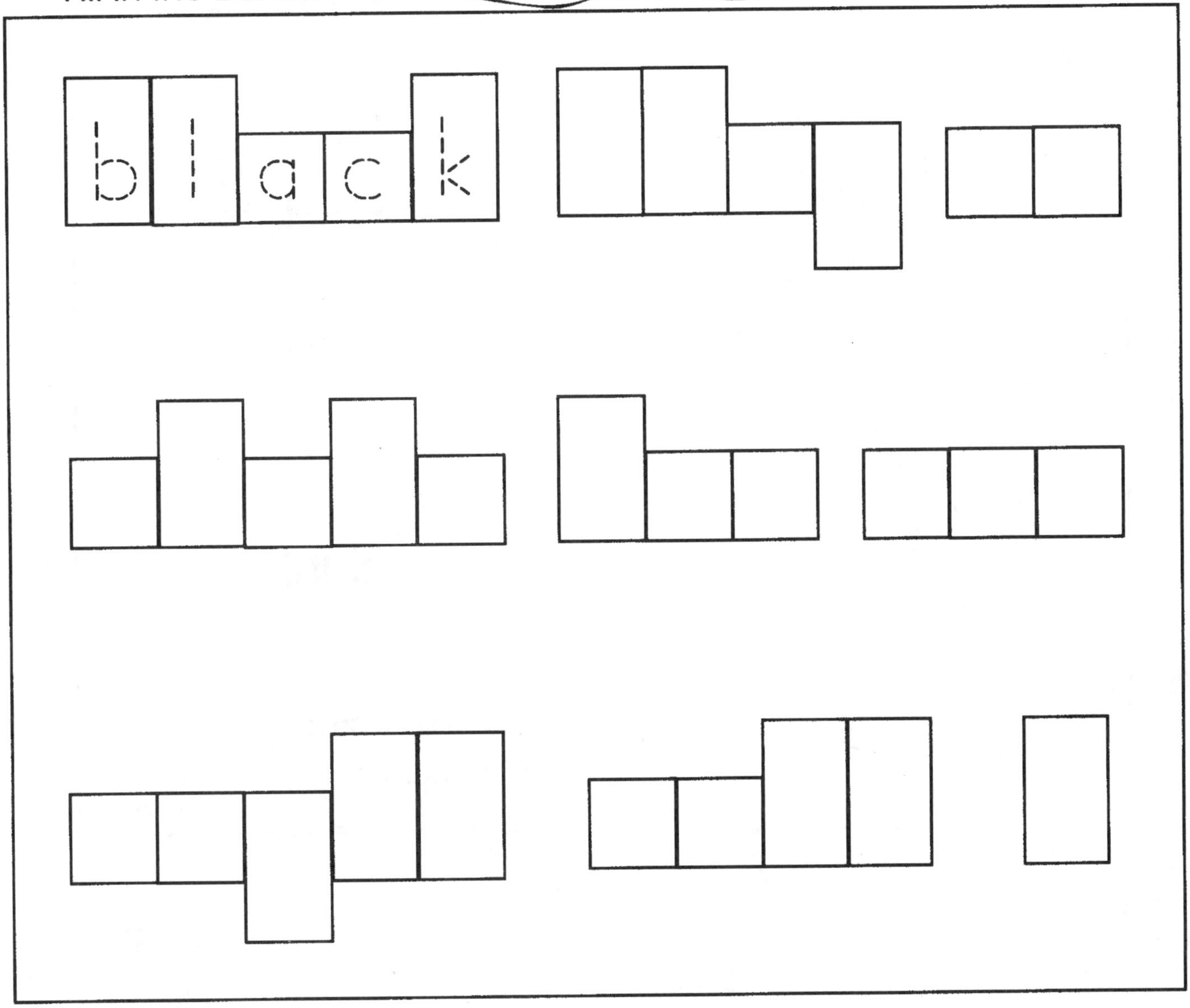

b l a c k

Trace.
Match.

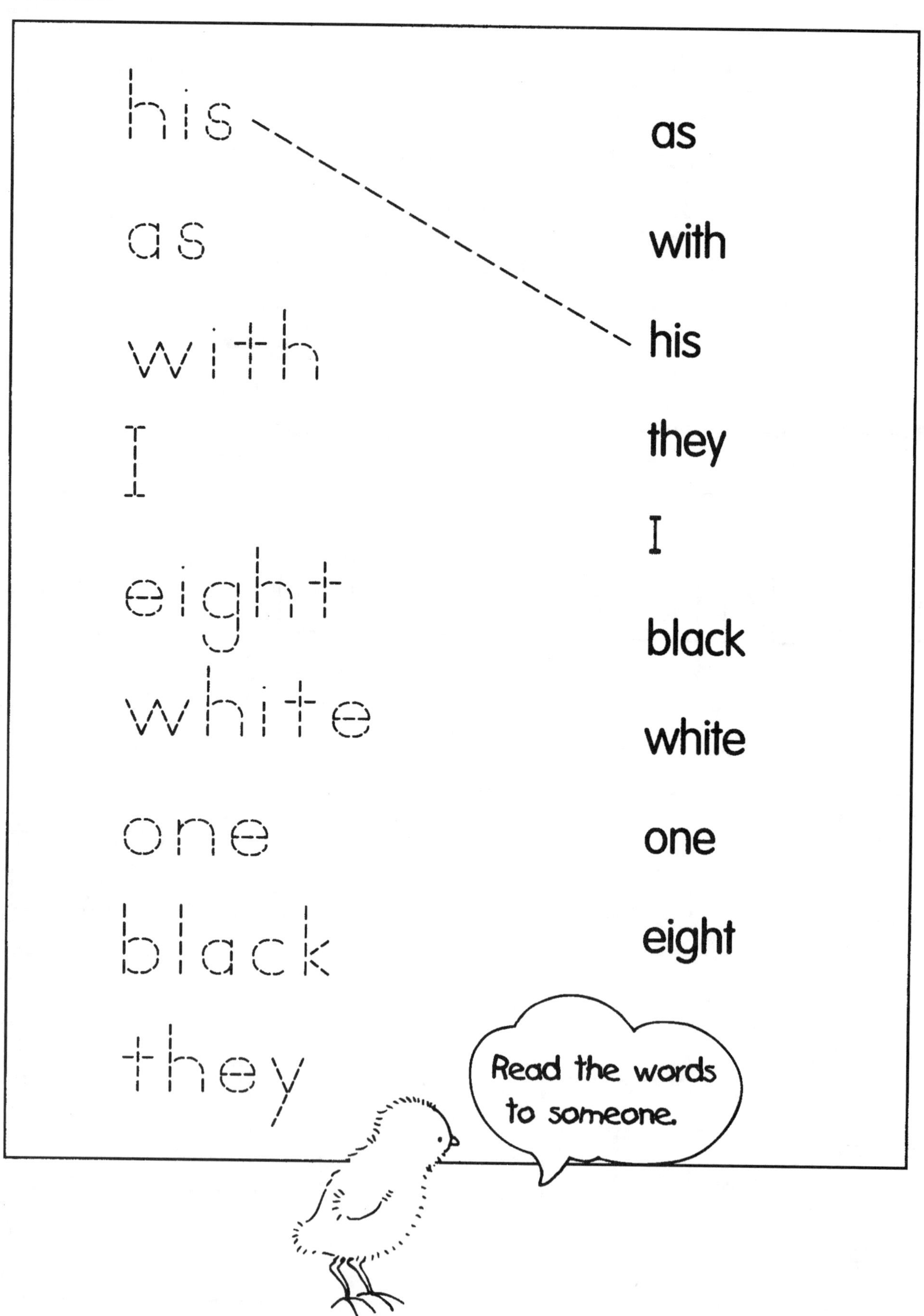
his
as
with
I
eight
white
one
black
they
as
with
his
they
I
black
white
one
eight
Read the words to someone.

Read and color.

white with black

His blue

I am the

a black

Read the words to someone.

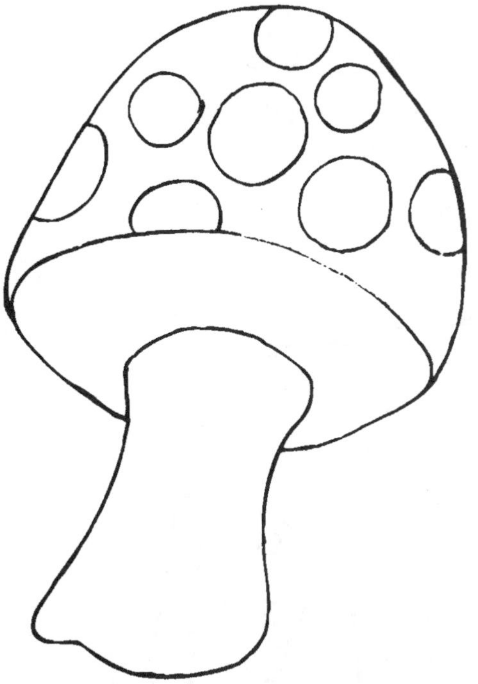

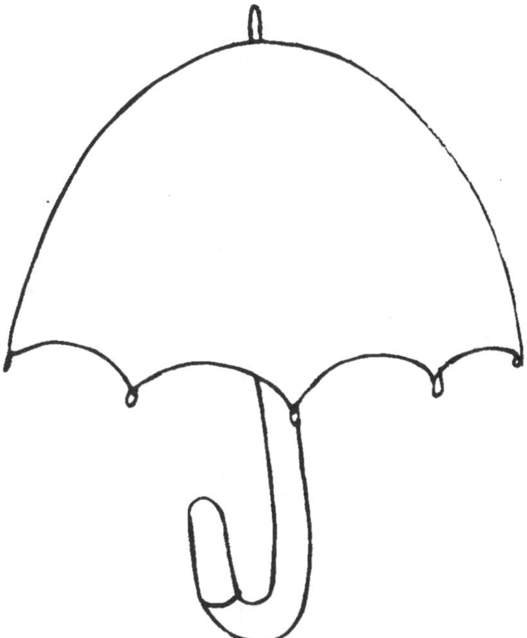

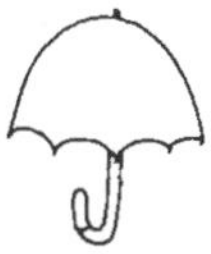

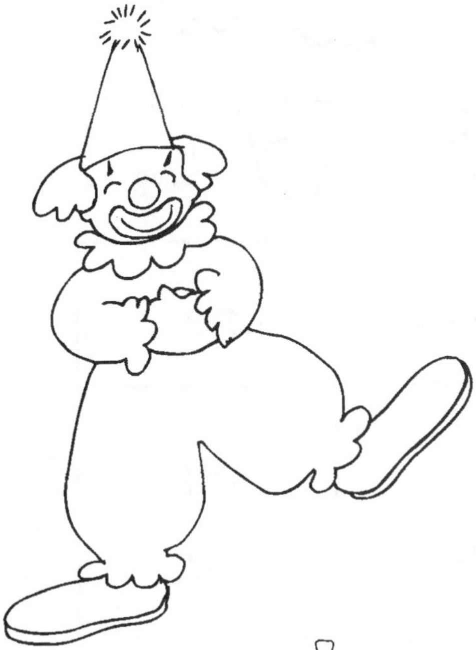

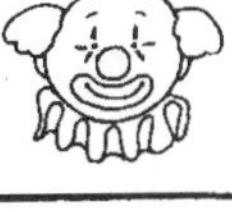

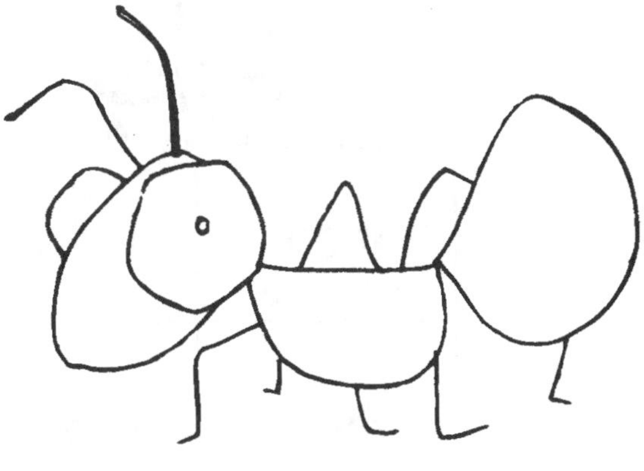

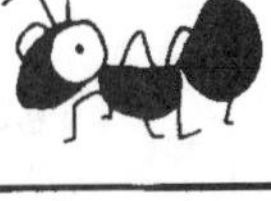

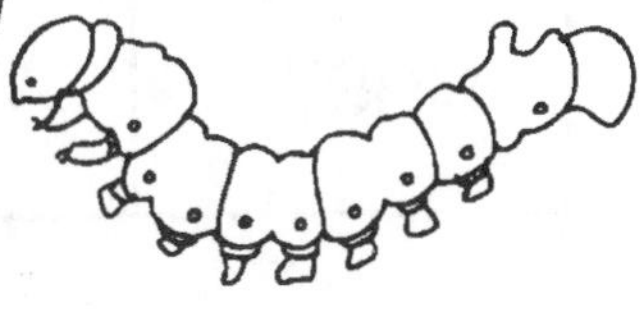

Find the Words

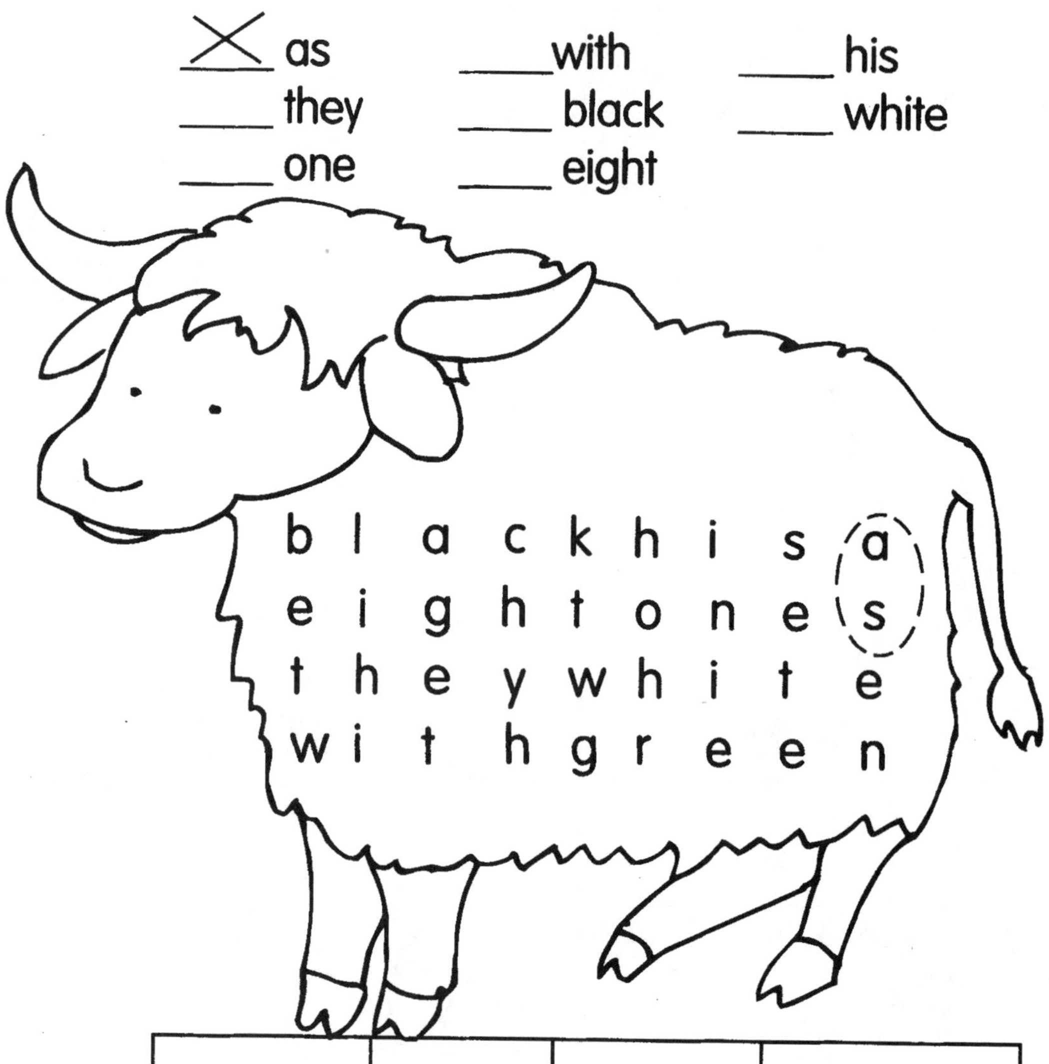

they	with	eight	one
they	white	they	and
they	with	eight	one
that	with	eight	one
two	was	white	of
they	with	eight	one
they	white	they	one

How to Wrap a Gift

1. Read 2. Cut 3. Paste in order	
	1 1
	2 3
	3 5
	4 6
	5
	6

Wrap the box in pretty paper.	Set the gift in a box.
Now put on the lid.	Tape a ribbon on the box.
Stick a card under the ribbon.	Take the gift to the party.

Draw what is in the box?

Who would you give the gift to? ______________________

Parents: Point to each word and say it for your child. Have him/her repeat the word back to you.

at	be	this
have	from	brown
four	seven	she

Fill in the boxes:

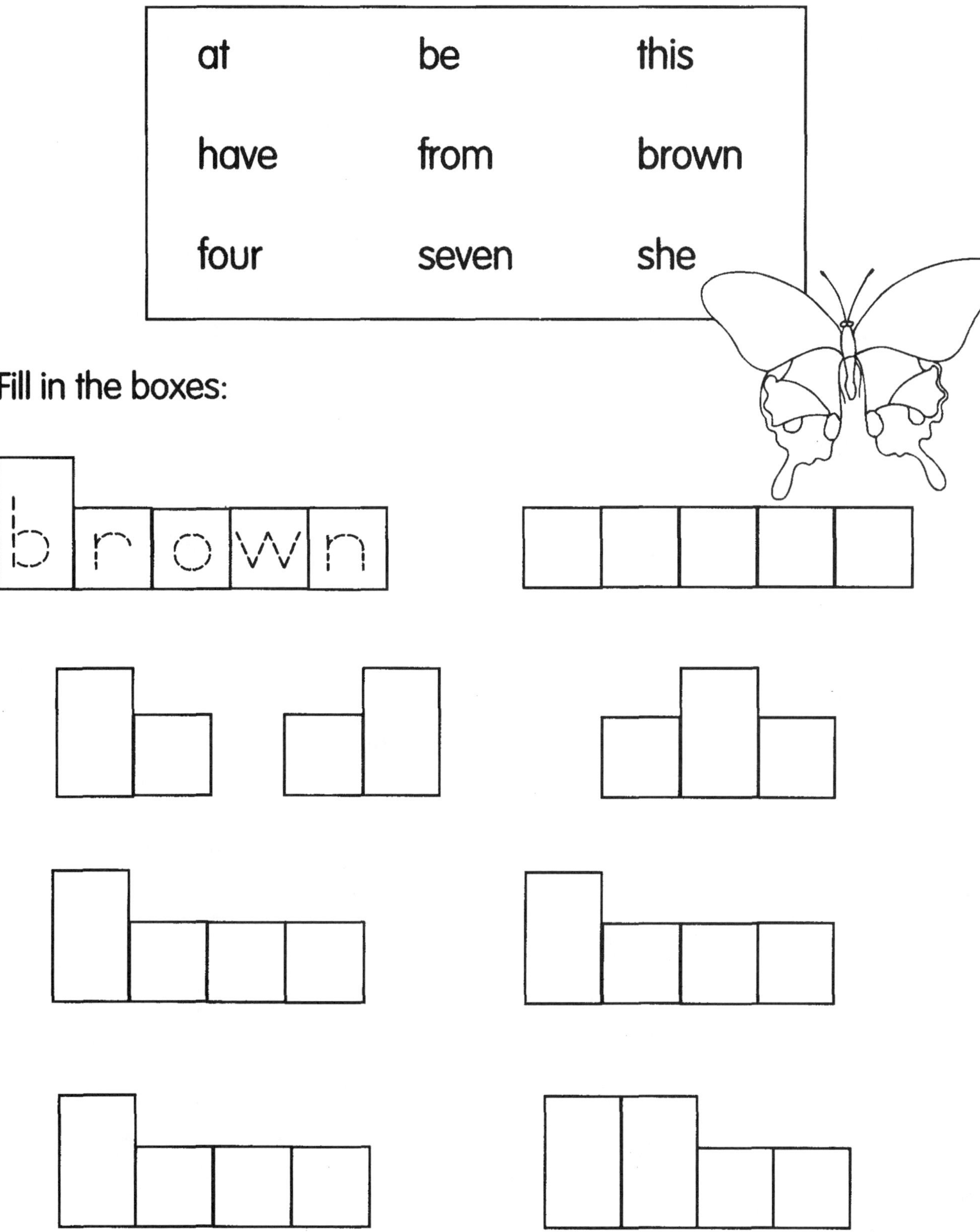

Read the words to someone.

the	of	red	one
a	to	green	two
and	in	blue	three
in	is	yellow	four
you	they	orange	five
that	I	purple	six
it	at	black	seven
was	be	white	eight
for	this	brown	nine
on	have		ten
he	from		
are	she		
as	with		
his			

I can read All words.

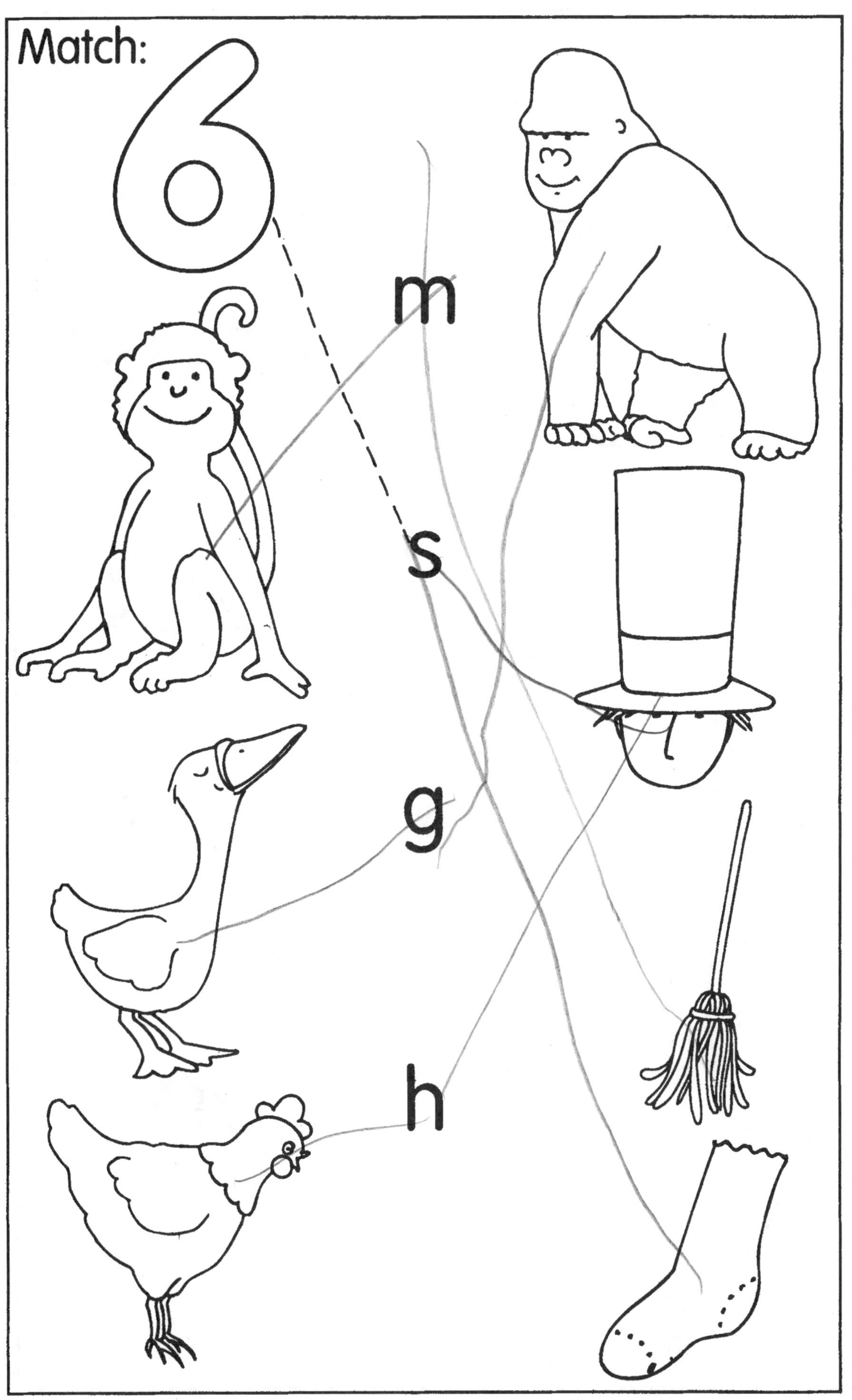
Match:
6
m
s
g
h

m s g h

m ouse

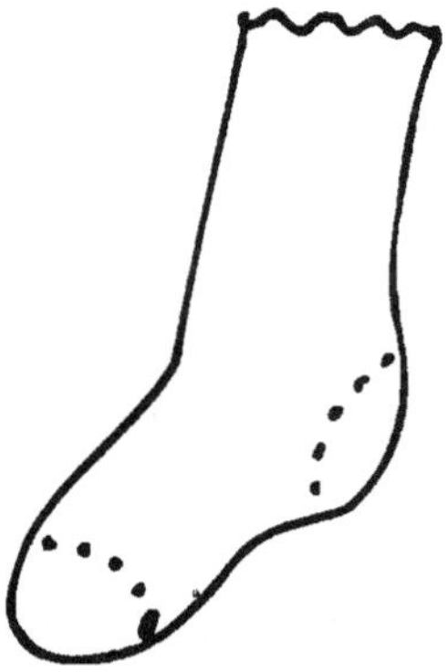

___ock

___oat

___en

Color the words that rhyme with **at**.

bug	can	dog	den / pat	let
big / bat	hop / fat	jam / hat	slat	fun / cat
mat / vat	splat	Nat	at	that
sat / met	Pat / fox	flat / get	brat	rat / nap
pot	win	man	tat / run	bed

I see a ________________.

Write the rhyming word.

log	wig	pen	box	vet

1. See the fox in that ______________.

2. A green frog sat on the ______________.

3. Can a pig put on a ______________ ?

4. I took my pet to see the ______________.

5. Put the hen in her ______________.

Mark the words that rhyme.

Write the rhyming words.

dock	hill	Muffet	clock	sheep
day	Peep	away	tuffet	Jill

1. Jack and ______________

Went up the ______________.

2. Little Bo ______________

Has lost her ______________

3. Hickory, dickory, ______________

The mouse ran up the ______________.

4. Little Miss ______________

Sat on a ______________.

5. Rain, rain go ______________

Come again another ______________.

Color the words that rhyme with:

funny — yellow

day — green

an — blue

back — brown

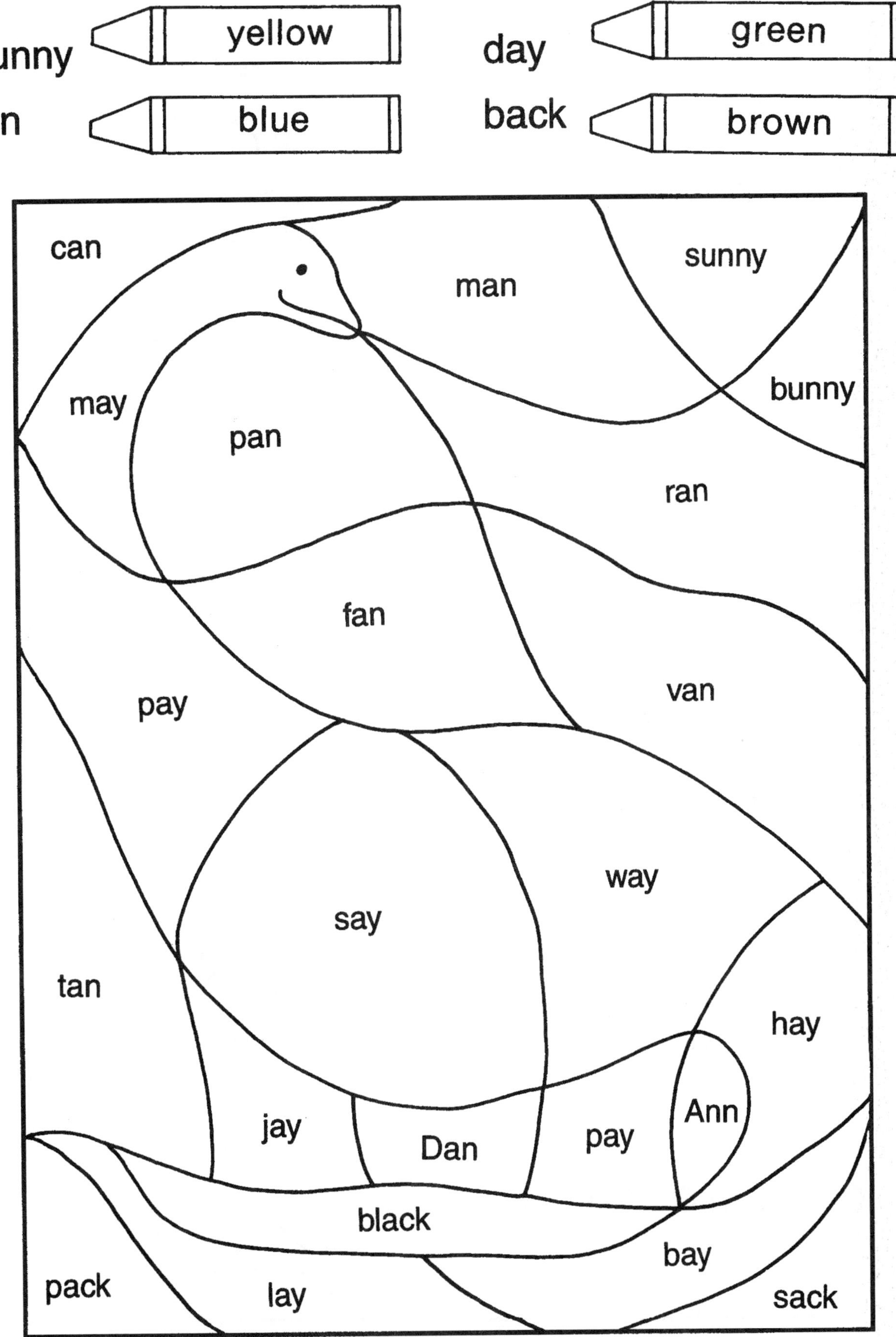

Read.
Match.

a rat on a hill

an egg in a pan

a hat on a man

a dog on a log

a bat in a net

a dog in a bed

Read.
Match.

The cat is fat.

The dog can run.

The fox is red.

The bed is big.

The man is hot.

The ant sat.

This is a big pond.

A log is in the pond.

A frog is on the log.

Jump, frog, jump.

I read this story to________________.

Draw:

frog	log

Fill in:

The pond is ______________ .

A ______________ is in the pond.

A ______________ is on the log.

the
bath

Pat and Sam

Sam digs in the mud.

Sam is a mess.

Pat is mad!

"Sam must get a bath."

I read this story to________________.

Match:

Pat

mud

bath

Sam

Sam digs in ________________ .

Pat is ________________ .

Sam must get a ________________ .

Note: Explain to your learner what usually happens when you add a **silent e** to a short vowel word. The vowel becomes a long sound.

Silent e

Read.	Add an e and read.	
can	can e	
cub	cub ___	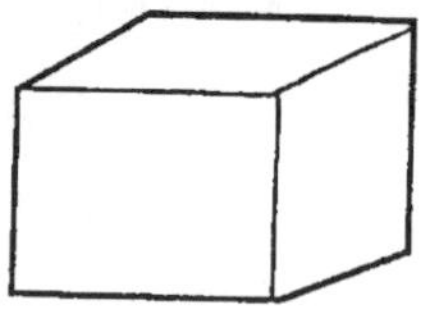
bit	bit ___	
tap	tap ___	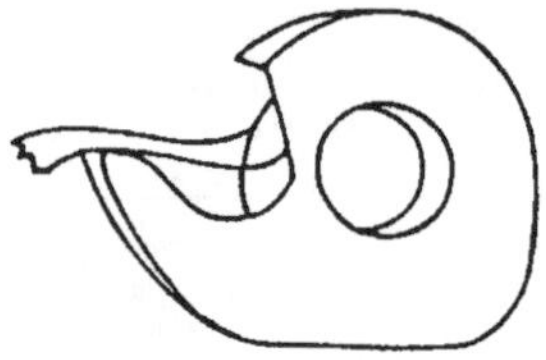
kit	kit ___	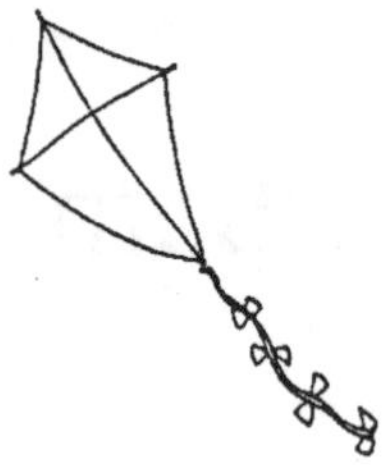
rob	rob ___	

Yes or No

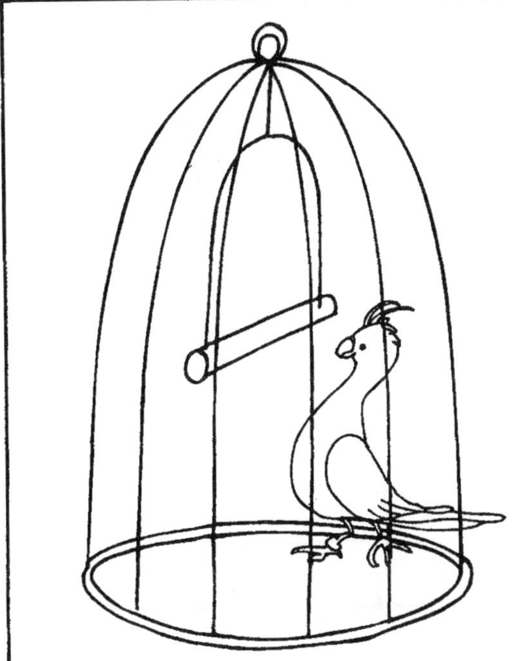 He is in the cage.  no	 Five eggs are on the plate. yes no
 Feed me a bone. yes no	 Kate can ride the bike. yes no

Match:

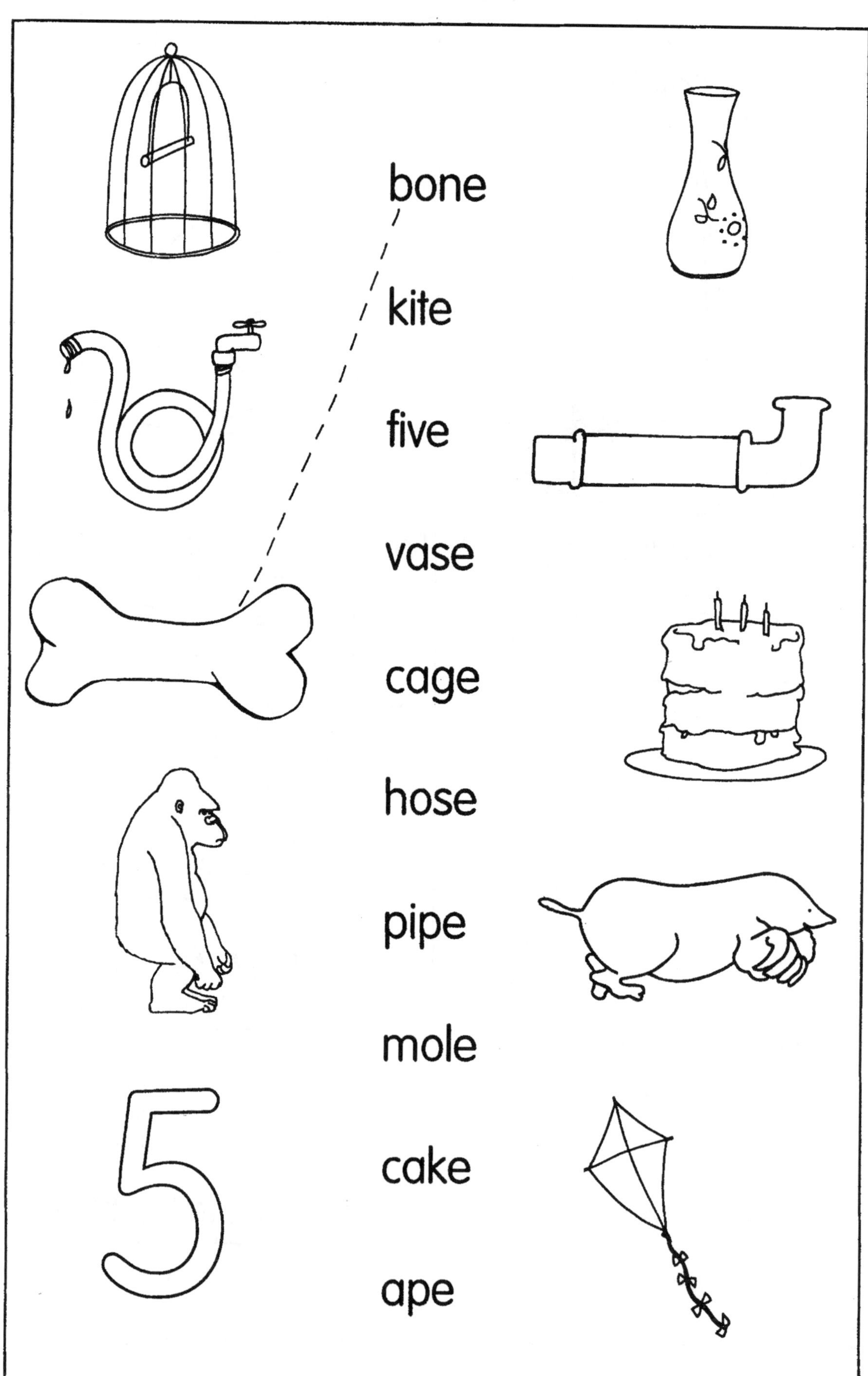
bone
kite
five
vase
cage
hose
pipe
mole
cake
ape

Color the Puzzle

blue	yellow	red
ai	oa	ee

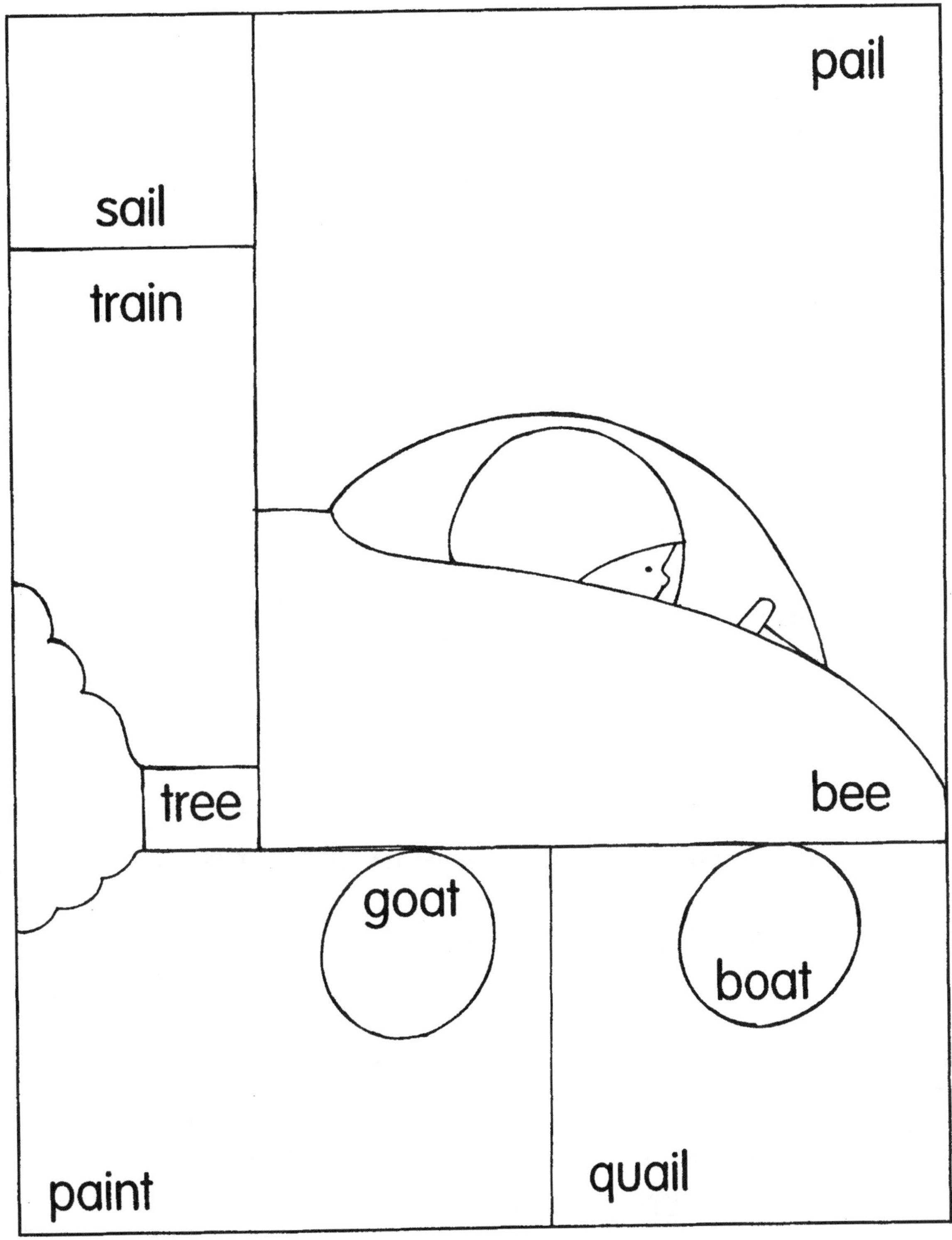

Pets at School

"Wake up, Eve," said June.

"Miss Lane said we can take pets to school.

I don't want to be late."

"This is my pet cat," said June.

"His name is Dave.

He likes to take naps on my bed."

"I have three pet mice," said Zeke.

"My mom and dad gave them to me.

My mice like to eat seeds."

I read this story to ______________________.

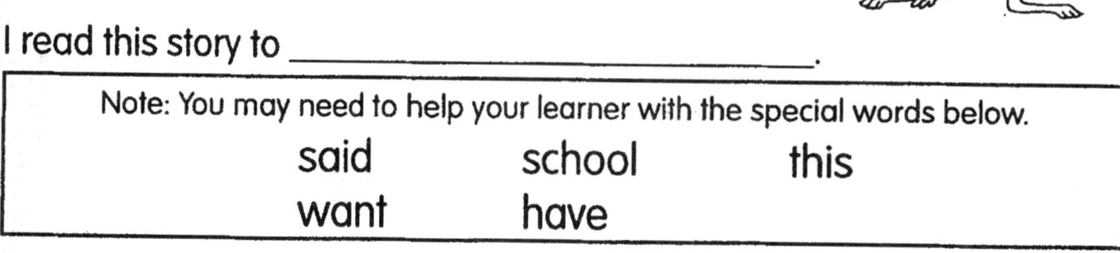

Note: You may need to help your learner with the special words below.

said school this
want have

"This is my dog, Mike," said Kate.
"Sit, Mike. Shake my hand.
He wants a bone to eat."

"I have a pet," said Miss Lane.
It is long and has scales.
"It is a black snake!"

We had fun with the pets at school.

I read this story to ______________________.

Read the story again.
Circle the long vowel words.

Note: Two vowels together can make a long vowel sound.

bee

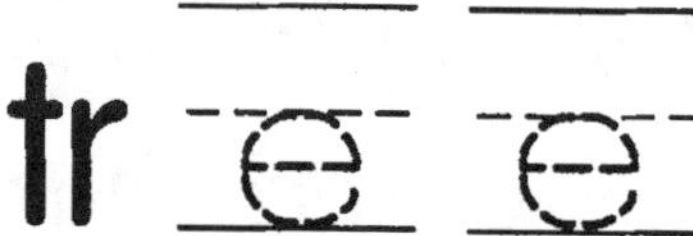

j __ __ p

thr __ __

__ __ l

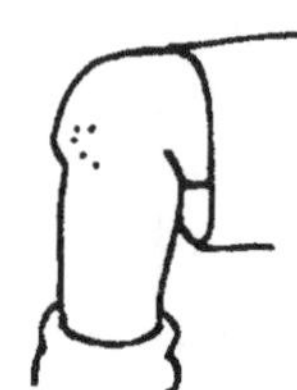

kn __ __

Read these words to someone.

How to Take a Bath

1. Read 2. Cut 3. Paste in order	
	1
	2
	3
	4
	5
	6

Add bubble bath.	Get dressed.
Get out of the tub and dry off.	Get into the tub.
Fill the tub with water.	Wash with soap and a rag.

Why do you have to take baths?

Do you like a bath or a shower best?

Do you like bubble bath in your tub?

Skill: identifies the consonant digraphs **ch**, **sh**, **wh**, and **th** and can give the sound each one represents

chip **sh**op **wh**at **th**is

Color the pictures.

ch – blue **sh** – red

wh – green **th** – brown

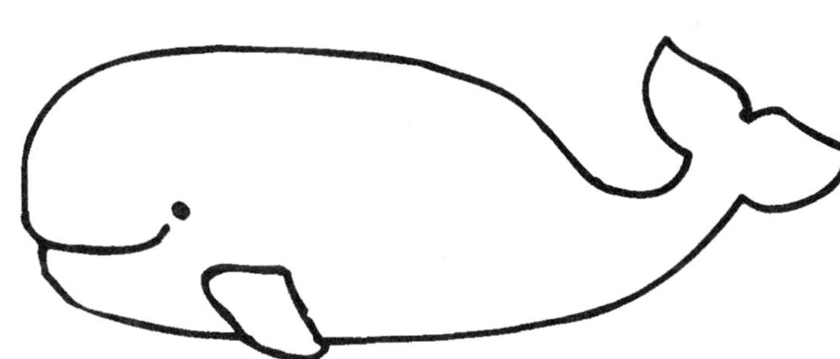

Read these words to someone.

the with

then bath

Skill: identifies and uses correct capitalization of the first word of a sentence

The sun is hot.

Fill in the capital letters.

1. my pet is not big.

2. it can run and hop.

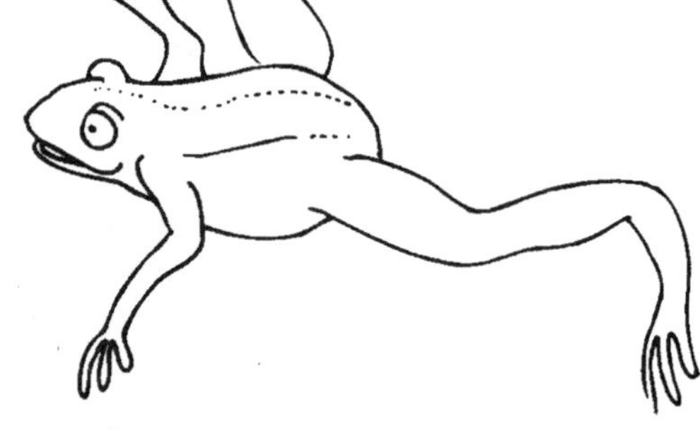

3. my pet can swim.

4. he is a green pet.

5. his name is Hopper.

6. can you tell what my pet is?

Skill: recognizes correct word order in a sentence

run. can I

I can run.

Put the words in order.
Read the sentence.

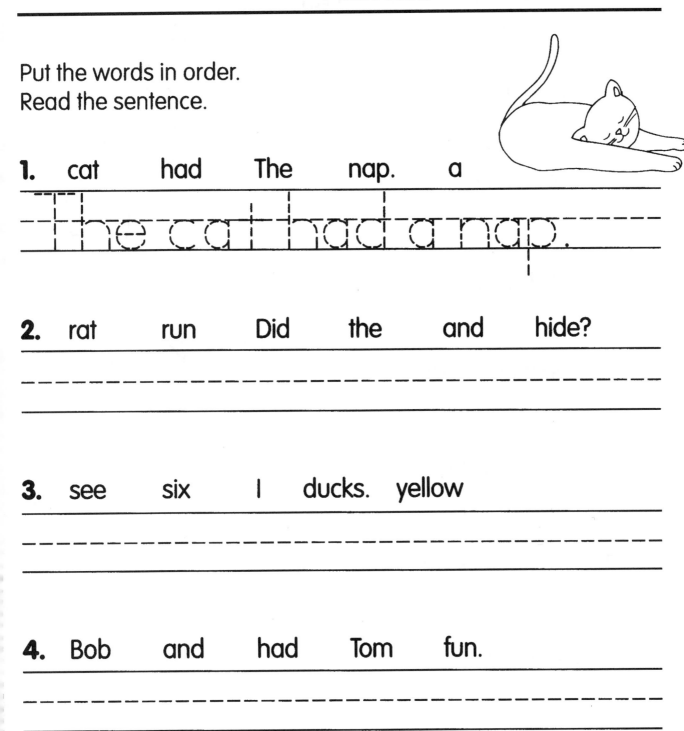

1. cat had The nap. a

The cat had a nap.

2. rat run Did the and hide?

3. see six I ducks. yellow

4. Bob and had Tom fun.

Skill: identifies and uses correct punctuation at the end of asking and telling sentences

- A **period** goes at the end of a sentence that **tells**.
- A **question mark** goes at the end of a sentence that **asks** a question

The fox is here. Do you see a fox**?**

Put in the . and **?**

1. The dog had a nap**.**

2. Is that a fox

3. Can you run fast

4. A cat is on my bed

5. Will the duck get wet

6. What is that

Skill: can write telling and asking sentences using correct capital letters and end punctuation

Write a sentence that **tells** about this monkey.

Write a sentence that **asks** a question about the monkey.

Skill: alphabetizes words through the first letter

ant	**b**ell
box	**g**o
cat	**n**ot

a b c d e f g h i j k l m n o p q r s t u v w x y z

Put the words in **a b c** order.

1. ______________________ 2. ______________________ 3. ______________________	cat ant box
1. ______________________ 2. ______________________ 3. ______________________	kite jam nest
1. ______________________ 2. ______________________ 3. ______________________	zebra skunk whale

Parents: You may read this to your child and have him/her give you the answer ***or*** *have your child read it on his/her own.*

Skill: draw conclusions from given facts

The sky is dark.
Water is falling from the sky.
Conclusion: It is raining.

Circle the answer.

1. I get a can.
I take the lid off.
I put food in a dish.
I am feeding the...?

2. I get a rag.
I get soap.
I get a tub.
I am washing...?

3. It is cold.
Snow comes down.
The wind blows.
I put on...?

4. I am sad.
I made a mess.
It is hard to clean.
I spilled...?

Skill: identifies and uses naming words (**nouns**)

A **noun** names a person, place, or thing.

Tom **school** **hat**

Put a ring around the **naming** words.

1. Dad has a box in the car.

2. Ted got a red kite and a blue ball.

3. The bike is at the park.

4. Six dogs ran up the street.

5. That cup has milk in it.

6. Mom and Dad went to school.

Name the things in this picture.

Skill: identifies plural nouns ending in **s**

one - cat
more than one - cat**s**

Write.

Skill: identifies and uses action words (**verbs**)

A **verb** tells what the subject is doing.

run **sing** **jump**

Put a line under **doing** words.

1. Tom rides his bike.
2. The cat sleeps on a rug.
3. A green frog hops to the pond.
4. Matt played with his dog.
5. I skip and jump.
6. Kim painted a fish.

Draw what you can do.

Skill: identifies and uses words that describe

big **hot** **six** **red**

Put a ring around the word that describes.
Match the words and pictures.

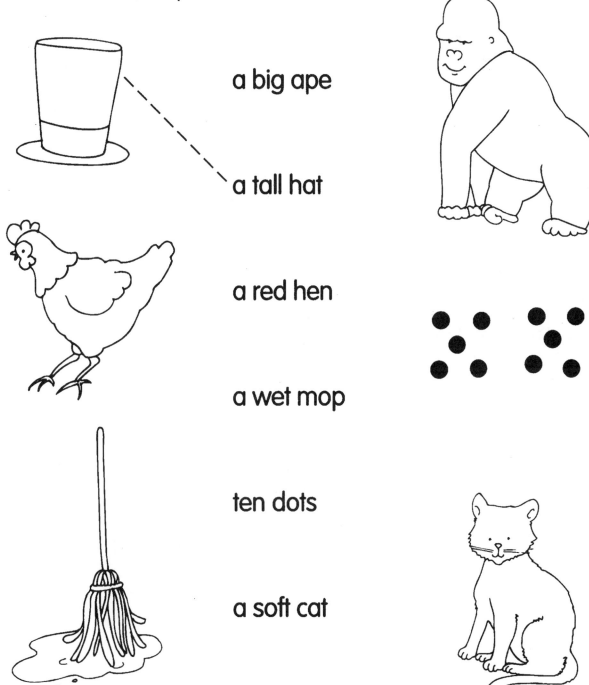

a big ape

a tall hat

a red hen

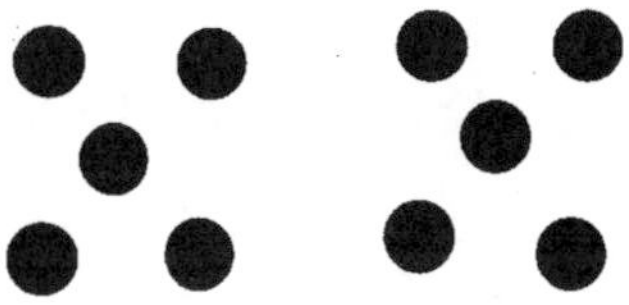

a wet mop

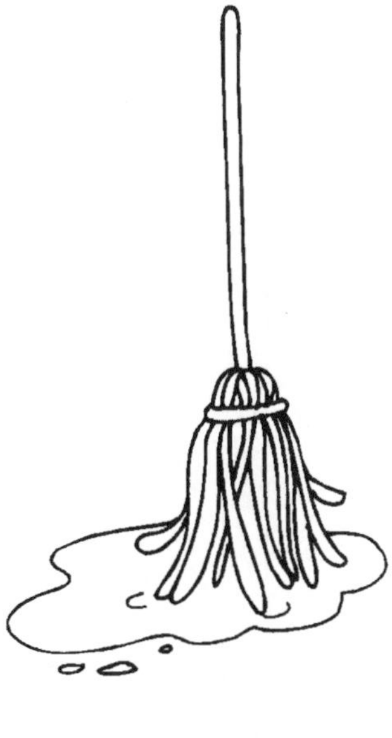

ten dots

a soft cat

Answer Key

Please take time to go over the work your child has completed. Ask your child to explain what he/she has done. Praise both success and effort. If mistakes have been made, explain what the answer should have been and how to find it. Let your child know that mistakes are a part of learning. The time you spend with your child helps let him/her know you feel learning is important.

page 4

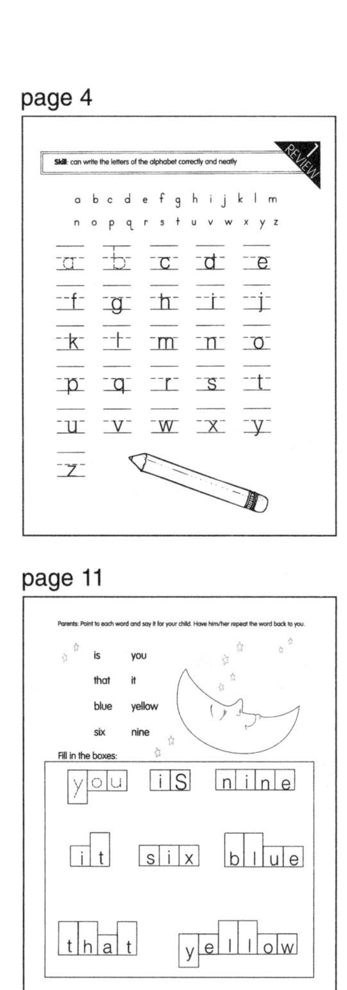

page 6

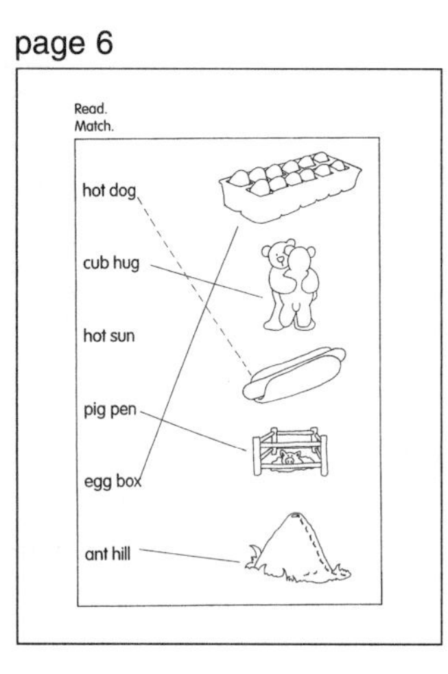

page 8

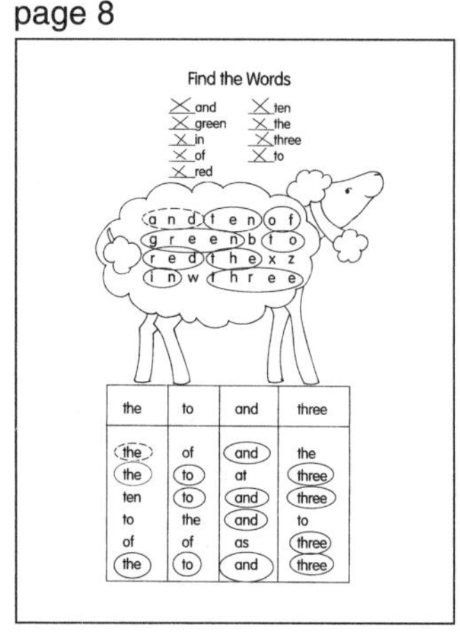

page 9

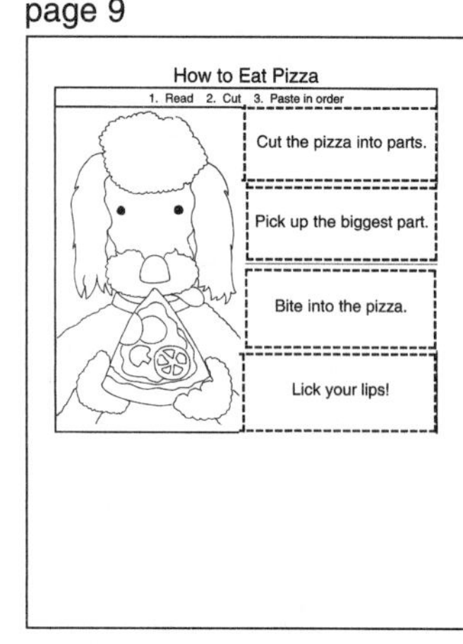

page 11

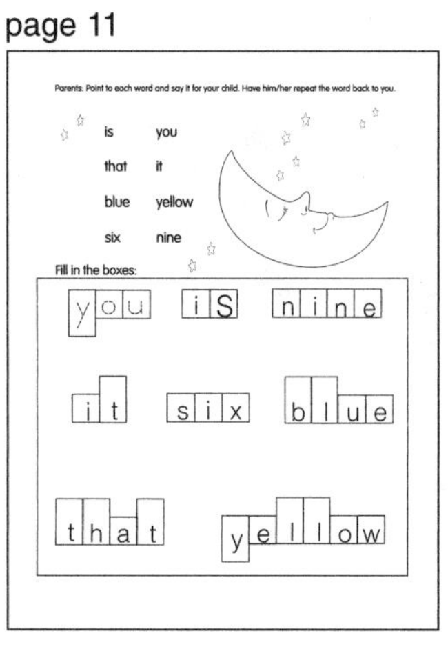

page 12

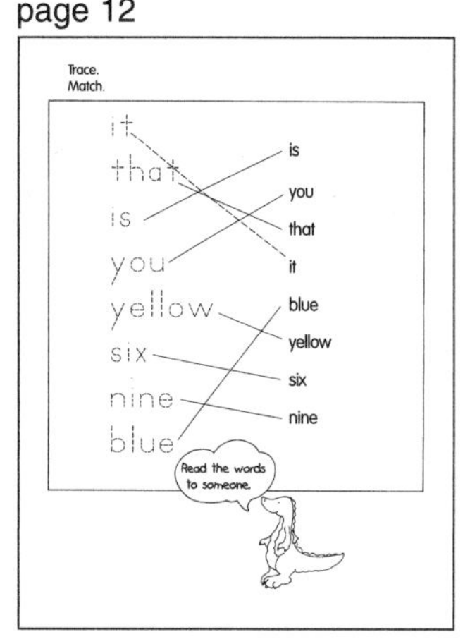

page 13

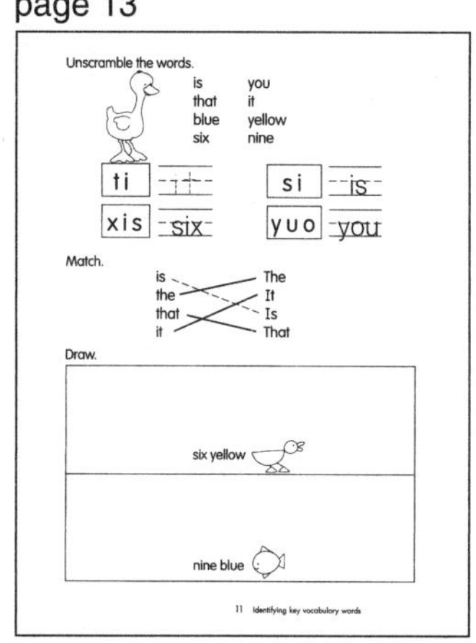

page 16

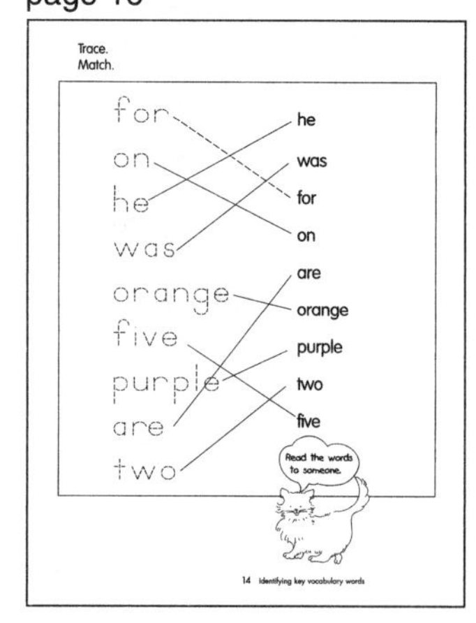

page 17

page 20

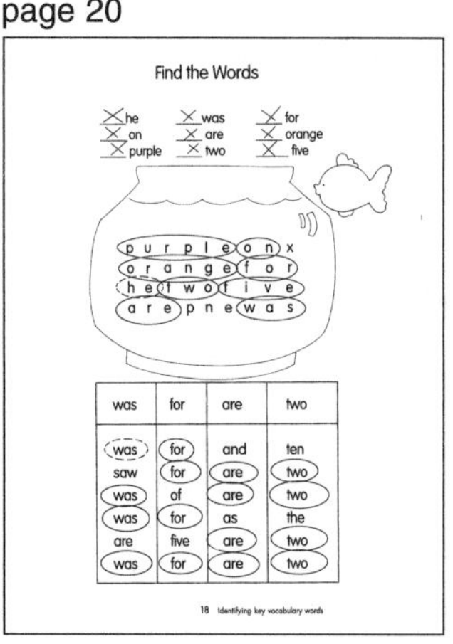

page 21

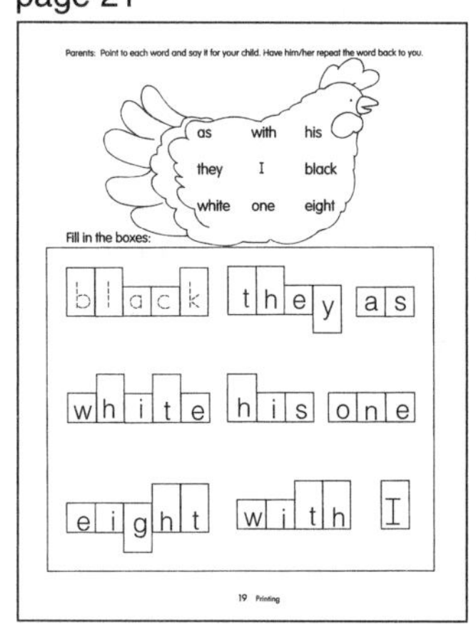

page 22

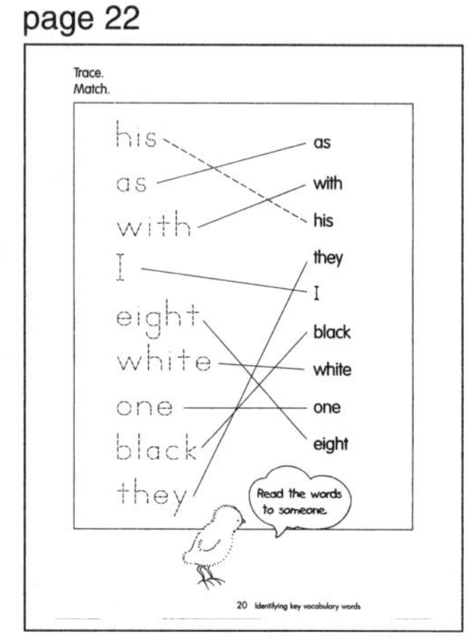

page 24

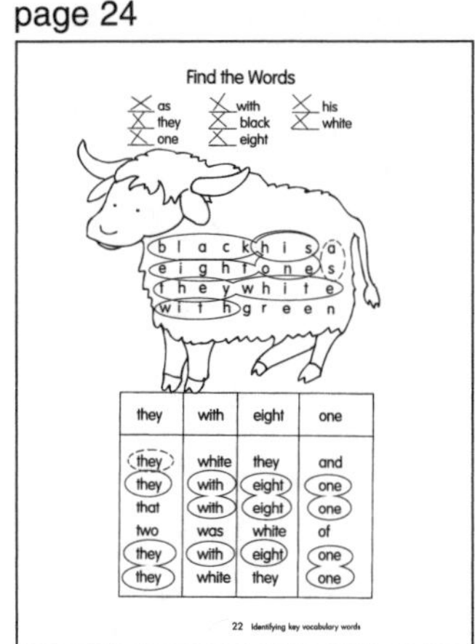
Find the Words
as
they
one
with
black
eight
his
white
b l a c k h i s a
e i g h t o n e s
t h e y w h i t e
w i t h g r e e n
they
with
eight
one
they white they and
they with eight one
that with eight one
two was white of
they with eight one
they white they one
22 Identifying key vocabulary words

page 25

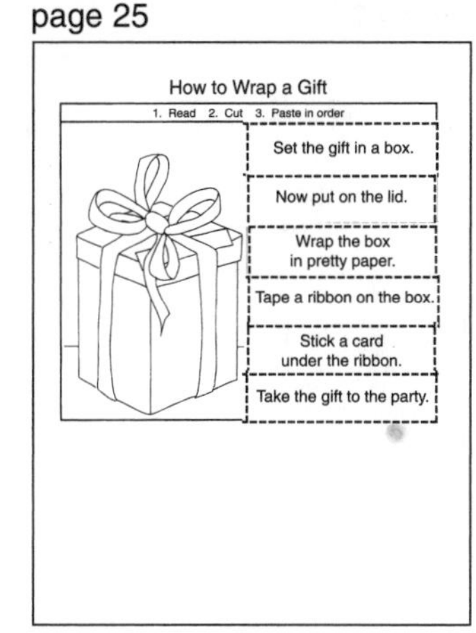
How to Wrap a Gift
1. Read 2. Cut 3. Paste in order
Set the gift in a box.
Now put on the lid.
Wrap the box in pretty paper.
Tape a ribbon on the box.
Stick a card under the ribbon.
Take the gift to the party.

page 27

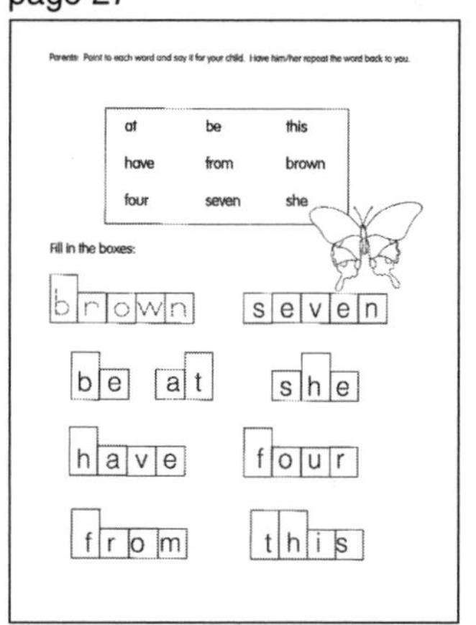
at
be
this
have
from
brown
four
seven
she
Fill in the boxes:
brown
seven
be
at
she
have
four
from
this

page 29

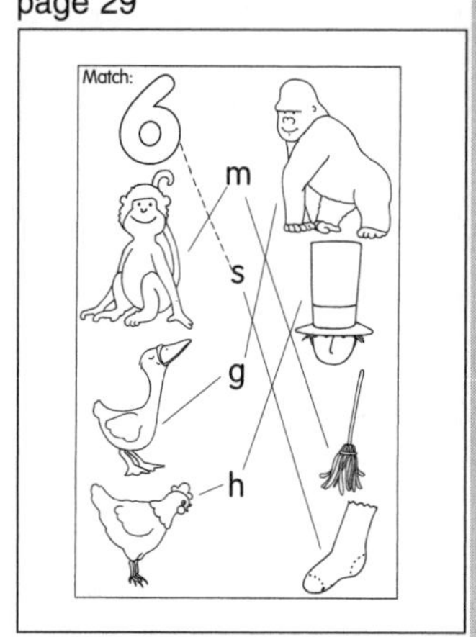
Match:
6
m
s
g
h

page 30

m s g h
mouse
sock
goat
hen

page 31

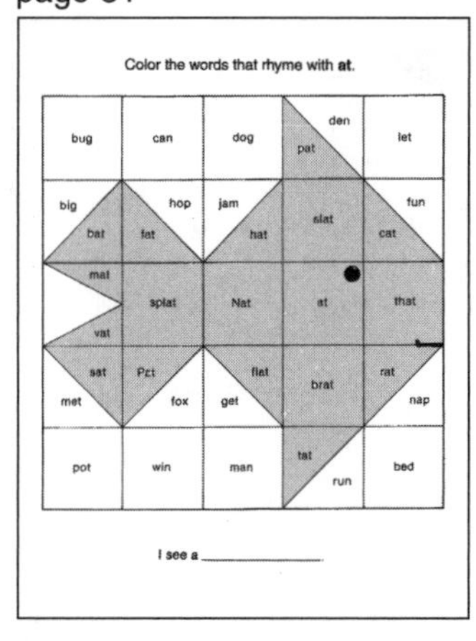
Color the words that rhyme with at.
bug
can
dog
den
pat
let
big
hop
jam
fun
bat
fat
hat
slat
cat
mat
splat
Nat
at
that
vat
sat
Pat
flat
rat
met
fox
get
brat
nap
pot
win
man
tat
run
bed
I see a

page 33

Mark the words that rhyme.
hog
at
oat

page 34

Write the rhyming words.
dock
day
hill
Peep
Muffet
away
clock
tuffet
sheep
Jill
1. Jack and Jill
Went up the hill
2. Little Bo Peep
Has lost her sheep
3. Hickory, dickory, dock
The mouse ran up the clock
4. Little Miss Muffet
Sat on a tuffet
5. Rain, rain go away
Come again another day

page 35

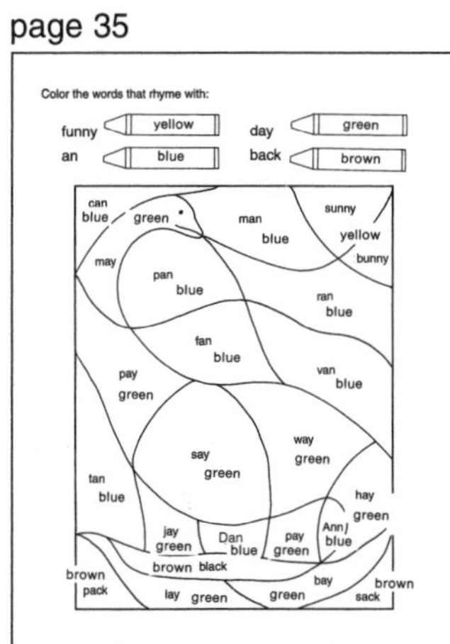
Color the words that rhyme with:
funny yellow
an blue
day green
back brown
can blue
green
man blue
sunny yellow
bunny
may
pan blue
ran blue
fan blue
pay green
van blue
say green
way green
tan blue
hay green
jay green
Dan blue
pay green
Ann blue
brown black
brown pack
bay
brown sack
lay green
green

page 36

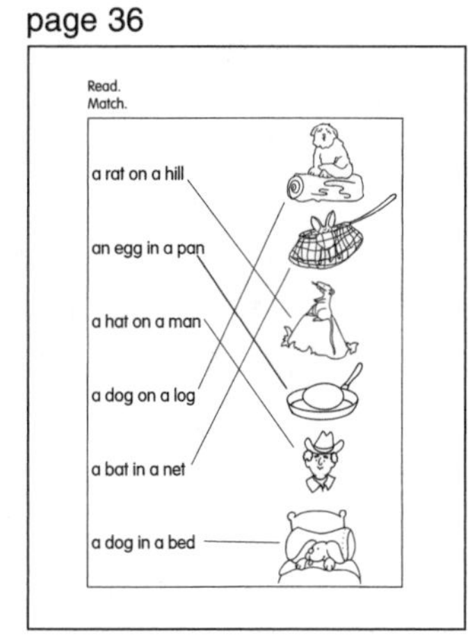
Read.
Match.
a rat on a hill
an egg in a pan
a hat on a man
a dog on a log
a bat in a net
a dog in a bed

page 37

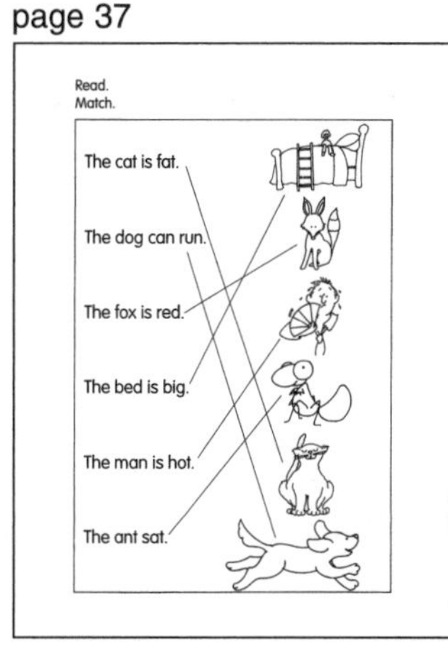
Read.
Match.
The cat is fat.
The dog can run.
The fox is red.
The bed is big.
The man is hot.
The ant sat.

page 39

Draw:
frog
log
Fill in:
The pond is big.
A log is in the pond.
A frog is on the log.

page 41

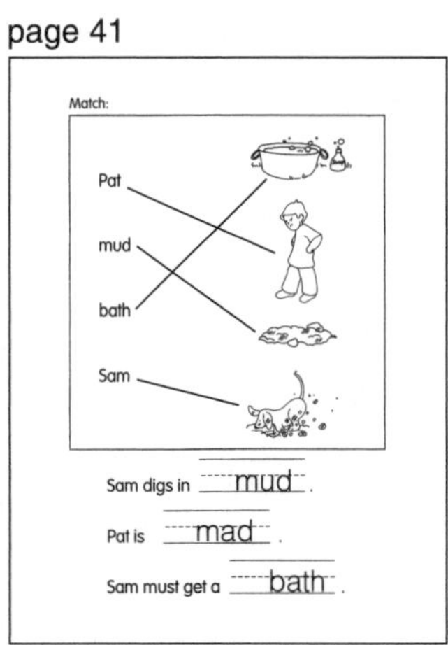
Match:
Pat
mud
bath
Sam
Sam digs in mud.
Pat is mad.
Sam must get a bath.

page 42

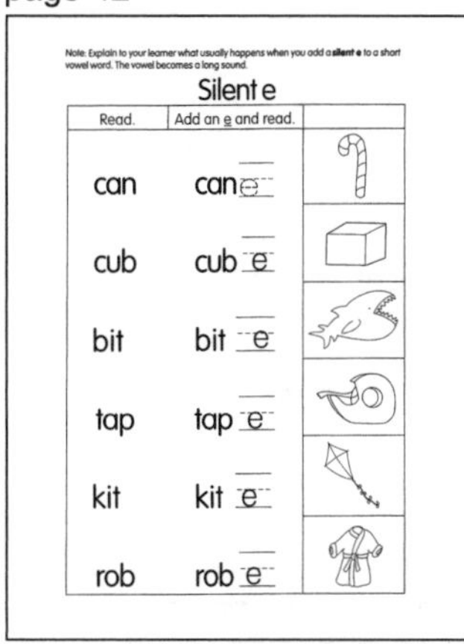
Silent e
Read.
Add an e and read.
can cane
cub cube
bit bite
tap tape
kit kite
rob robe

page 43

Yes or No
He is in the cage.
yes no
Five eggs are on the plate.
yes no
Feed me a bone.
yes no
Kate can ride the bike.
yes no

page 44

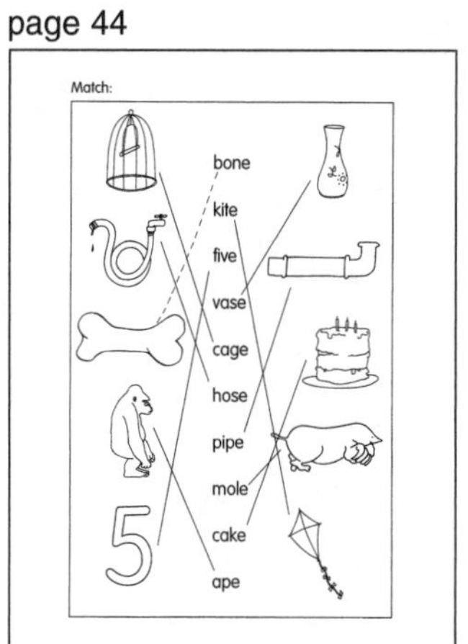
Match:
bone
kite
five
vase
cage
hose
pipe
mole
cake
ape

page 45

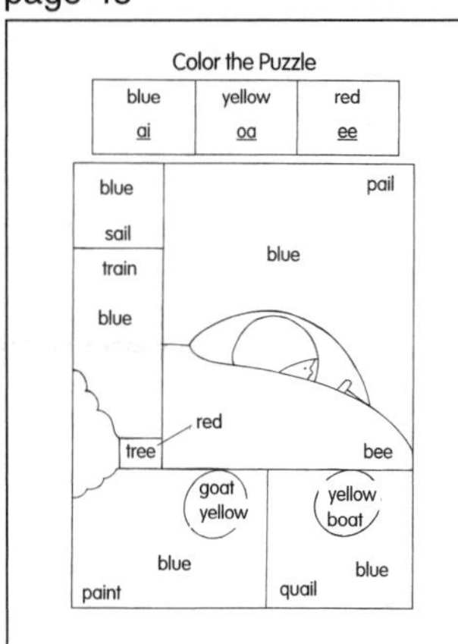

Color the Puzzle

blue	yellow	red
ai	oa	ee

blue
sail
train
blue
blue
pail
red
tree
bee
goat
yellow
yellow
boat
blue
paint
quail
blue

page 46

Pets at School

"Wake up, Eve," said June.
"Miss Lane said we can take pets to school.
I don't want to be late."

"This is my pet cat," said June.
"His name is Dave.
He likes to take naps on my bed."

"I have three pet mice," said Zeke.
"My mom and dad gave them to me.
My mice like to eat seeds."

I read this story to ____________

Note: You may need to help your learner with the special words below.
said school this
want have

page 47

"This is my dog, Mike," said Kate.
"Sit, Mike. Shake my hand.
He wants a bone to eat."

"I have a pet," said Miss Lane.
It is long and has scales.
"It is a black snake!"

We had fun with the pets at school.

I read this story to ____________

Read the story again.
Circle the long vowel words.
"Wake up, Eve."

page 48

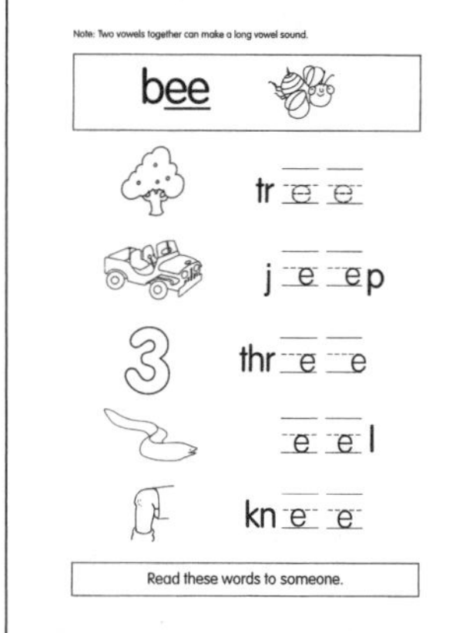

Note: Two vowels together can make a long vowel sound.

bee

tr e e
j e e p
thr e e
e e l
kn e e

Read these words to someone.

page 49

How to Take a Bath

1. Read 2. Cut 3. Paste in order

Fill the tub with water.
Add bubble bath.
Get into the tub.
Wash with soap and a rag.
Get out of the tub and dry off.
Get dressed.

page 51

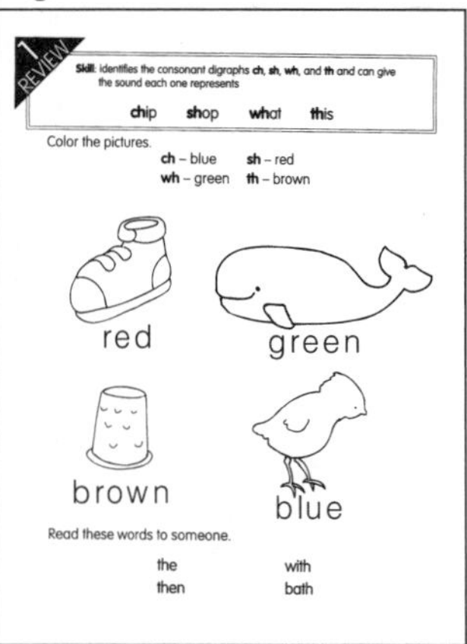

Skill: identifies the consonant digraphs ch, sh, wh, and th and can give the sound each one represents

chip shop what this

Color the pictures.
ch – blue sh – red
wh – green th – brown

red green
brown blue

Read these words to someone.
the with
then bath

page 52

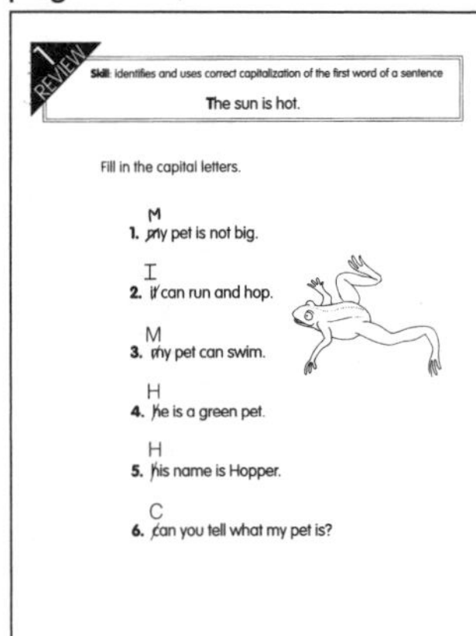

Skill: identifies and uses correct capitalization of the first word of a sentence

The sun is hot.

Fill in the capital letters.

1. M my pet is not big.
2. I i can run and hop.
3. M my pet can swim.
4. H he is a green pet.
5. H his name is Hopper.
6. C can you tell what my pet is?

page 53

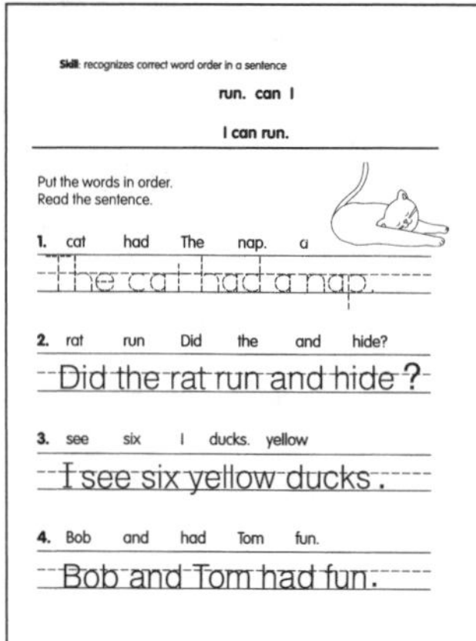

Skill: recognizes correct word order in a sentence

run. can I
I can run.

Put the words in order.
Read the sentence.

1. cat had The nap. a
The cat had a nap.
2. rat run Did the and hide?
Did the rat run and hide?
3. see six I ducks. yellow
I see six yellow ducks.
4. Bob and had Tom fun.
Bob and Tom had fun.

page 54

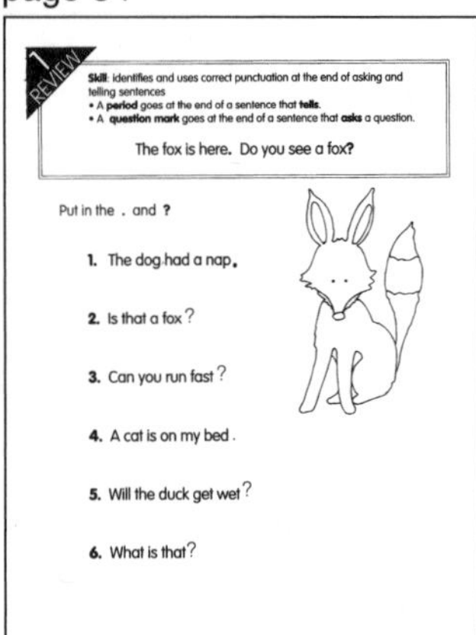

Skill: identifies and uses correct punctuation at the end of asking and telling sentences
• A period goes at the end of a sentence that tells.
• A question mark goes at the end of a sentence that asks a question.

The fox is here. Do you see a fox?

Put in the . and ?

1. The dog had a nap.
2. Is that a fox?
3. Can you run fast?
4. A cat is on my bed.
5. Will the duck get wet?
6. What is that?

page 55

Skill: can write telling and asking sentences using correct capital letters and end punctuation

Write a sentence that tells about this monkey.

answers will vary

Write a sentence that asks a question about the monkey.

page 56

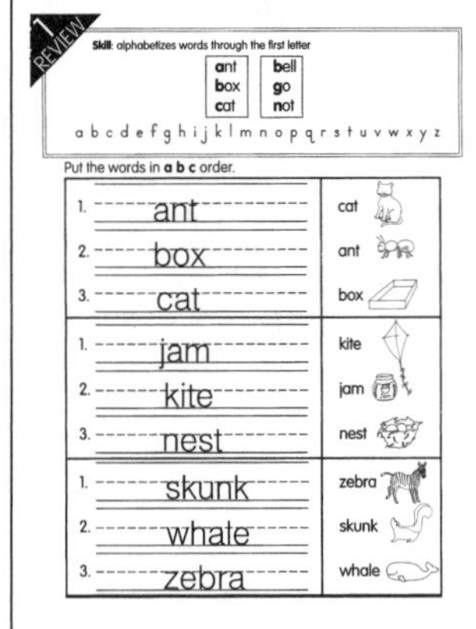

Skill: alphabetizes words through the first letter

ant bell
box go
cat not

a b c d e f g h i j k l m n o p q r s t u v w x y z

Put the words in a b c order.

1. ant 2. box 3. cat	cat ant box
1. jam 2. kite 3. nest	kite jam nest
1. skunk 2. whale 3. zebra	zebra skunk whale

page57

Parents: You may read this to your child and have him/her give you the answer or have your child read it on his/her own.
Skill: draw conclusions from given facts

The sky is dark.
Water is falling from the sky.
Conclusion: It is raining.

Circle the answer.

1. I get a can.
I take the lid off.
I put food in a dish.
I am feeding the...?

2. I get a rag.
I get soap.
I get a tub.
I am washing...?

3. It is cold.
Snow comes down.
The wind blows.
I put on...?

4. I am sad.
I made a mess.
It is hard to clean.
I spilled...?

page 58

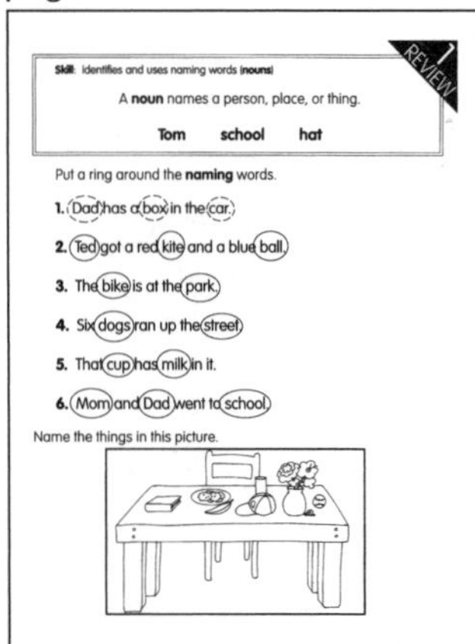

Skill: identifies and uses naming words (nouns)

A noun names a person, place, or thing.

Tom school hat

Put a ring around the naming words.

1. Dad has a box in the car.
2. Ted got a red kite and a blue ball.
3. The bike is at the park.
4. Six dogs ran up the street.
5. That cup has milk in it.
6. Mom and Dad went to school.

Name the things in this picture.

page 59

Skill: identifies plural nouns ending in s

one - cat
more than one - cats

Write.

dogs	cup
cups	bats
bat	dog

page 60

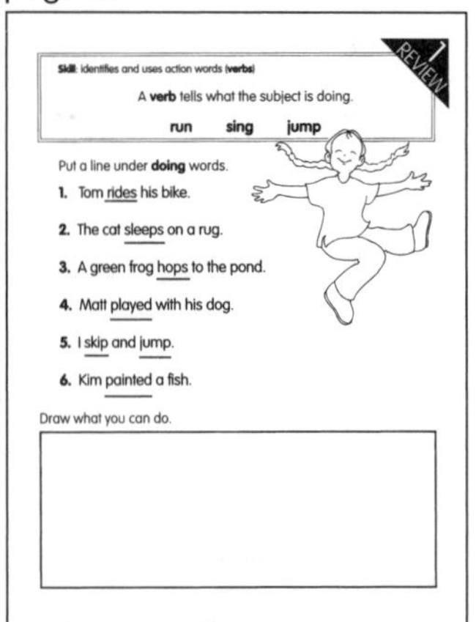

Skill: identifies and uses action words (verbs)

A verb tells what the subject is doing.

run sing jump

Put a line under doing words.

1. Tom rides his bike.
2. The cat sleeps on a rug.
3. A green frog hops to the pond.
4. Matt played with his dog.
5. I skip and jump.
6. Kim painted a fish.

Draw what you can do.

page 61

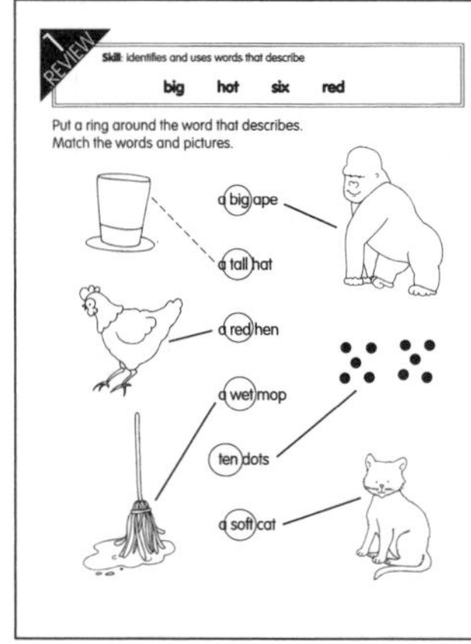

Skill: identifies and uses words that describe

big hot six red

Put a ring around the word that describes.
Match the words and pictures.

a big ape
a tall hat
a red hen
a wet mop
ten dots
a soft cat

On the City Streets

Do you see any plants? ______________________

Color Puzzle

The number names will be purple.
The color names will be red.
The boy's names will be black.
The girl's names will be yellow.

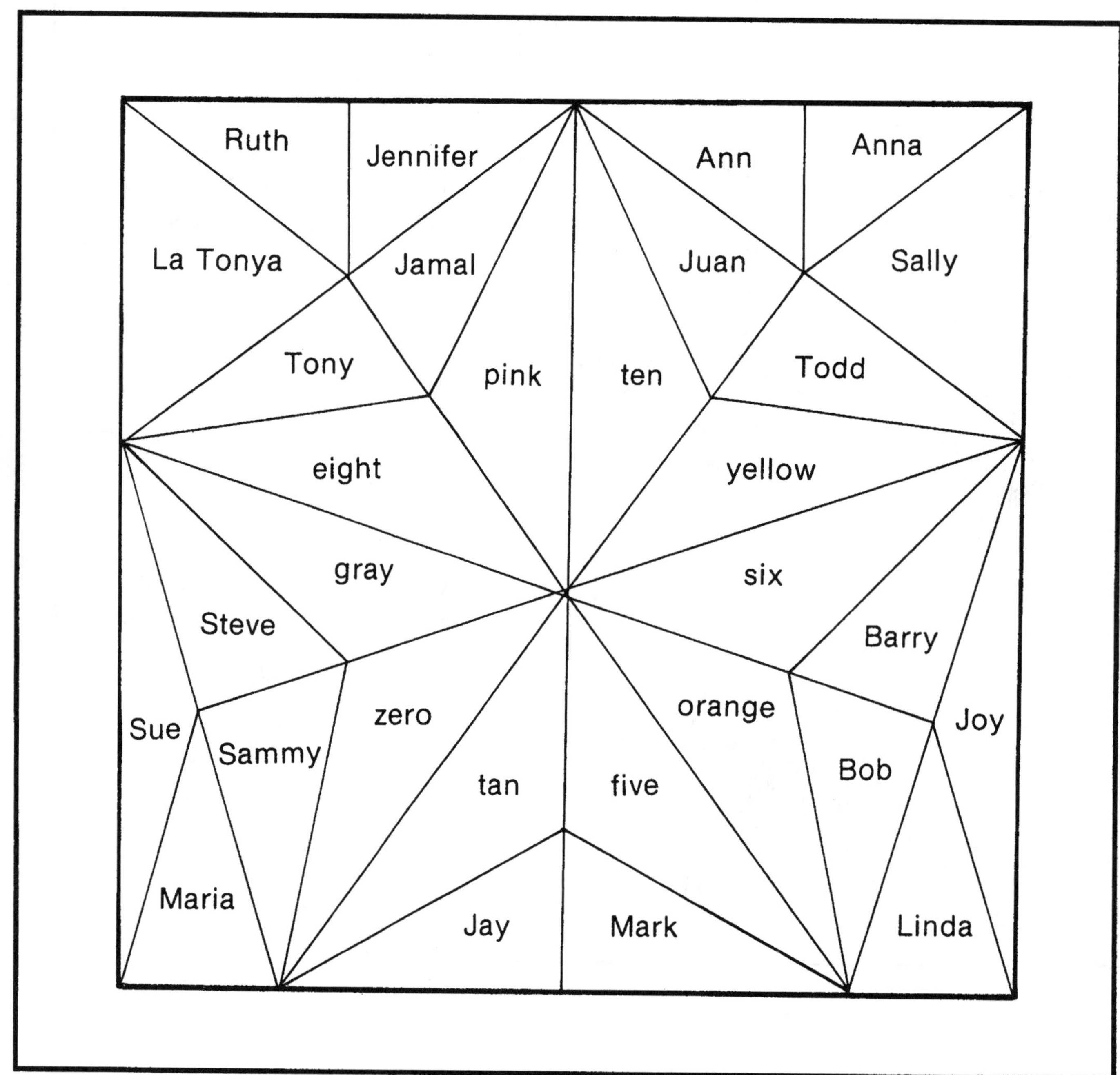

What Will You Find?

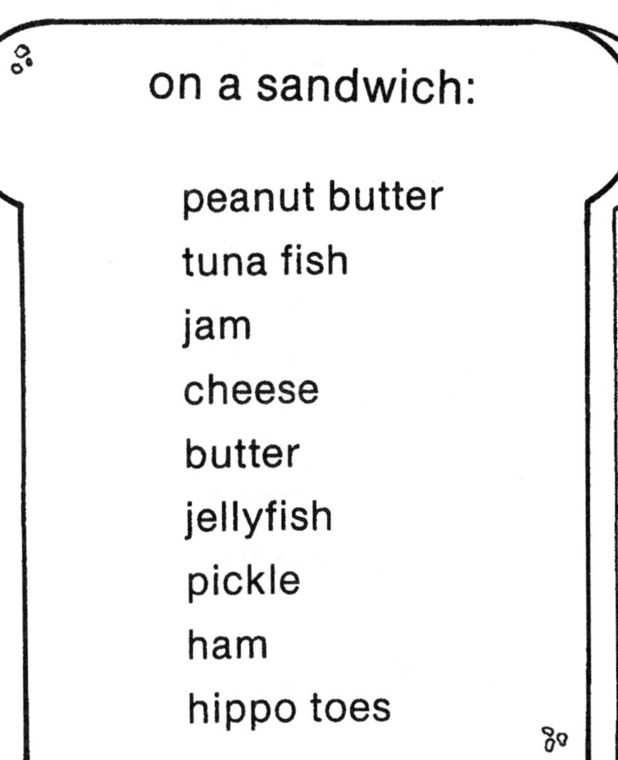

on a sandwich:

peanut butter
tuna fish
jam
cheese
butter
jellyfish
pickle
ham
hippo toes

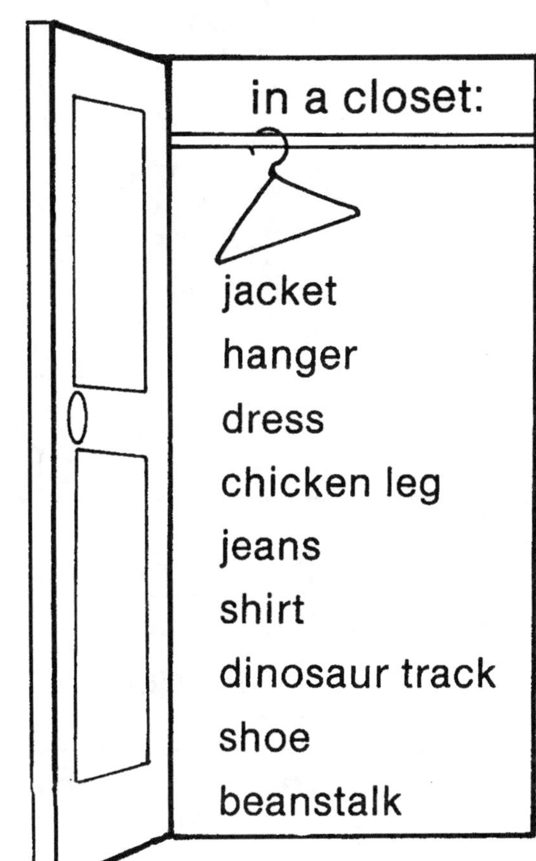

in a closet:

jacket
hanger
dress
chicken leg
jeans
shirt
dinosaur track
shoe
beanstalk

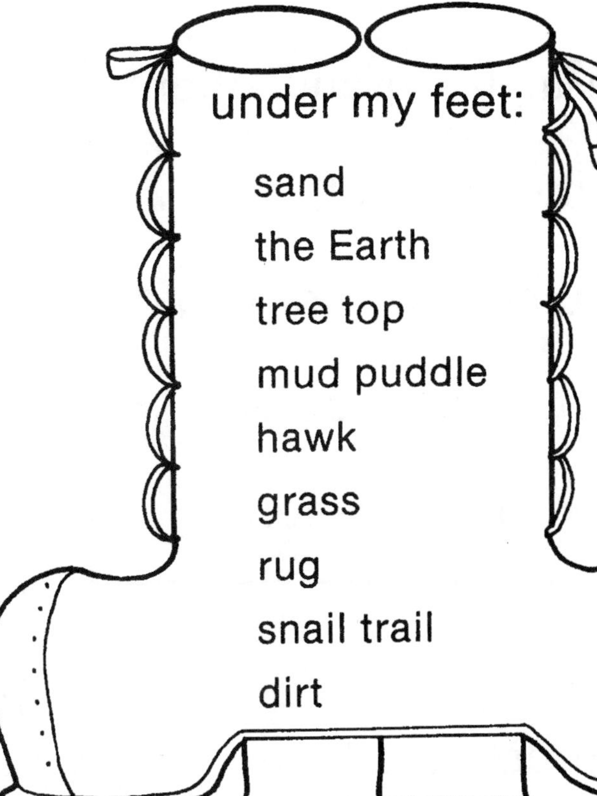

under my feet:

sand
the Earth
tree top
mud puddle
hawk
grass
rug
snail trail
dirt

over my head:

sun
rainbow
green grass
stars
hat
moon
sidewalk
footprints
cloud

Who Where When

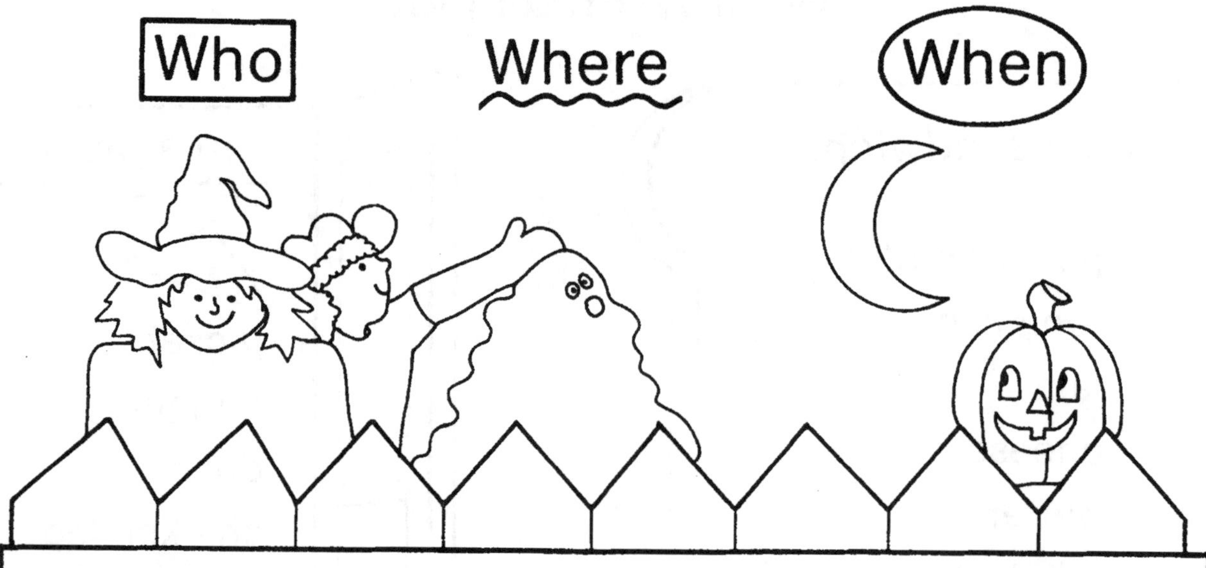

by the fence	during the night
last Halloween	under the table
excited children	a tired farmer
in a jar	in the lunch box
the funny clown	Ralph's grandfather
every day	after school
huge football players	tomorrow morning
around the school	the busy doctor
on my head	on my vacation

How many who words? ______

How many where words? ______

How many when words? ______

How to Catch a Tadpole

1. Read 2. Cut 3. Paste in order

	1
	2
	3
	4
	5
	6

Put holes in the lid.	Look in the water until you see tadpoles.
Put the lid on the jar and take them home.	Find a jar at your house.
Go to a pond.	Scoop up some tadpoles in your jar.

The little tadpoles will grow up to be frogs.

Draw a big frog sitting on a log.
Make the log in a pond.

Write the Missing Letter

Read and Answer

yes no

1. Did the pig get in the mud? ______________
2. Is the rat on the mat? ______________
3. Is the pig wet? ______________
4. Did the rat get a rag? ______________
5. Is the bug big? ______________
6. Is a hat on the pig? ______________

Read and Answer

yes no

1. Did the snake hide in the cave? ____________

2. Did Kate ride up the hill? ____________

3. Did Kate and Pete meet at the top? ____________

4. Is it a hot day? ____________

5. Did Pete hike up the hill? ____________

6. Can a snake ride a bike? ____________

Read and Draw

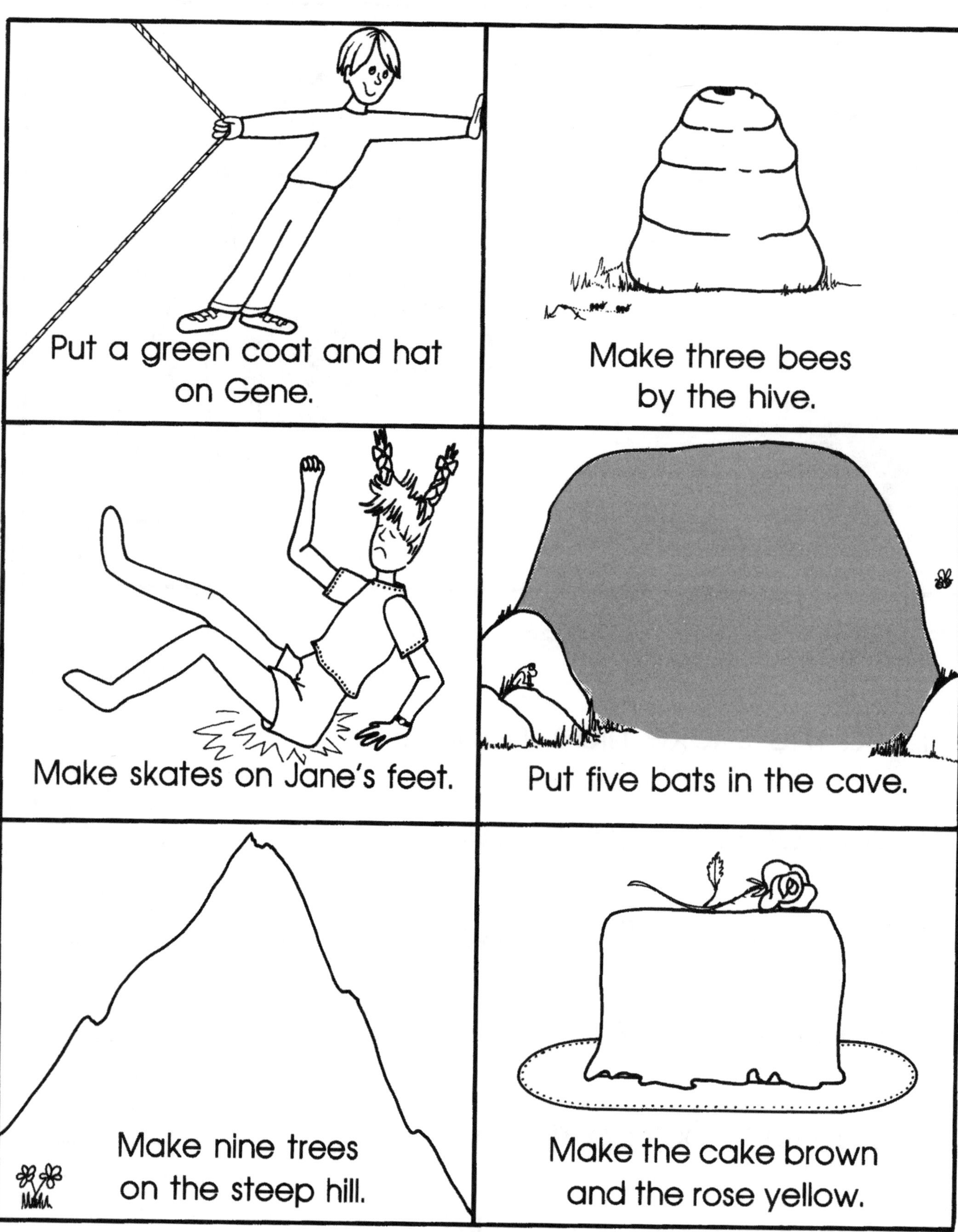

Put a green coat and hat on Gene.
Make three bees by the hive.
Make skates on Jane's feet.
Put five bats in the cave.
Make nine trees on the steep hill.
Make the cake brown and the rose yellow.

Write the words that rhyme in the boxes.

see	get	zoo

bow	bee	three
bet	shoe	set
we	too	wet
let	he	moo

Follow the words that rhyme with **take** to get to the **cake**.

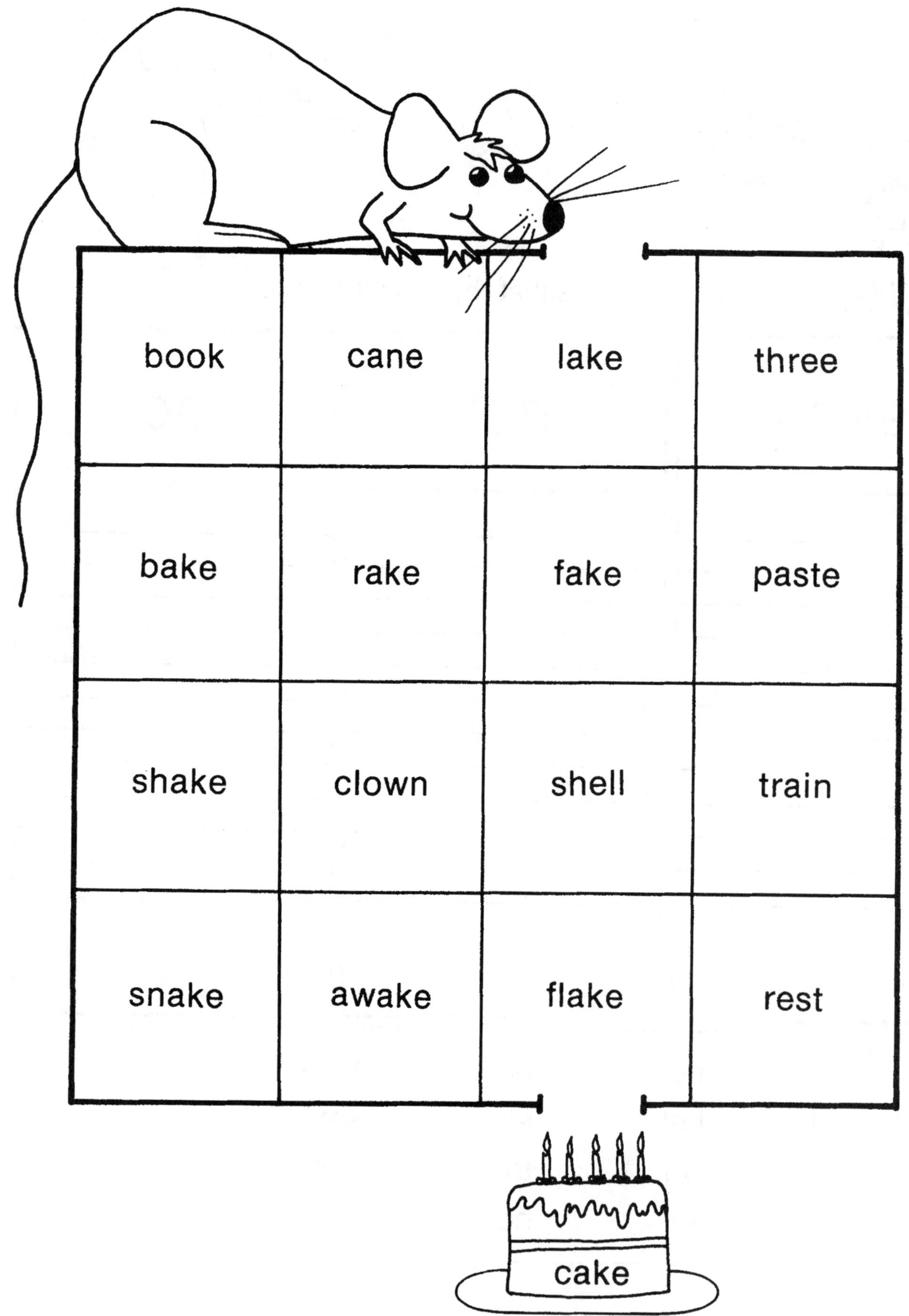

Making Big Words

Write the compound words.

rain + bow =

cup + cake =

basket + ball =

jelly + fish =

skate + board =

gold + fish =

Draw pictures of the new words.

Making Big Words

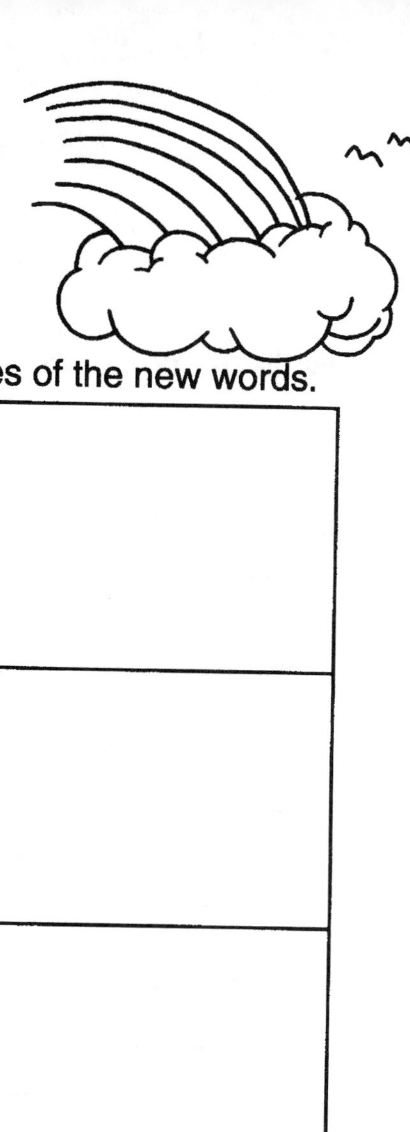

Write the compound words.

Draw pictures of the new words.

rain + bow =

cup + cake =

basket + ball =

jelly + fish =

skate + board =

gold + fish =

Fill in the Blanks

Think about the underlined word.
Write a new word that means the same thing.

1. The <u>small</u> frog hopped into the pond. __________

2. I saw a <u>large</u> elephant at the zoo. __________

3. Did you hear the teacher <u>speak</u>? __________

4. Please <u>build</u> me a swing. __________

5. Don't <u>scream</u>, the baby is asleep. __________

6. Please <u>close</u> the door. __________

little	hard	big
make	leap	yell
shut	talk	fast

Name the Picture

Write two words that name each picture.

Word Box

baby	infant	scream
bright	jump	shiny
build	leap	sick
ill	make	yell

Match Opposites

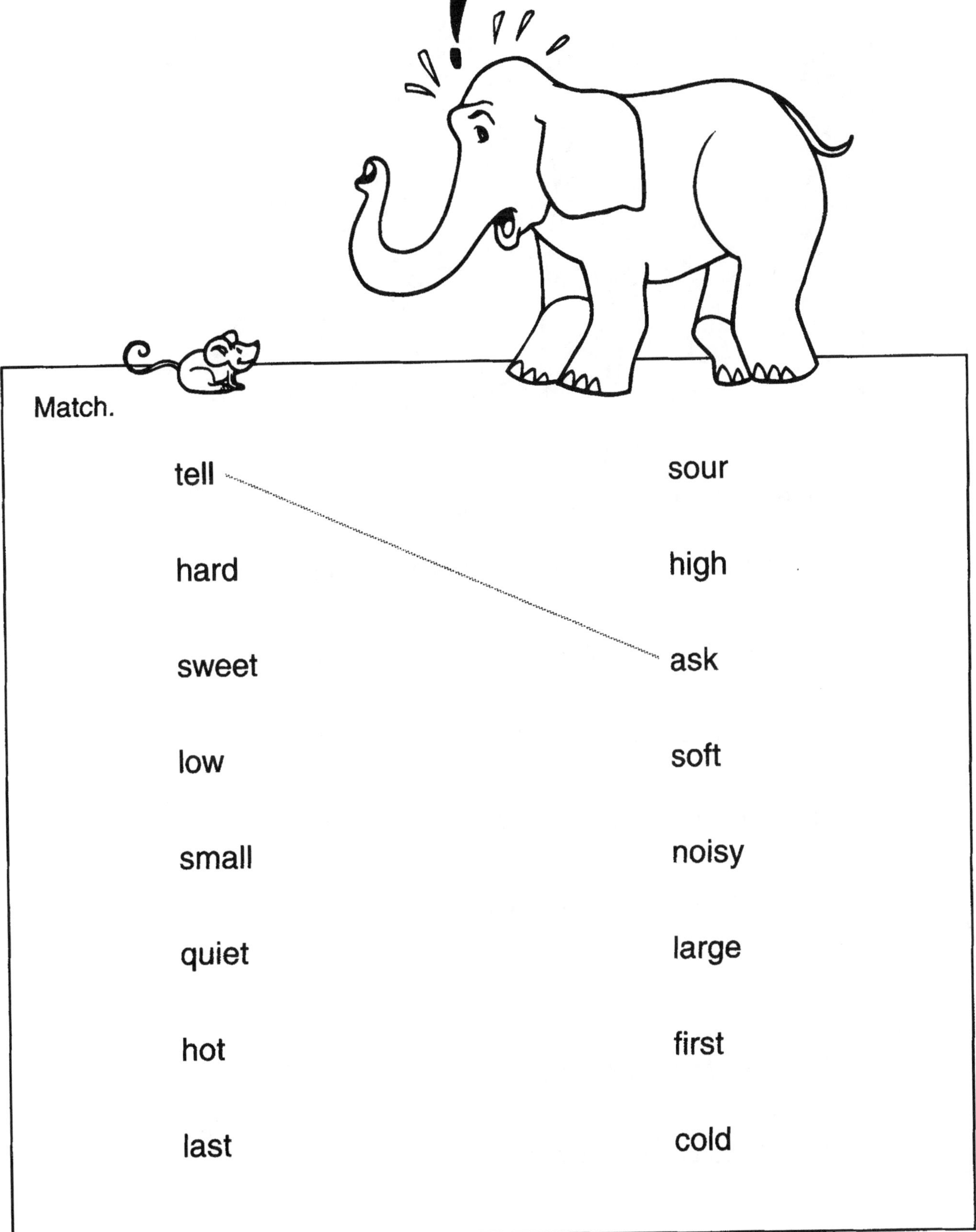

Match.

tell	sour
hard	high
sweet	ask
low	soft
small	noisy
quiet	large
hot	first
last	cold

Homophones

Circle the right word.

1. Do you (know no) how to make your lunch?

2. I read a story about a brave (night knight).

3. Dad put a new (pane pain) of glass in the window.

4. Tim didn't (know no) the way to the store.

5. May I have a (peace piece) of pie?

6. How many (rose rows) of beans did you plant?

7. We had to wait an (our hour) to catch the bus.

8. Did you eat the (hole whole) pizza?

Read the Words

clown

gown

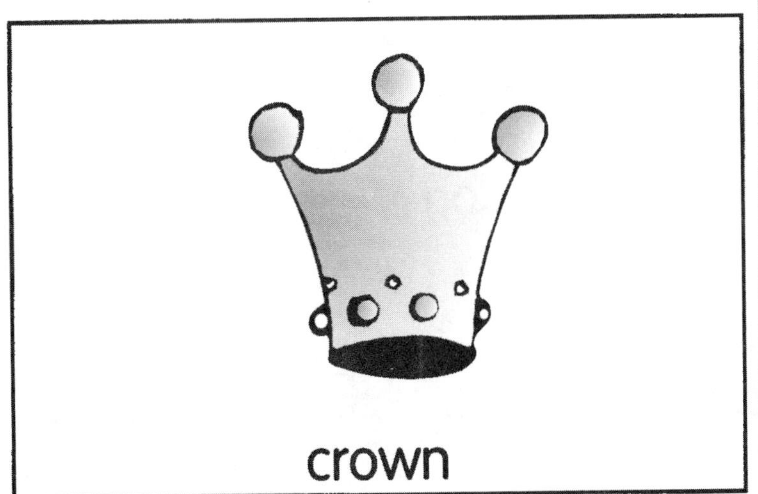

crown

down

brown

drown

gown

clown

frown

town

crown

I read these words to ________________.

Write the name of the picture on the line.

crown

____

______________ ______________

Fill in the blanks.

1. She had a rip in her yellow gown.

2. The cl__________ did tricks with a br__________ dog.

3. The king went d__________ t__________ to get his cr__________.

I read these sentences to ______________.

Read the story.
Put an X on the words that rhyme with <u>down</u>.

The Sad King

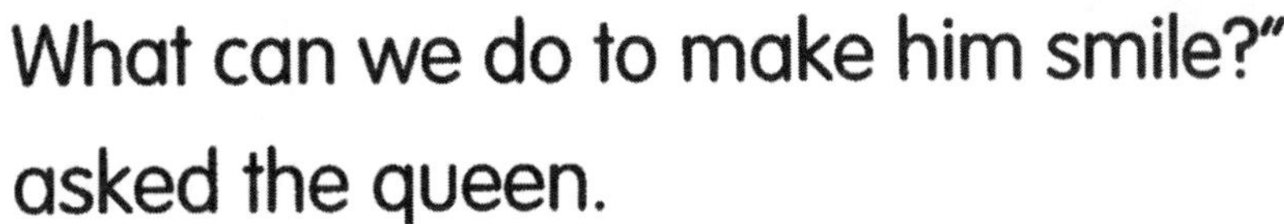

"The king is not happy.
See that big frown.
What can we do to make him smile?"
asked the queen.

"I saw a clown when I was downtown,"
said the prince.
We can get her to make the king smile."

The clown came in a funny, brown gown.
She did tricks for the king.

"I will not frown now," said the king.
"I like the tricks you did."
And the king gave the clown his crown.

I read this story to ______________.

Note: Your learner may need help reading the special words on this page.

happy smile asked prince king queen

Telling Sentences

A **period** is used at the end of a sentence that tells you something.

Put a . at the end of the sentences.

1. I am Jim
2. My sister is Ann
3. We can go to the park
4. It will be fun
5. We will see lions
6. We will see monkeys
7. Then we can eat ice cream

Asking Sentences

A **question mark** is used at the end of a sentence that **asks** something.

Put a **?** at the end of the sentences.

1. Can you jump rope
2. Do you want to go to my house
3. Can we go to the pet shop
4. Was the dog funny
5. Is that a fox
6. What is that
7. Do you like pizza

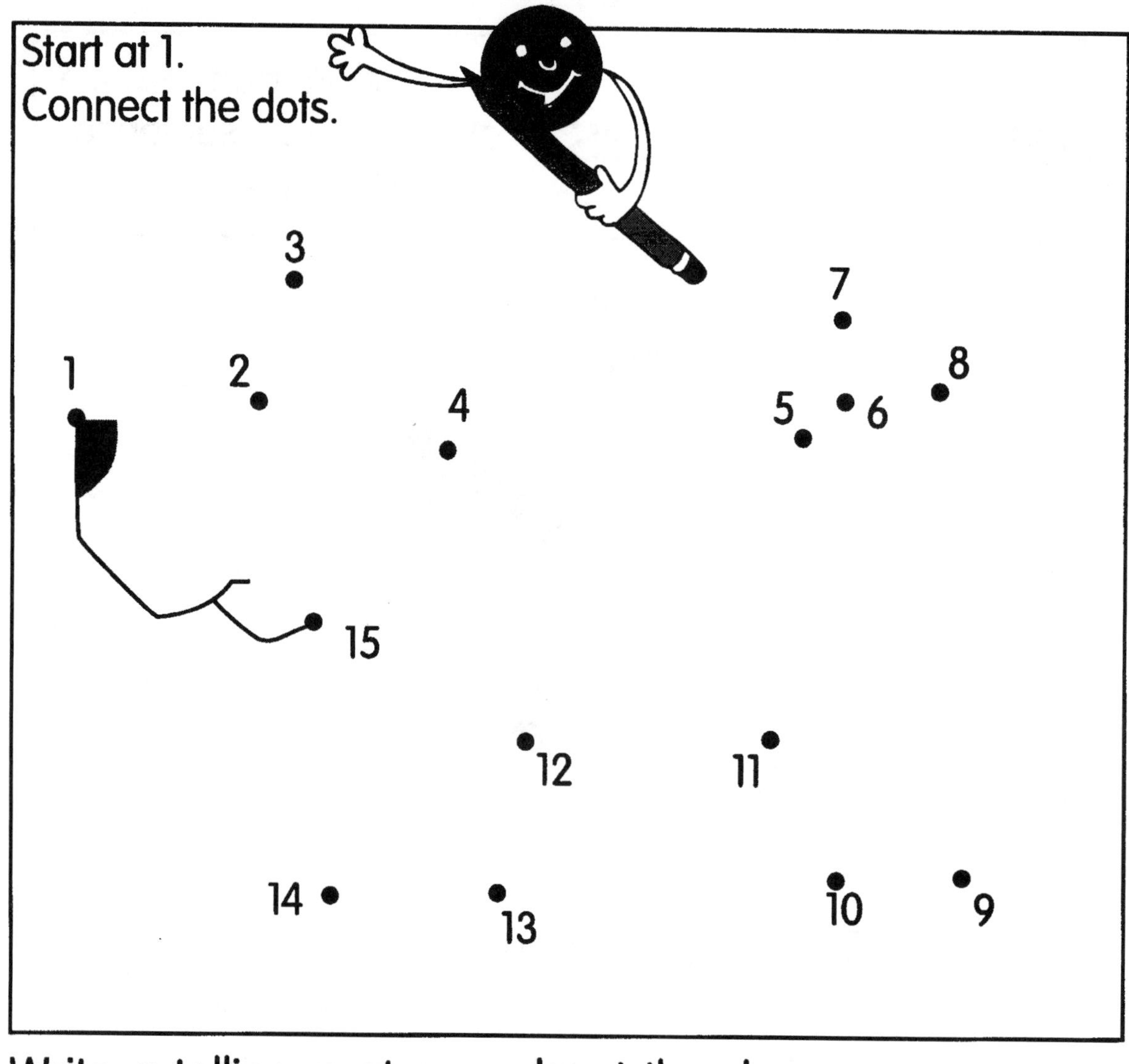

Write a telling sentence about the dog.

Write an asking sentence about the dog.

Names start with capital letters.

A H T B N C K D E Q Y

A B C D E F G H I J K L M N O P Q R S T U V W X Y Z

ann Ann

bob

kim

dan

jamal

ben

jose

nancy

My name is

Write capital letters.
Use periods or question marks.

T
the fox is in a box.
C
can it get out?

is that a cat

no, it is a skunk

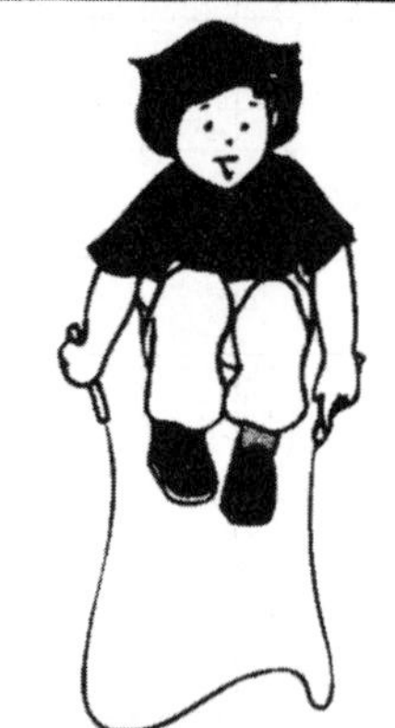

do you like to jump rope

i think it is fun

when did you get that toy

can I play with it

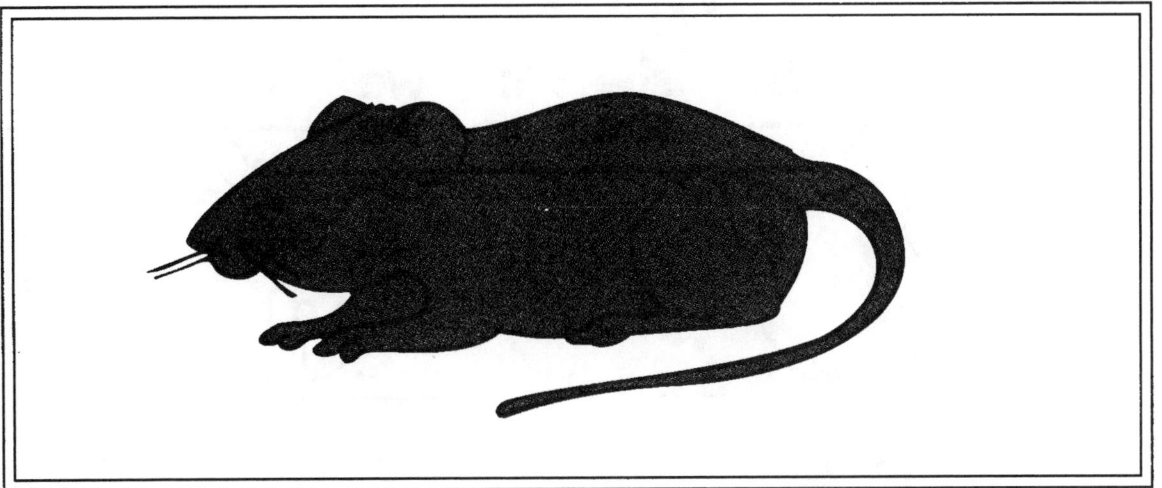

What is missing in this story?

Bud

can you come over

my pet rat bud got out

can you help me catch him

i got him

quick, get his pen

lock the lid

thank you

you were a big help

Who Is It?

he she it we

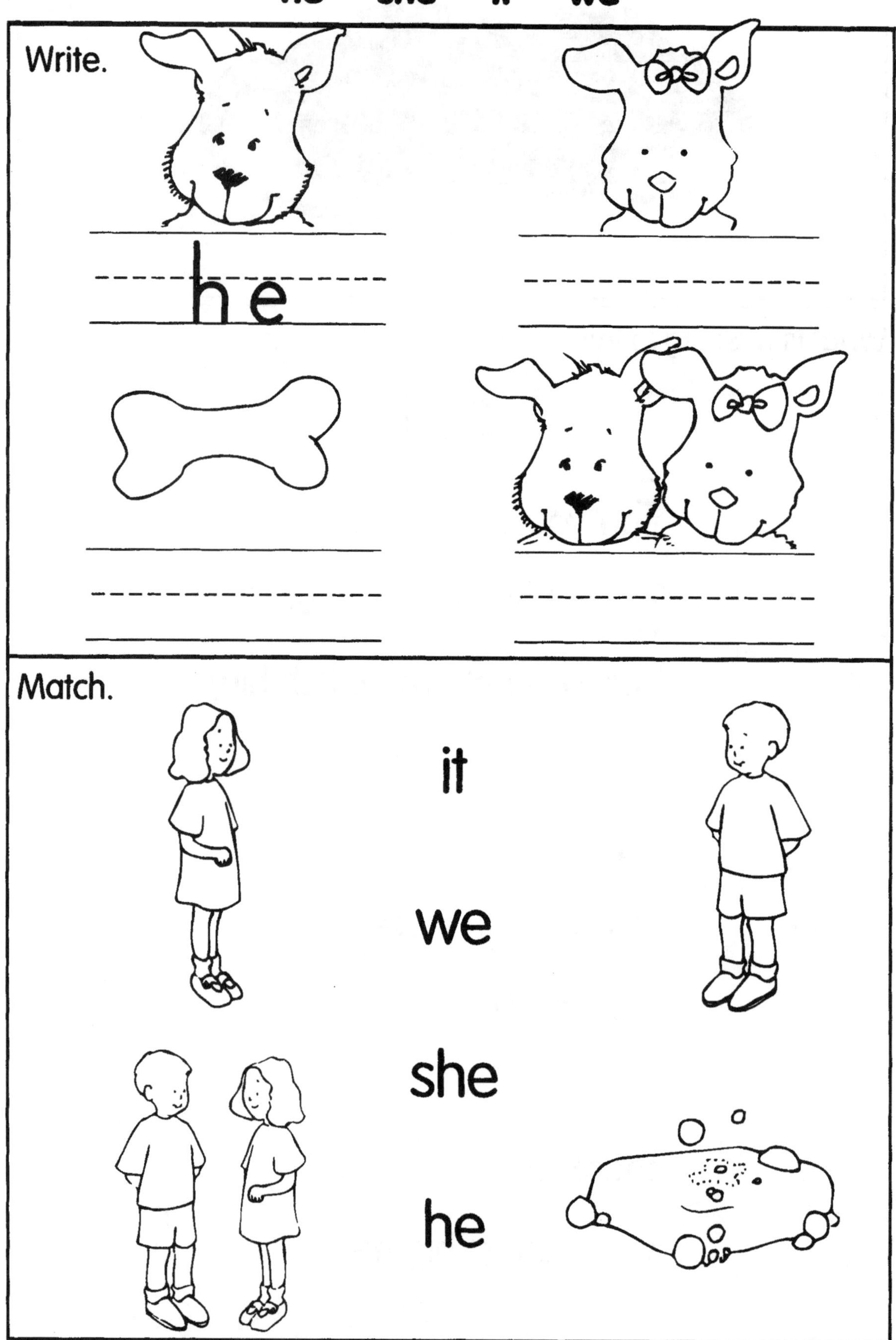

Write.

He **She** **We** **it**

Dad has a box.

He puts tools in it.

Ted has a red kite.

__________ likes to fly __________.

Ann and I got a big ball.

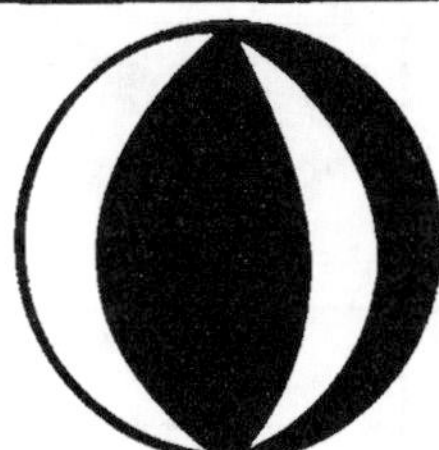

__________ play with __________.

Betty has a bike.

__________ can ride __________.

One and More Than One

Add s if it is more than one.

cup		

The Toy Elephant

Color **one** orange.
Color **more than one** brown.

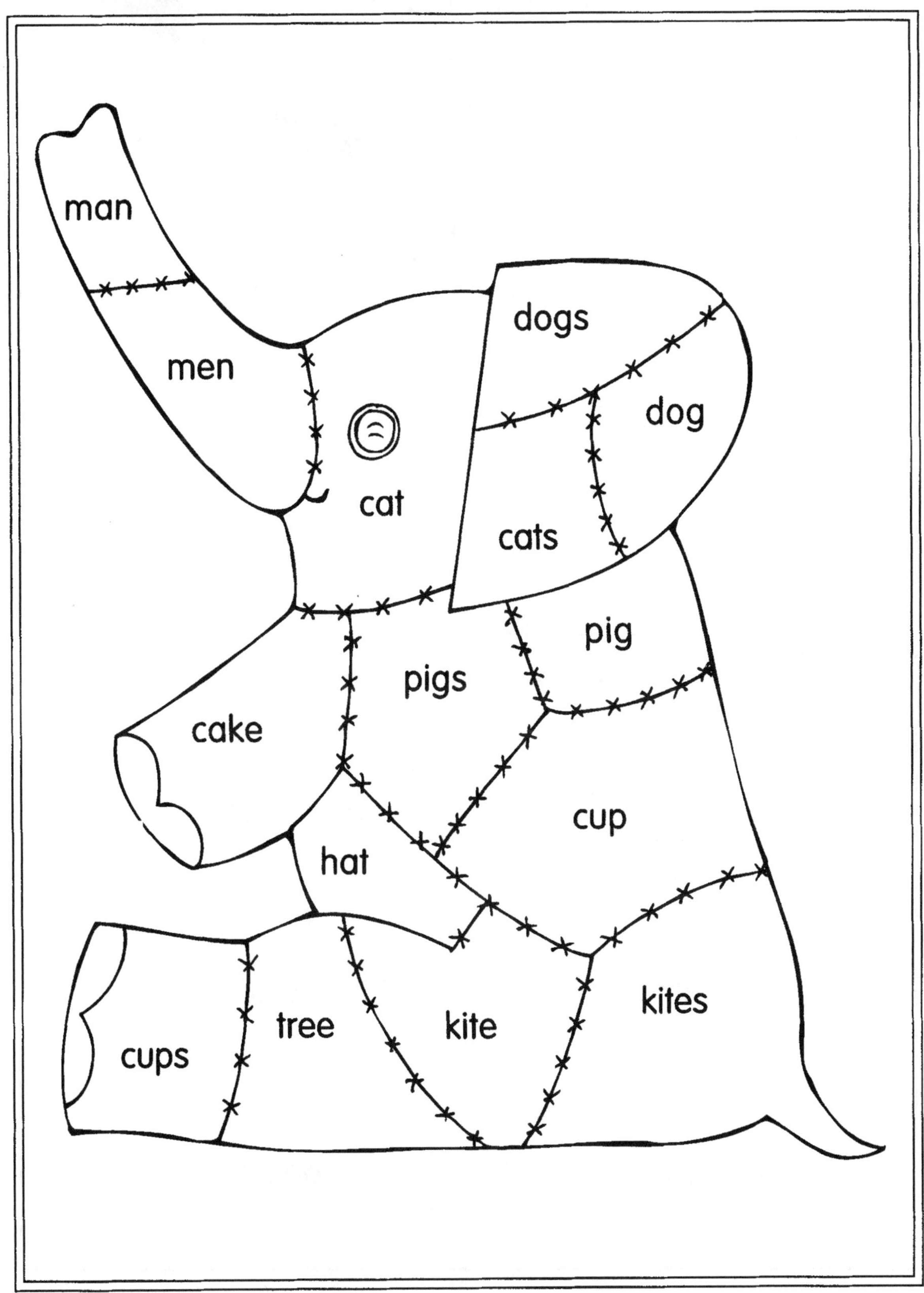

Making Smaller Words

is not - **isn't**

cannot - **can't**

do not - **don't**

Write.

1. That isn't my cat.

2. I ____________ find my kite.

3. I ____________ want to go.

4. I ____________ like snakes.

5. That ____________ my dog.

6. Mom ____________ go now.

Match.

isn't	cannot
don't	is not
can't	do not

Write.

1. Bob cannot ride a bike.

   Bob can't ride a bike.

2. I do not want to go.

   I ______ want to go.

3. That is not his pet.

   That ______ his pet.

4. We cannot run in the street.

   We ______ run in the street.

Using <u>is</u> and <u>are</u>

one - **is**	more than one - **are**

Circle the right word.

The dog (**is** **are**) small.

Sam and Tom (**is** **are**) here.

My kite (**is** **are**) yellow.

The cats (**is** **are**) playing.

We (**is** **are**) going to Disneyland.

What Does It Look Like?

Circle the picture that matches the words.

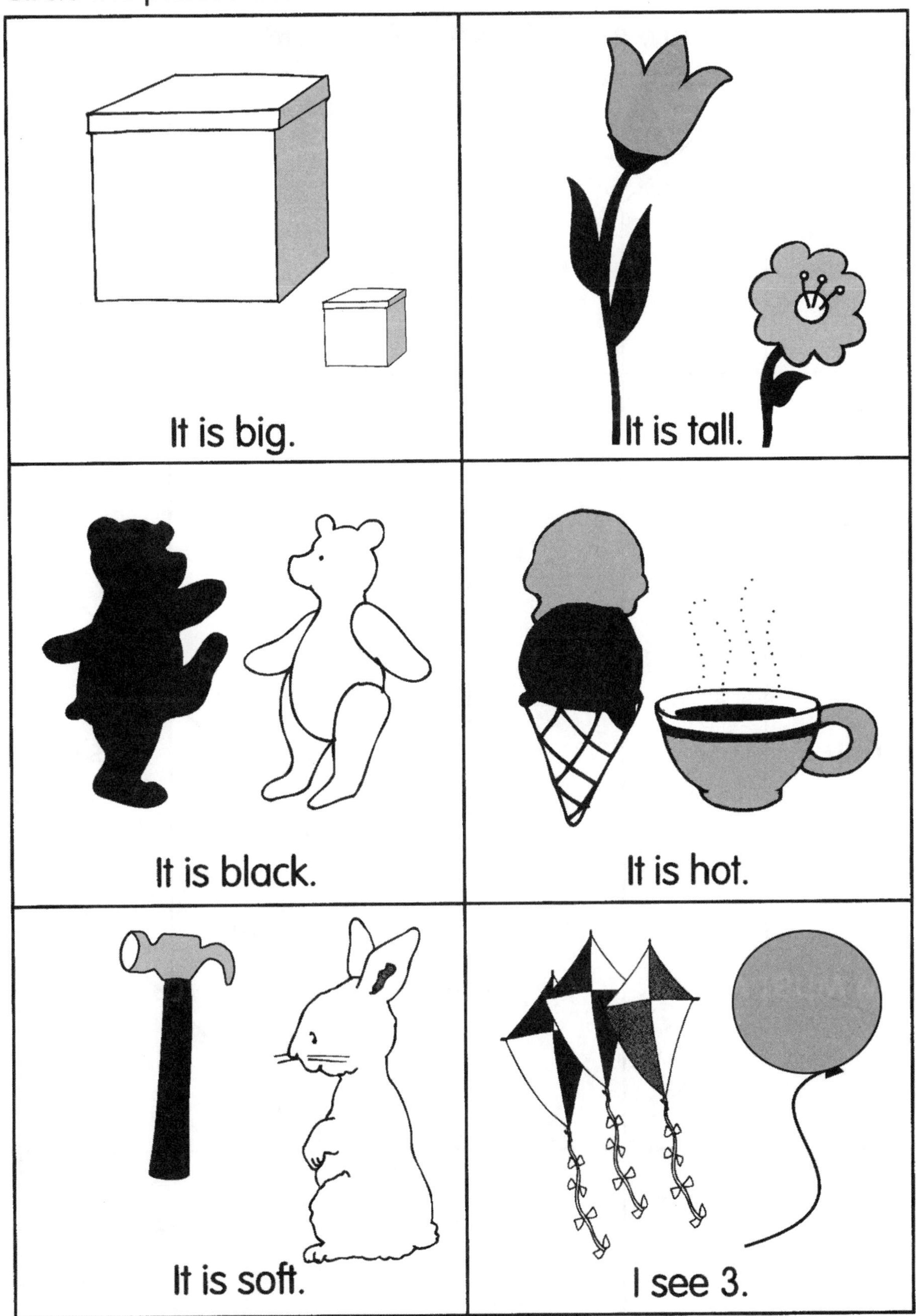
It is big.
It is tall.
It is black.
It is hot.
It is soft.
I see 3.

Find the Surprise

things you can do - Color **green.**
names of things - Color **blue.**
how things look - Color **red.**

box nut dog pig

bed big red ten six kite

pan fast tall brown fat nest

hop sit

yell skip run

fox sand

TV dig tree

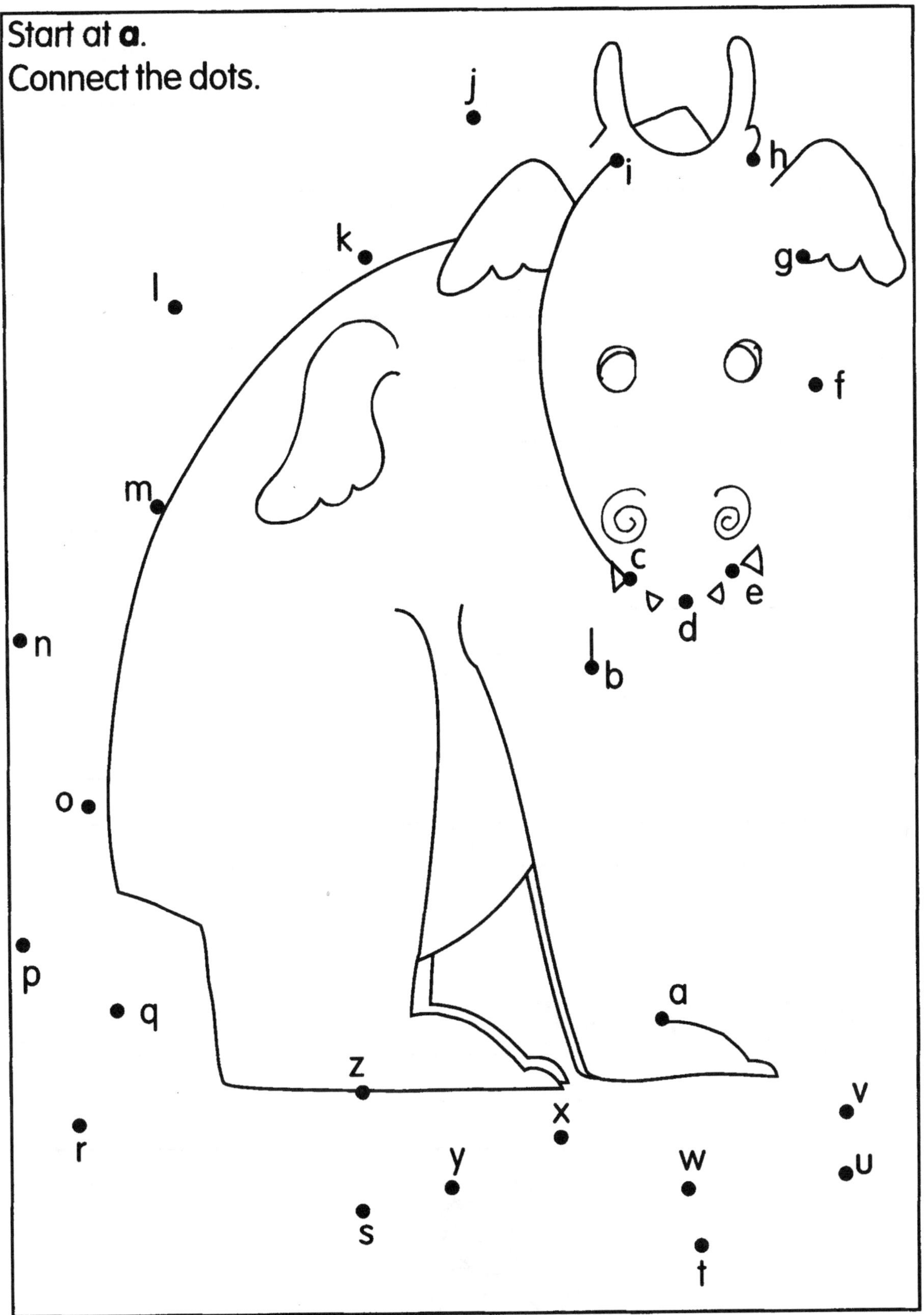

This dragon ____________ green.

is are

Games I Have Played

1. ______________________

2. ______________________

3. ______________________

4. ______________________

5. ______________________

6. ______________________

7. ______________________

8. ______________________

9. ______________________

10. ______________________

My favorite game is:

____

This is how to play ______________________.
my favorite game

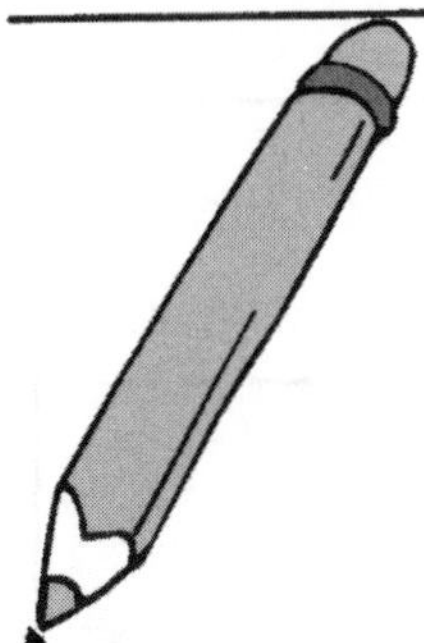

Draw you and your friends playing the game.

Second Grade Language

When I was only one year old...

I couldn't...

I was able to...

I looked like this.

When I am grown...

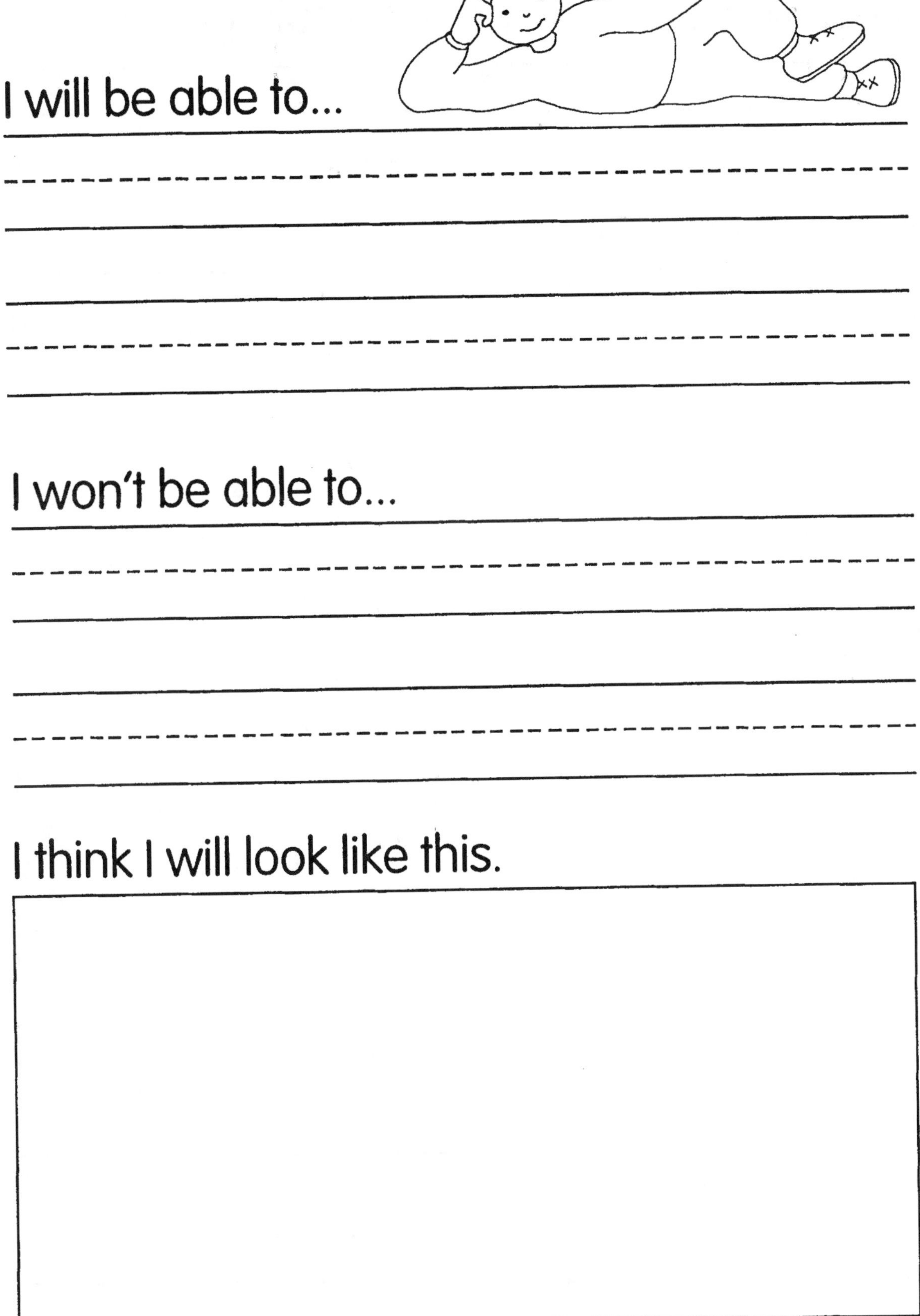

I will be able to...

I won't be able to...

I think I will look like this.

A New Pet

If I could have a new pet, I would get a:

It would look like this:

I would name it:

How to Make a Sandwich

1. Read 2. Cut 3. Paste in order
1
2
3
4
5
6

Cut the sandwich in two.	Open the jar of peanut butter.
Eat it up!	Get out the bread, peanut butter, and a knife.
Sit down and take a big bite.	Put a lot of peanut butter on the bread.

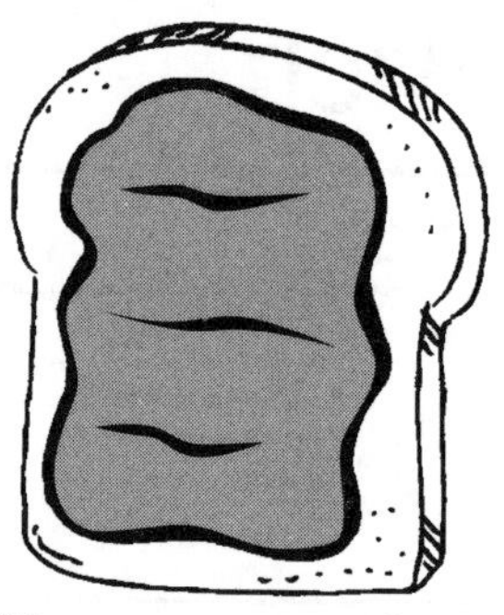 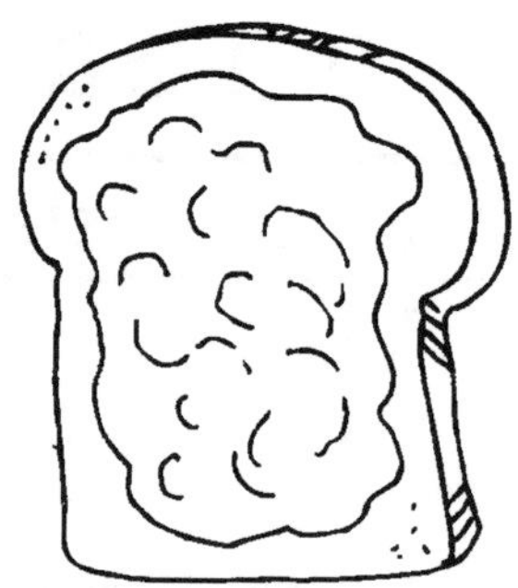

Do you like peanut butter and jelly sandwiches? ____________

What kind of sandwich do you like best?

How do you make it?

How to Plant a Seed

1. Read 2. Cut 3. Paste in order

	1
	2
	3
	4
	5
	6

Water the seeds.	Pick out the seeds you want to plant.
Fill the hole with dirt and pat it down.	Now the seeds can grow.
Next you must dig a hole in the dirt.	Drop the seeds into the hole.

Second Grade Language

Draw what you think will grow from the seeds in the pot.

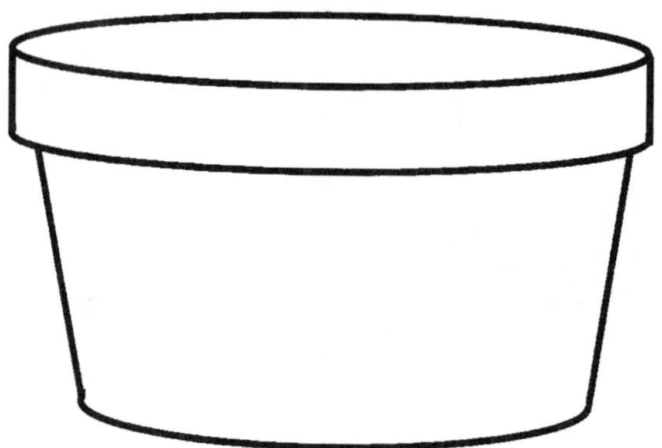

REVIEW 2

Skill: Arranges words in order to form a sentence.

hat was The red.

The hat was red.

Put the words in order to make a sentence.

1. funny. That was pig a

That was a funny pig.

2. you Can swim?

3. pizza? Do like you

4. dog down ran My the street.

5. milk Put in cup. my the

Second Grade Language

2 REVIEW

Skill: Begins a sentence with a capital letter.

Bob went to the zoo.

Will you play with me?

Fill in the capital letters.

1. M
my dog is small.

2. his name is Pepper.

3. he can run and jump.

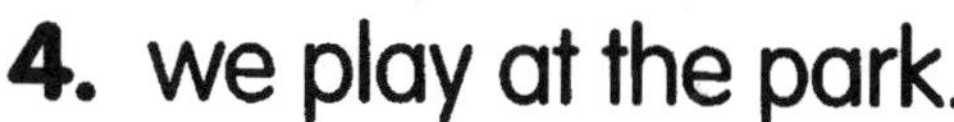

4. we play at the park.

5. he can fetch a ball.

6. mother won't let him sleep with me.

Skill: Can write a statement and a question using correct end punctuation.

Write a telling sentence about this cat.

Write an asking sentence about this cat.

2 REVIEW

Skill: Identify proper nouns. A **proper noun** is the name of a special person, place, or thing.

Tom   Bishop School   Cheerios®

Put a ring around the proper nouns.

Patty	Jan	Barbie®
Goat	Yellowstone Park	Anna
What	Bob	Texas
Green Street	Jello®	Jose
Play	Ten	Tony

Skill: Begins proper nouns with a capital letter.

Amy **J**amal **K**elly

Write the names.

sam Sam

tim

kisha

lee

mary

carlos

pete

joe

tina

rosa

Skill: Identifies words that tell what is happening. These **doing** words are called **verbs**.

Put a ring around the doing words.

run	work	sing
red	trunk	cut
peek	swim	hat

Draw.

jump	sleep

Skill: Uses the correct forms of **doing** words (verbs) with added endings.

jump	jump**s**	jump**ing**	jump**ed**
hop	hop**s**	hopp**ing**	hopp**ed**

Put a ring around the right word.

The dog (run runs) to get his dinner.

Bob and Tom (

runs) to dinner too.

The kangaroo is (hopping hopped).

He (hopping hopped) all day.

The monkey (jumping jumped) up in the tree.

It will (jump jumps) to the top.

Connie (ride rides) the bike.

Sam will (ride rides) it next.

Matt is (looking looked) for his pet.

He has (looking looked) all day.

2 REVIEW

Skill: Recognizes and uses words that describe things. **Describing words** are called **adjectives**.

big small

Match the picture and the words.
Put a line under the word that tells how it looks.

The box is big.

It is sweet.

Get the black cat.

I saw six fish.

The oatmeal is hot.

My bunny is soft.

Skill: Identifies the two parts of a simple sentence. One part tells **who** or **what** the sentence is about. The other part tells **what happened**.

The monkey ate a banana.

The monkey - *who the sentence is about*
ate a banana - *what happened*

Put a ring around the **who** or **what** part.
Put a line under the **what happened** part.

1. The girls went to the zoo.

2. My birthday cake fell on the floor.

3. His dogs barked all day.

4. The rain came down on my umbrella.

5. The children played a game.

6. The funny clown did tricks.

Skill: Recognize and use short vowel sounds in reading and spelling words.

a - pat   e - ten   i - in

o - hot   u - cup

Read and match.

fox

sun

pen

bat

six

Write.

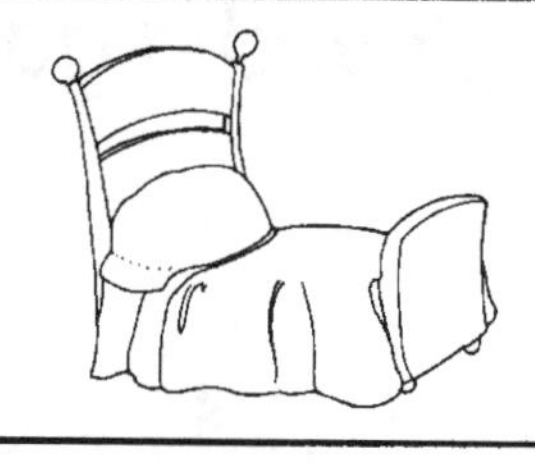

Skill: A word with a single vowel usually has the short sound.

cat **cup** **hop** **sit** **ten**

An **e** at the end of a one-syllable word usually makes the vowel long.

like **cake** **hope** **cute** **Pete**

Read.	Add an **e** and read again.	
can	c a n e	
cub	c u b ___	
bit	b i t ___	
tap	t a p ___	
kit	k i t ___	
rob	r o b ___	

Skill: Recognize and use long vowel sounds in reading and spelling words.

a - cake e - be i - bike
o - go u - cute

Read and match.

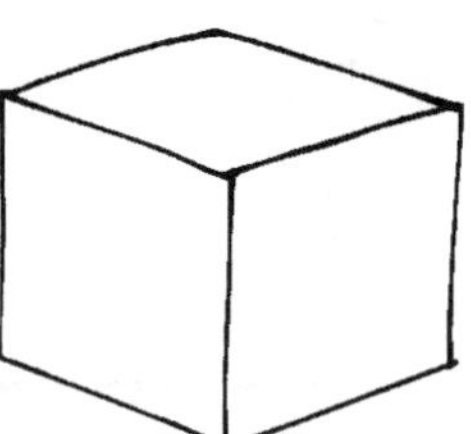

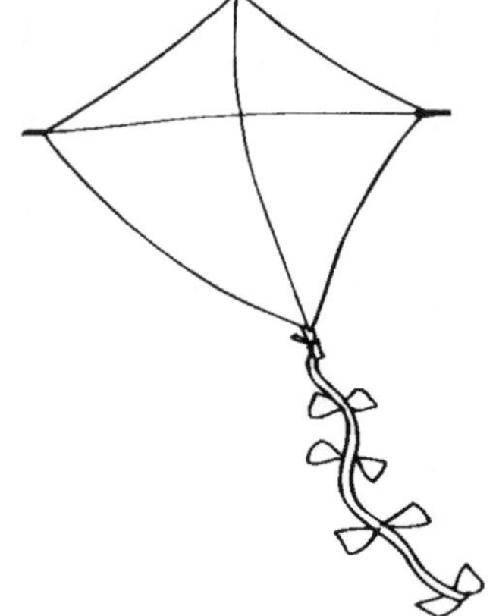

bee

kite

skate

cube

hose

Write.

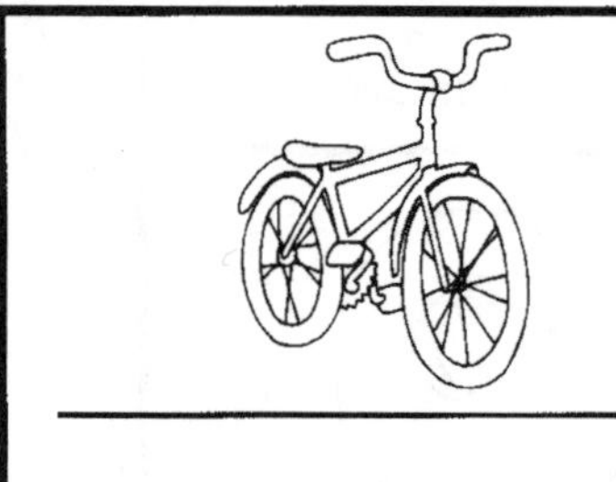

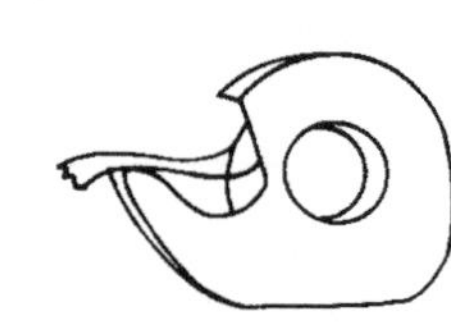

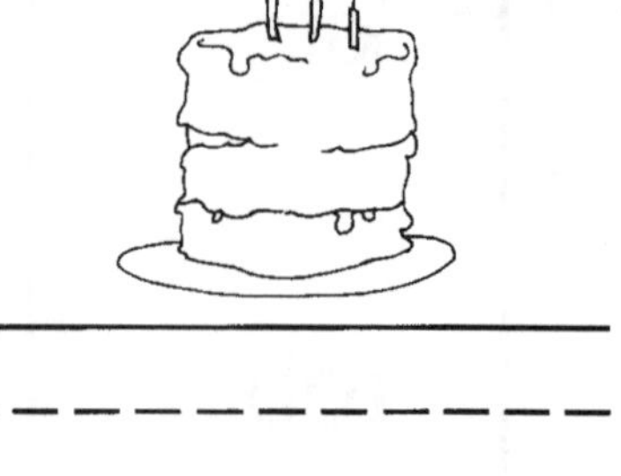

2 REVIEW

Skill: If two vowels are together in a one-syllable word, the first is usually long and the second is silent.

boat **sleep** **tie** **train**

Read the words.
Match.

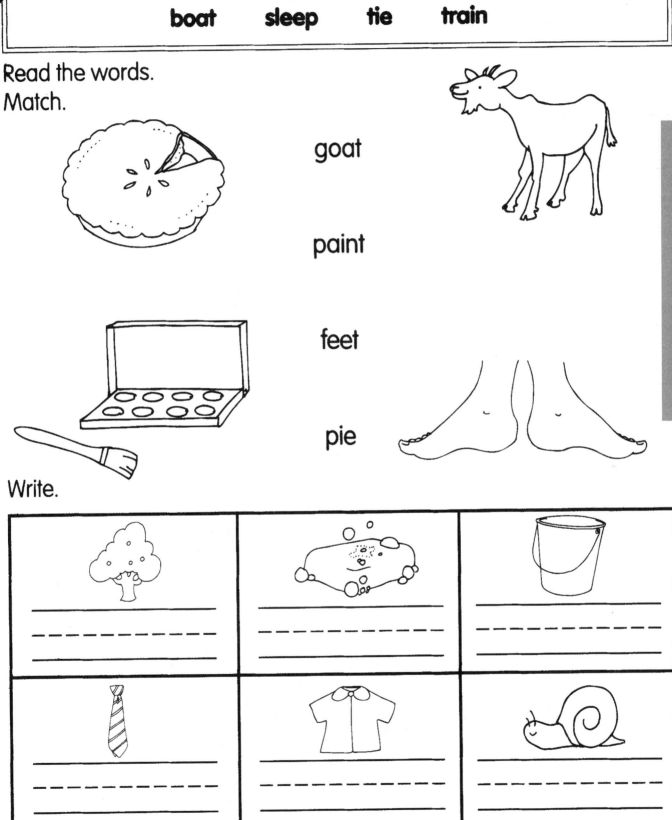

goat

paint

feet

pie

Write.

Skill: Reads and spells words containing vowels changed by an **r**.

An **r** following a vowel changes the vowel's sound.

ar - car	**er** - her	**ur**- fur
or - horn	**ir** - first	**wor** - worm

Read and fill in the missing letters.

H er c ____

h ____ is beeping.

The cat's f ____

is ____ range.

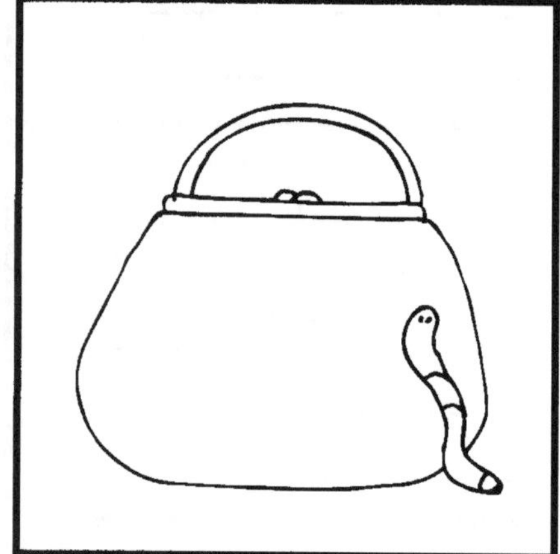

A fat ____ m

went up h ____

p ____ se.

2 REVIEW

Skill: Alphabetizes words using the second letter.

c**a**n	t**e**n	w**a**ll
c**e**nt	t**h**e	w**e**t
c**o**at	t**o**p	w**h**at

a b c d e f g h i j k l m n o p q r s t u v w x y z

Put these words in alphabetical order.

big bee bag bag	duck dad did	help hot hill
run ring red	tag trick the	zoo zebra zipper

Second Grade Language

Answer Key

Please take time to go over the work your child has completed. Ask your child to explain what he/she has done. Praise both success and effort. If mistakes have been made, explain what the answer should have been and how to find it. Let your child know that mistakes are a part of learning. The time you spend with your child helps let him/her know you feel learning is important.

page 65

On the City Streets

people animals vehicles

Color the stores.

Do you see any plants?

page 66

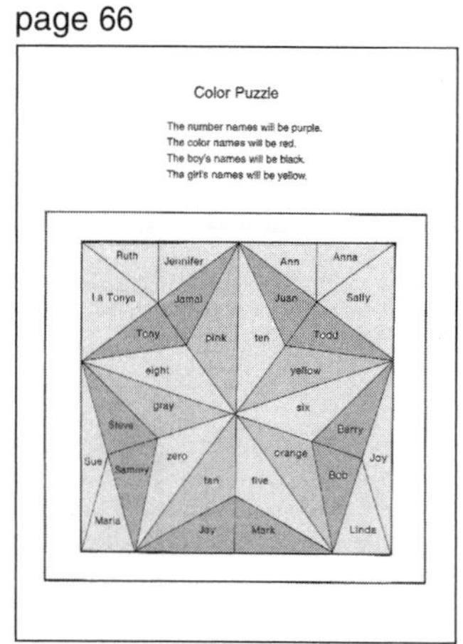

Color Puzzle

The number names will be purple.
The color names will be red.
The boy's names will be black.
The girl's names will be yellow.

page 67

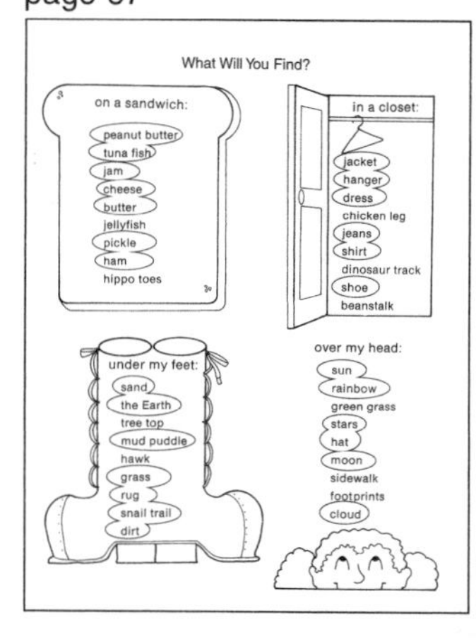

What Will You Find?

on a sandwich: peanut butter, tuna fish, jam, cheese, butter, jellyfish, pickle, ham, hippo toes

in a closet: jacket, hanger, dress, chicken leg, jeans, shirt, dinosaur track, shoe, beanstalk

under my feet: sand, the Earth, tree top, mud puddle, hawk, grass, rug, snail trail, dirt

over my head: sun, rainbow, green grass, stars, hat, moon, sidewalk, footprints, cloud

page 68

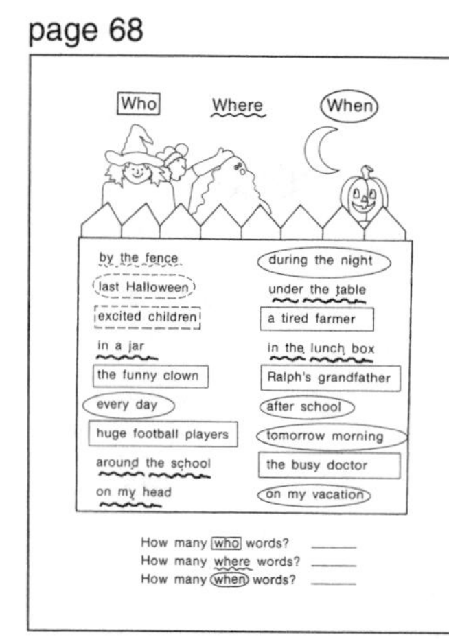

Who Where When

by the fence	during the night
last Halloween	under the table
excited children	a tired farmer
in a jar	in the lunch box
the funny clown	Ralph's grandfather
every day	after school
huge football players	tomorrow morning
around the school	the busy doctor
on my head	on my vacation

How many who words? ____
How many where words? ____
How many when words? ____

page 69

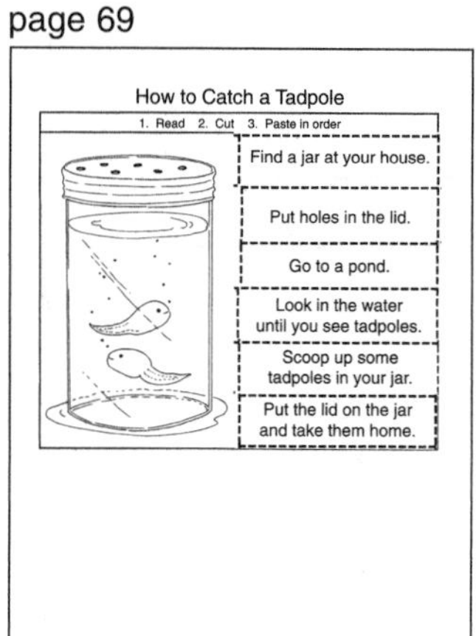

How to Catch a Tadpole

1. Read 2. Cut 3. Paste in order

Find a jar at your house.

Put holes in the lid.

Go to a pond.

Look in the water until you see tadpoles.

Scoop up some tadpoles in your jar.

Put the lid on the jar and take them home.

page 71

Write the Missing Letter

man	net	hen
sun	bat	lid
bed	top	wig
cup	six	jet

page 72

Read and Answer

yes no

1. Did the pig get in the mud? yes
2. Is the rat on the mat? no
3. Is the pig wet? yes
4. Did the rat get a rag? yes
5. Is the bug big? no
6. Is a hat on the pig? yes

page 73

Read and Answer

yes no

1. Did the snake hide in the cave? yes
2. Did Kate ride up the hill? yes
3. Did Kate and Pete meet at the top? no
4. Is it a hot day? yes
5. Did Pete hike up the hill? yes
6. Can a snake ride a bike? no

page 74

Read and Draw

drawings will vary

page 75

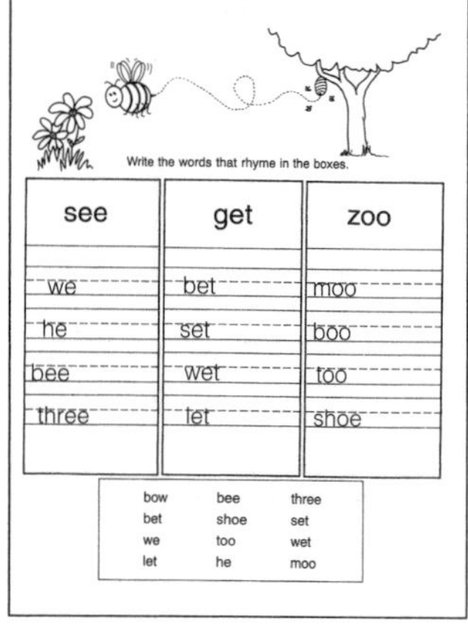

Write the words that rhyme in the boxes.

see	get	zoo
we	bet	moo
he	set	boo
bee	wet	too
three	let	shoe

bow	bee	three
bet	shoe	set
we	too	wet
let	he	moo

page 76

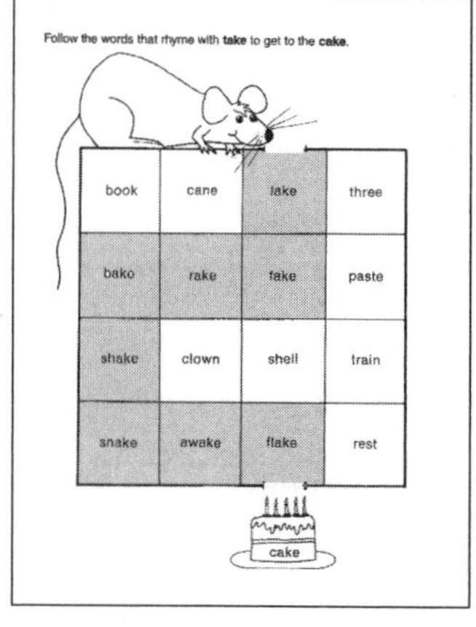

Follow the words that rhyme with **take** to get to the **cake**.

book	cane	lake	three
bake	rake	fake	paste
shake	clown	shell	train
snake	awake	flake	rest

cake

page 77

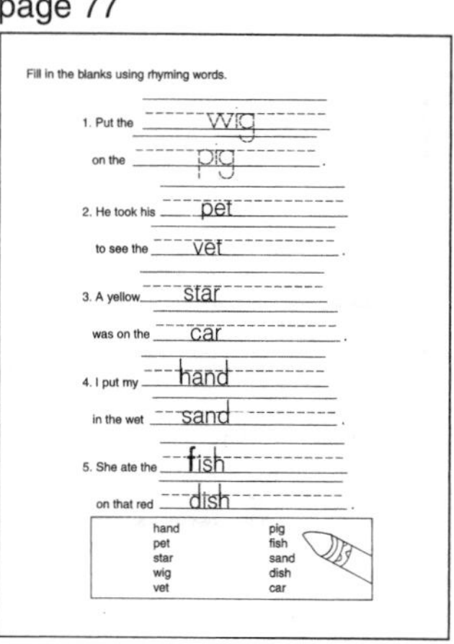

Fill in the blanks using rhyming words.

1. Put the wig on the pig.
2. He took his pet to see the vet.
3. A yellow star was on the car.
4. I put my hand in the wet sand.
5. She ate the fish on that red dish.

hand	pig
pet	fish
star	sand
wig	dish
vet	car

page 78

Making Big Words

Write the compound words. Draw pictures of the new words.

rain + bow = rainbow

cup + cake = cupcake

basket + ball = basketball

jelly + fish = jellyfish

skate + board = skateboard

gold + fish = goldfish

page 79

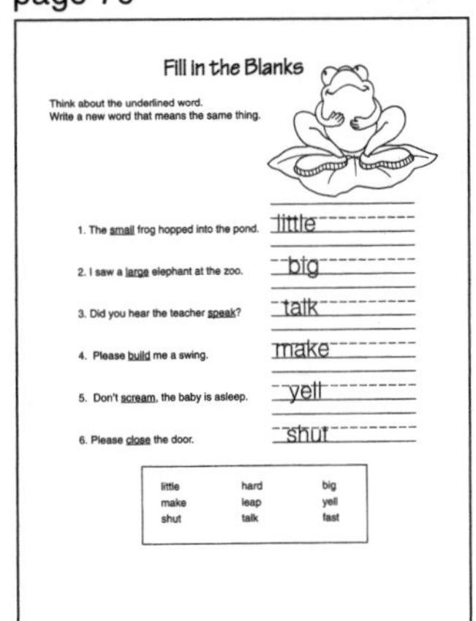

Fill in the Blanks

Think about the underlined word.
Write a new word that means the same thing.

1. The small frog hopped into the pond. little
2. I saw a large elephant at the zoo. big
3. Did you hear the teacher speak? talk
4. Please build me a swing. make
5. Don't scream, the baby is asleep. yell
6. Please close the door. shut

little	hard	big
make	leap	yell
shut	talk	fast

page 80

Name the Picture

Write two words that name each picture.

scream, yell — baby, infant — ill, sick — jump, leap

Word Box

baby	infant	scream
bright	jump	shiny
build	leap	sick
ill	make	yell

page 81

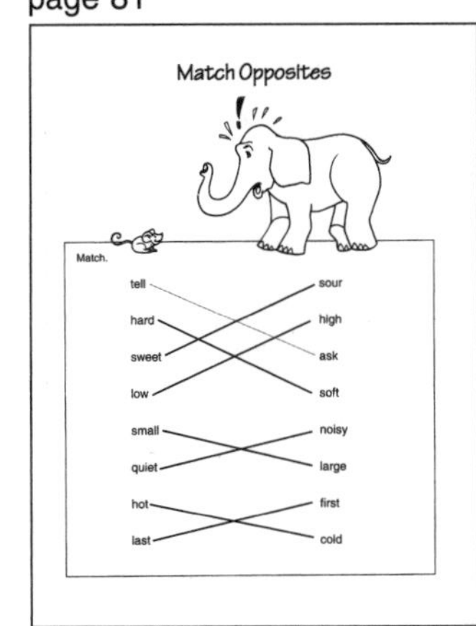

Match Opposites

Match.

tell — ask
hard — soft
sweet — sour
low — high
small — large
quiet — noisy
hot — cold
last — first

page 82

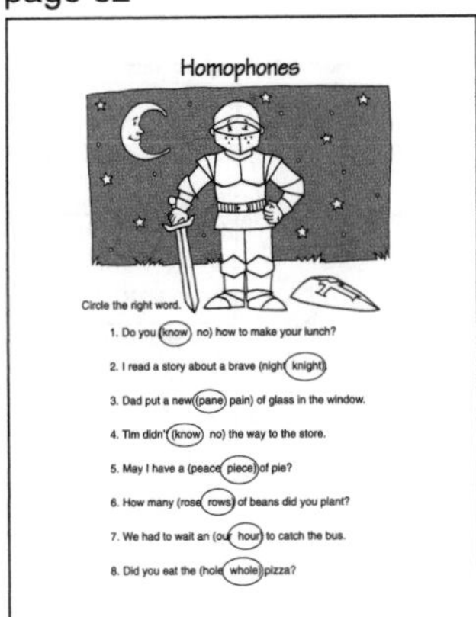

Homophones

Circle the right word.

1. Do you (know) no) how to make your lunch?
2. I read a story about a brave (night (knight).
3. Dad put a new (pane) pain) of glass in the window.
4. Tim didn't (know) no) the way to the store.
5. May I have a (peace (piece) of pie?
6. How many (rose (rows) of beans did you plant?
7. We had to wait an (our (hour) to catch the bus.
8. Did you eat the (hole (whole) pizza?

page 84

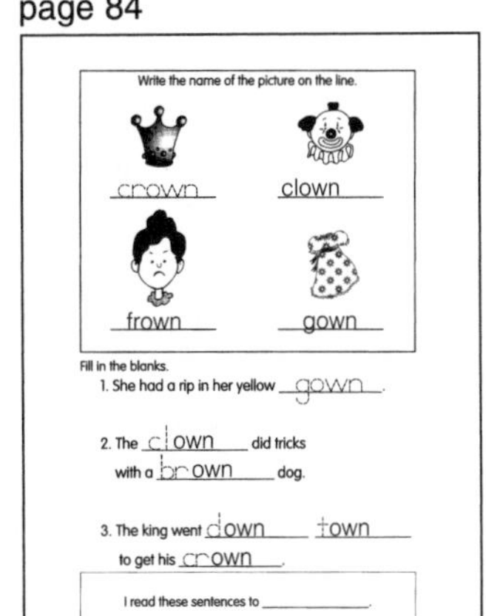

Write the name of the picture on the line.

crown — clown — frown — gown

Fill in the blanks.

1. She had a rip in her yellow gown.
2. The clown did tricks with a brown dog.
3. The king went down town to get his crown.

I read these sentences to ________.

page 85

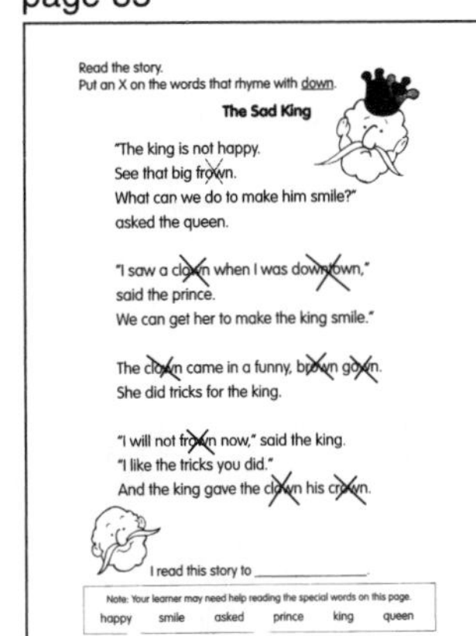

Read the story.
Put an X on the words that rhyme with down.

The Sad King

"The king is not happy.
See that big frown.
What can we do to make him smile?"
asked the queen.

"I saw a clown when I was down town,"
said the prince.
We can get her to make the king smile."

The clown came in a funny, brown gown.
She did tricks for the king.

"I will not frown now," said the king.
"I like the tricks you did."
And the king gave the clown his crown.

I read this story to ________.

Note: Your learner may need help reading the special words on this page.
happy smile asked prince king queen

page 86

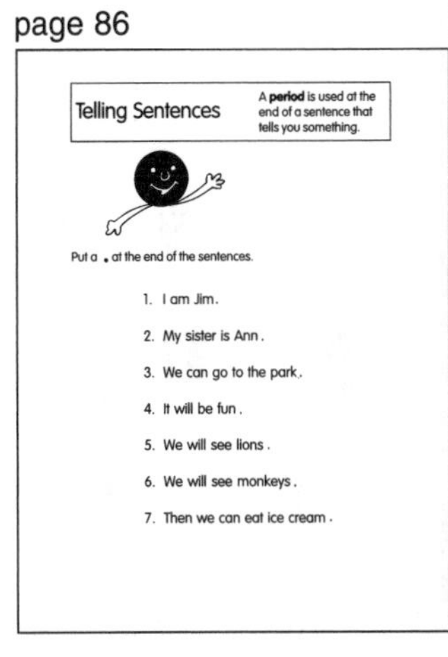

Telling Sentences

A **period** is used at the end of a sentence that tells you something.

Put a . at the end of the sentences.

1. I am Jim.
2. My sister is Ann.
3. We can go to the park.
4. It will be fun.
5. We will see lions.
6. We will see monkeys.
7. Then we can eat ice cream.

page 87

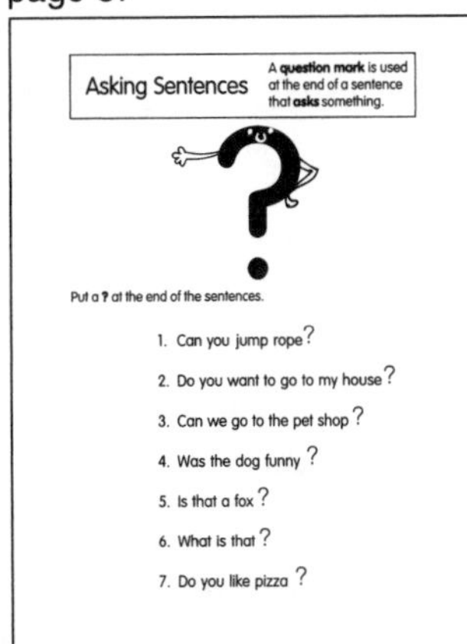

Asking Sentences

A **question mark** is used at the end of a sentence that **asks** something.

Put a ? at the end of the sentences.

1. Can you jump rope?
2. Do you want to go to my house?
3. Can we go to the pet shop?
4. Was the dog funny?
5. Is that a fox?
6. What is that?
7. Do you like pizza?

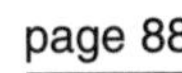

page 88

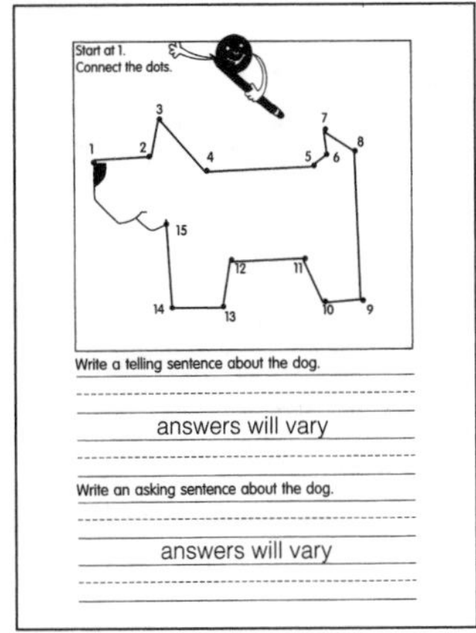

Start at 1.
Connect the dots.

Write a telling sentence about the dog.
answers will vary

Write an asking sentence about the dog.
answers will vary

page 89

Names start with capital letters.

A B C D E F G H I J K L M N O P Q R S T U V W X Y Z

ann Ann — bob Bob
kim Kim — dan Dan
jamal Jamal — ben Ben
jose Jose — nancy Nancy

My name is ________

page 90

Write capital letters.
Use periods or question marks.

The fox is in a box.
Can it get out?

Is that a cat?
No, it is a skunk.

Do you like to jump rope?
I think it is fun.

When did you get that toy?
Can I play with it?

page 91

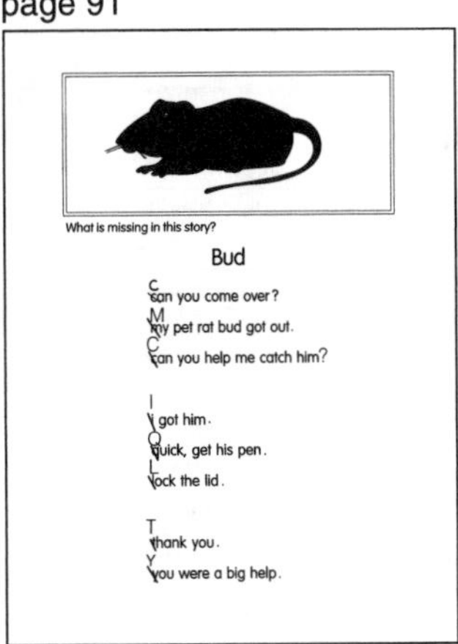

What is missing in this story?

Bud

Can you come over?
My pet rat bud got out.
Can you help me catch him?

I got him.
Quick, get his pen.
Lock the lid.

Thank you.
You were a big help.

page 92

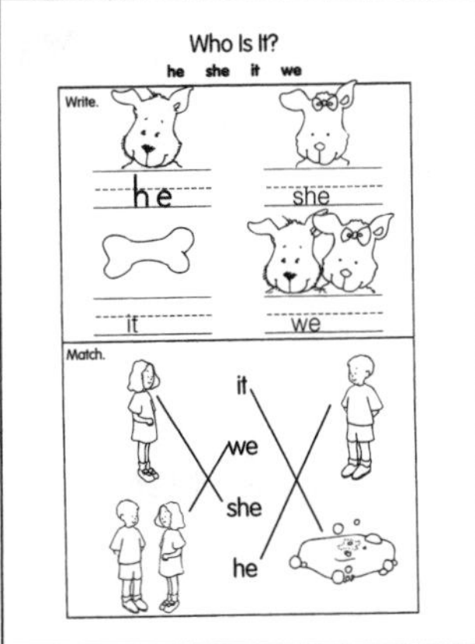

Who Is It?

he she it we

Write.

he — she — it — we

Match.

it — we — she — he

page 93

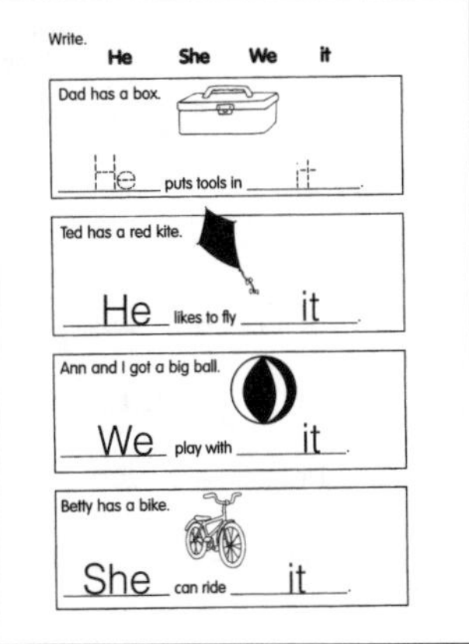

Write. He She We it

Dad has a box.
He puts tools in it.

Ted has a red kite.
He likes to fly it.

Ann and I got a big ball.
We play with it.

Betty has a bike.
She can ride it.

page 94

One and More Than One

Add s if it is more than one.

cup — pig — hat
ants — hats — cups
pins — pigs — ant

Second Grade Language

page 95

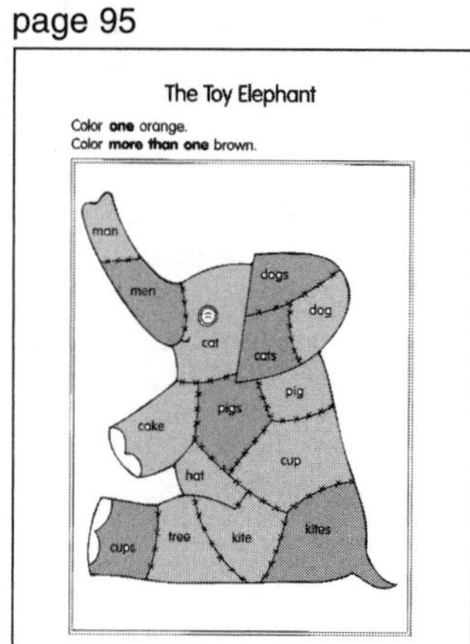
The Toy Elephant

Color **one** orange.
Color **more than one** brown.

page 96

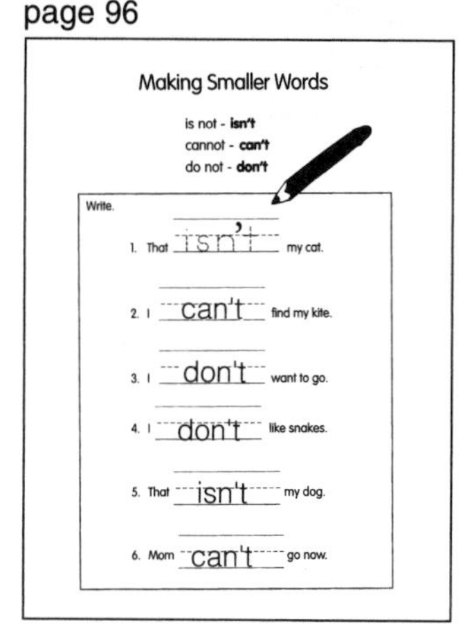
Making Smaller Words

is not - **isn't**
cannot - **can't**
do not - **don't**

Write.

1. That isn't my cat.
2. I can't find my kite.
3. I don't want to go.
4. I don't like snakes.
5. That isn't my dog.
6. Mom can't go now.

page 97

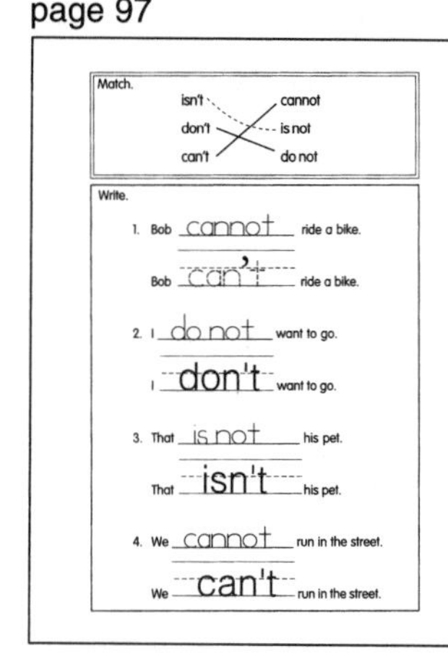
Match.

isn't — is not
don't — do not
can't — cannot

Write.

1. Bob cannot ride a bike.
   Bob can't ride a bike.
2. I do not want to go.
   I don't want to go.
3. That is not his pet.
   That isn't his pet.
4. We cannot run in the street.
   We can't run in the street.

page 98

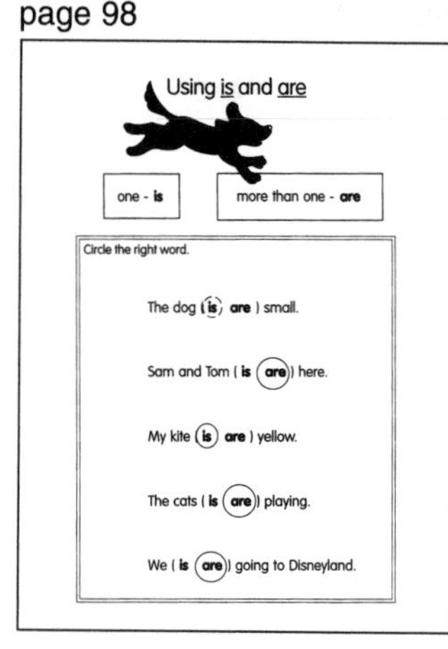
Using is and are

one - **is** more than one - **are**

Circle the right word.

The dog (**is** are) small.
Sam and Tom (is **are**) here.
My kite (**is** are) yellow.
The cats (is **are**) playing.
We (is **are**) going to Disneyland.

page 99

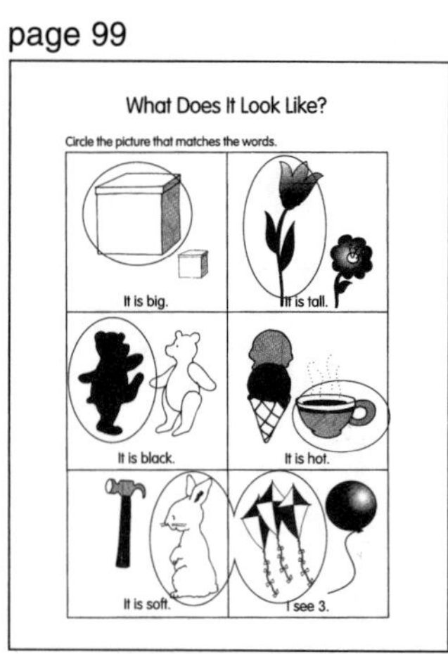
What Does It Look Like?

Circle the picture that matches the words.

It is big.
It is tall.
It is black.
It is hot.
It is soft.
I see 3.

page 100

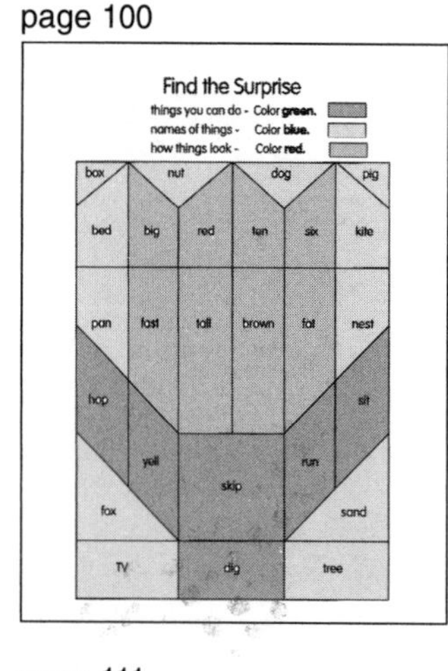
Find the Surprise

things you can do - Color **green.**
names of things - Color **blue.**
how things look - Color **red.**

page 101

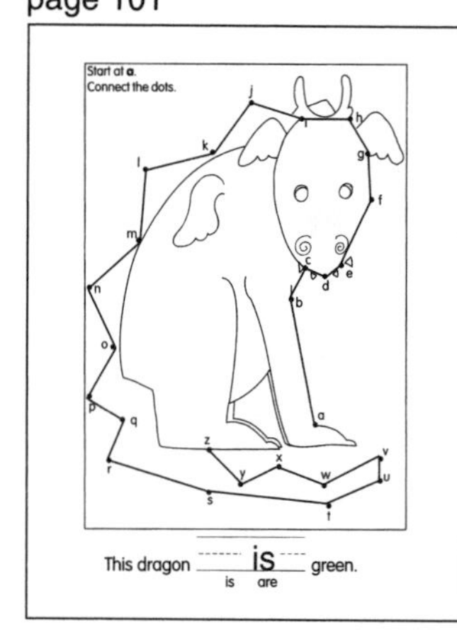
Start at **a.**
Connect the dots.

This dragon is green.
is are

page 107

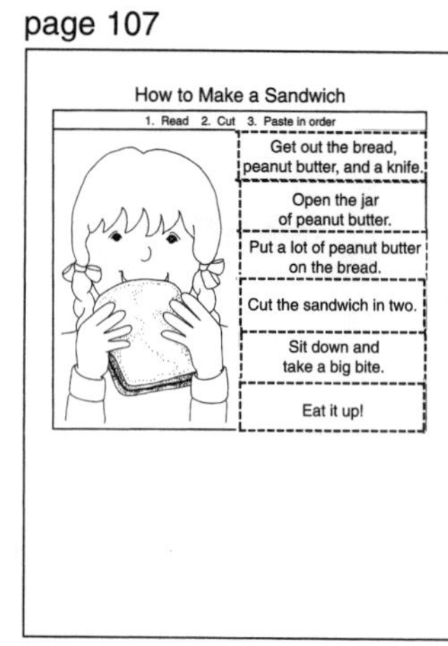
How to Make a Sandwich

1. Read 2. Cut 3. Paste in order

Get out the bread, peanut butter, and a knife.
Open the jar of peanut butter.
Put a lot of peanut butter on the bread.
Cut the sandwich in two.
Sit down and take a big bite.
Eat it up!

page 109

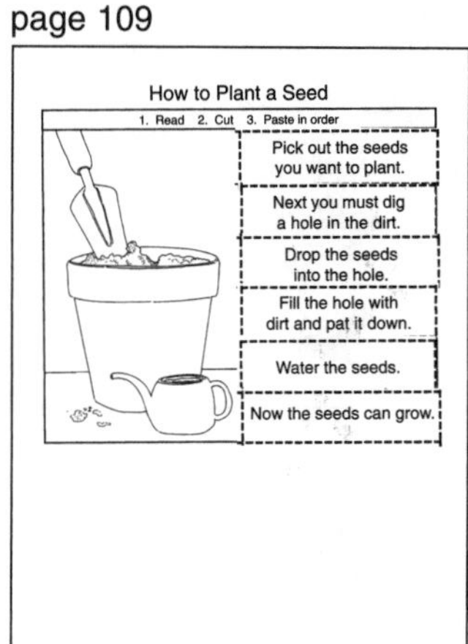
How to Plant a Seed

1. Read 2. Cut 3. Paste in order

Pick out the seeds you want to plant.
Next you must dig a hole in the dirt.
Drop the seeds into the hole.
Fill the hole with dirt and pat it down.
Water the seeds.
Now the seeds can grow.

page 111

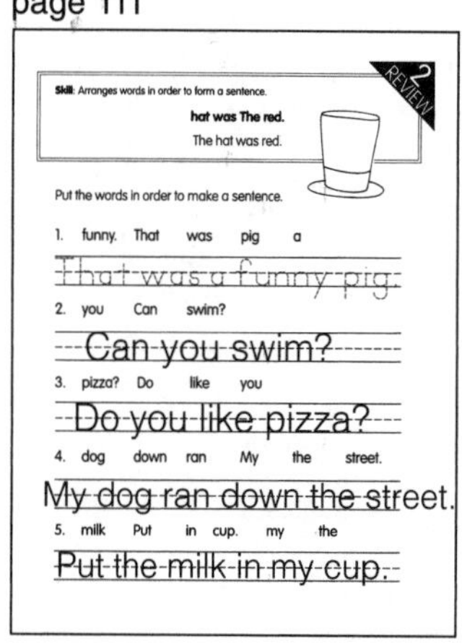
Skill: Arranges words in order to form a sentence.

hat was The red.
The hat was red.

REVIEW 2

Put the words in order to make a sentence.

1. funny. That was pig a
   That was a funny pig.
2. you Can swim?
   Can you swim?
3. pizza? Do like you
   Do you like pizza?
4. dog down ran My the street.
   My dog ran down the street.
5. milk Put in cup. my the
   Put the milk in my cup.

page 112

REVIEW 2

Skill: Begins a sentence with a capital letter.

Bob went to the zoo.
Will you play with me?

Fill in the capital letters.

1. My dog is small.
2. His name is Pepper.
3. He can run and jump.
4. We play at the park.
5. He can fetch a ball.
6. Mother won't let him sleep with me.

page 113

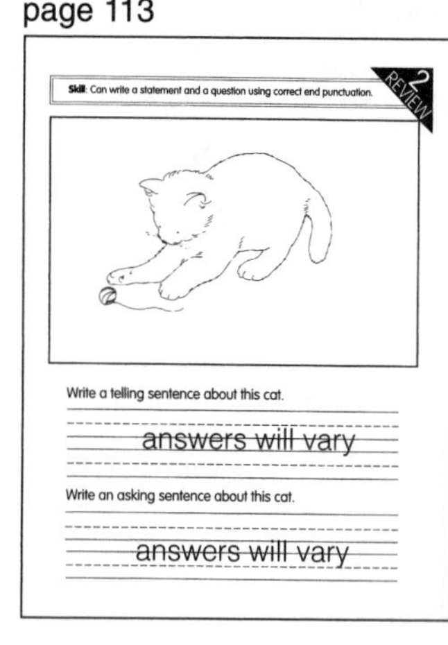
Skill: Can write a statement and a question using correct end punctuation.

REVIEW 2

Write a telling sentence about this cat.

answers will vary

Write an asking sentence about this cat.

answers will vary

page 114

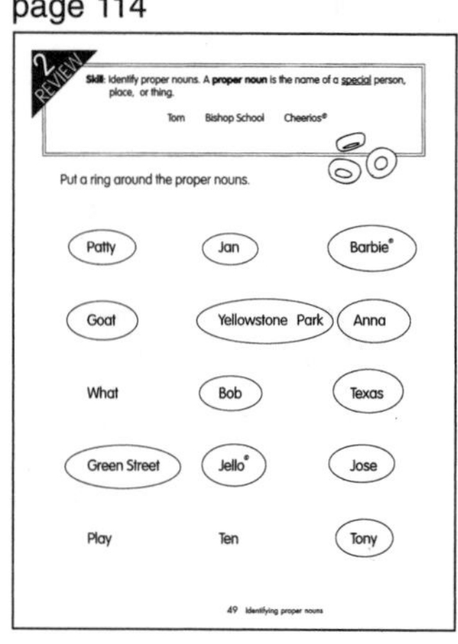
REVIEW 2

Skill: Identify proper nouns. A **proper noun** is the name of a special person, place, or thing.

Tom Bishop School Cheerios®

Put a ring around the proper nouns.

(Patty) (Jan) (Barbie®)
(Goat) (Yellowstone Park) (Anna)
What (Bob) (Texas)
(Green Street) (Jello®) (Jose)
Play Ten (Tony)

49 Identifying proper nouns

page 115

Skill: Begins proper nouns with a capital letter.

Amy Jamal Kelly

REVIEW 2

Write the names.

sam Sam tim Tim
kisha Kisha lee Lee
mary Mary carlos Carlos
pete Pete joe Joe
tina Tina rosa Rosa

page 116

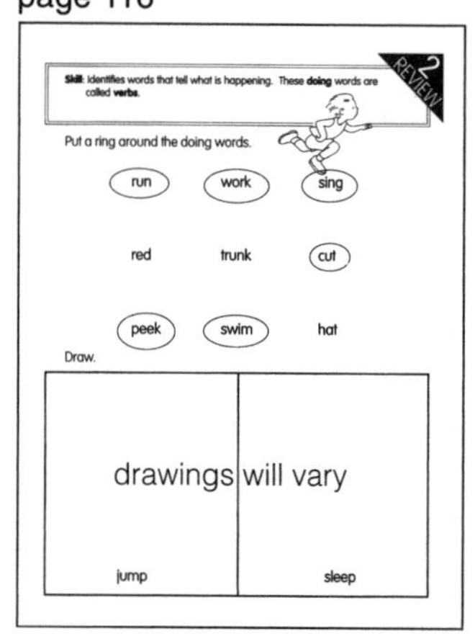
Skill: Identifies words that tell what is happening. These **doing** words are called **verbs.**

REVIEW 2

Put a ring around the doing words.

(run) (work) (sing)
red trunk (cut)
(peek) (swim) hat

Draw.

drawings will vary

jump sleep

page 117

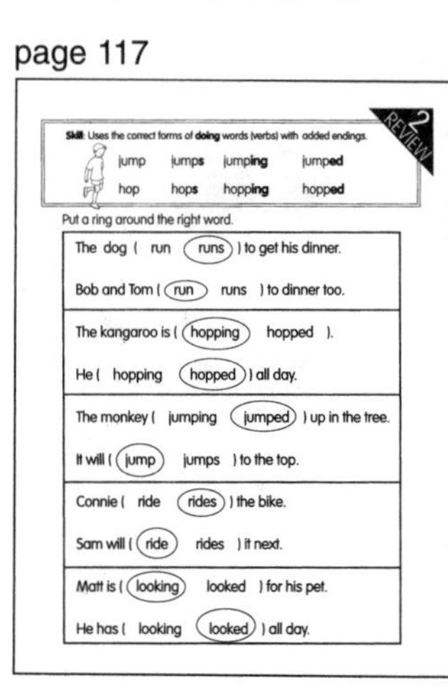
Skill: Uses the correct forms of **doing** words (verbs) with added endings.

REVIEW 2

jump	jumps	jump**ing**	jump**ed**
hop	hops	hop**ping**	hop**ped**

Put a ring around the right word.

The dog (run (runs)) to get his dinner.
Bob and Tom ((run) runs) to dinner too.
The kangaroo is ((hopping) hopped).
He (hopping (hopped)) all day.
The monkey (jumping (jumped)) up in the tree.
It will ((jump) jumps) to the top.
Connie (ride (rides)) the bike.
Sam will ((ride) rides) it next.
Matt is ((looking) looked) for his pet.
He has (looking (looked)) all day.

page 118

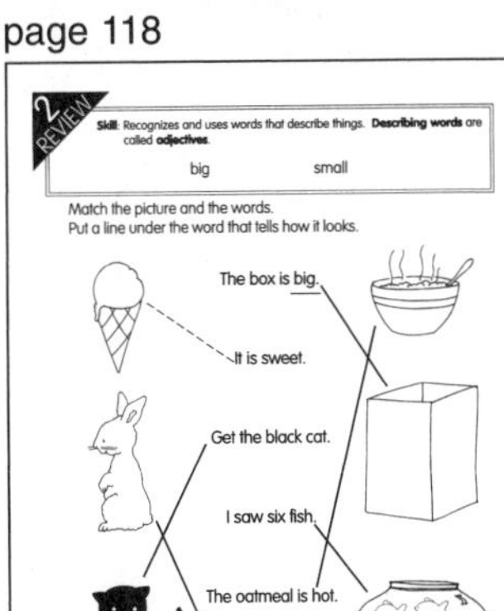

Skill: Recognizes and uses words that describe things. **Describing words** are called **adjectives**.

big small

Match the picture and the words.
Put a line under the word that tells how it looks.

The box is big.
It is sweet.
Get the black cat.
I saw six fish.
The oatmeal is hot.
My bunny is soft.

page 119

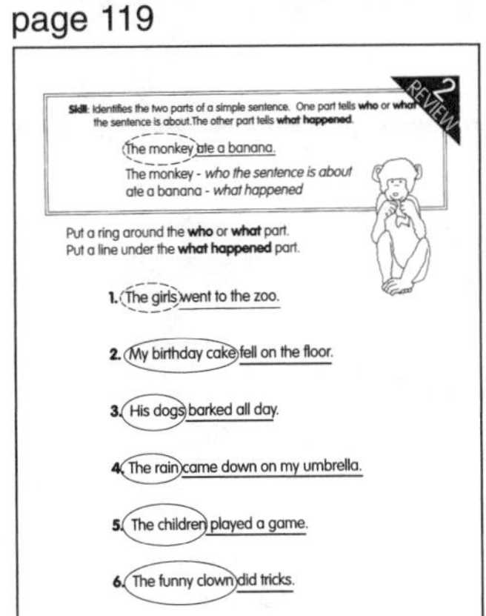

Skill: Identifies the two parts of a simple sentence. One part tells **who** or **what** the sentence is about. The other part tells **what happened**.

The monkey ate a banana.

The monkey - *who the sentence is about*
ate a banana - *what happened*

Put a ring around the **who** or **what** part.
Put a line under the **what happened** part.

1. The girls went to the zoo.
2. My birthday cake fell on the floor.
3. His dogs barked all day.
4. The rain came down on my umbrella.
5. The children played a game.
6. The funny clown did tricks.

page 120

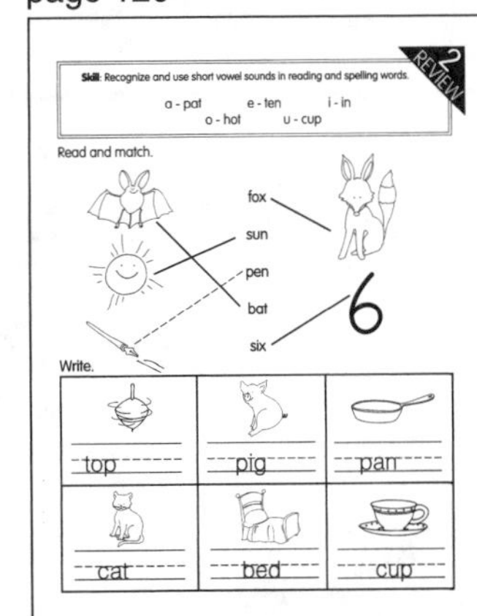

Skill: Recognize and use short vowel sounds in reading and spelling words.

a - pat e - ten i - in
o - hot u - cup

Read and match.

fox
sun
pen
bat
six

Write.

top	pig	pan
cat	bed	cup

page 121

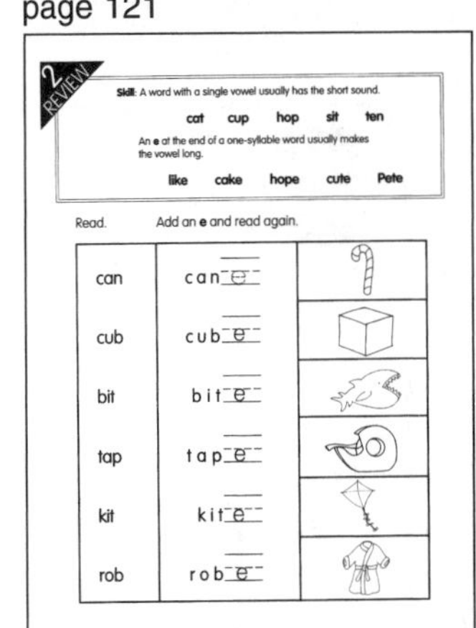

Skill: A word with a single vowel usually has the short sound.

cat cup hop sit ten

An **e** at the end of a one-syllable word usually makes the vowel long.

like cake hope cute Pete

Read. Add an **e** and read again.

can	cane
cub	cube
bit	bite
tap	tape
kit	kite
rob	robe

page 122

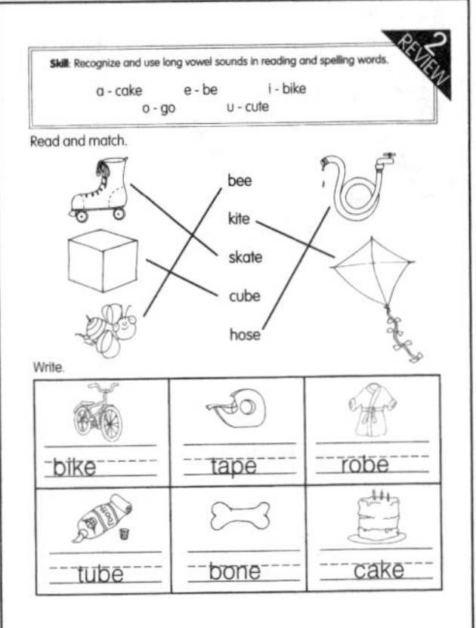

Skill: Recognize and use long vowel sounds in reading and spelling words.

a - cake e - be i - bike
o - go u - cute

Read and match.

bee
kite
skate
cube
hose

Write.

bike	tape	robe
tube	bone	cake

page 123

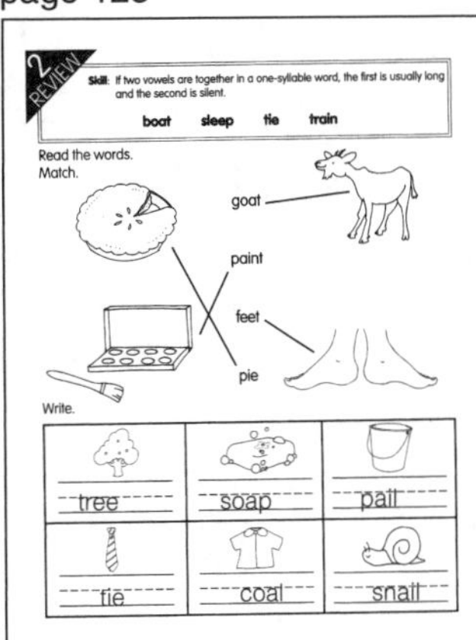

Skill: If two vowels are together in a one-syllable word, the first is usually long and the second is silent.

boat sleep tie train

Read the words.
Match.

goat
paint
feet
pie

Write.

tree	soap	pail
tie	coat	snail

page 124

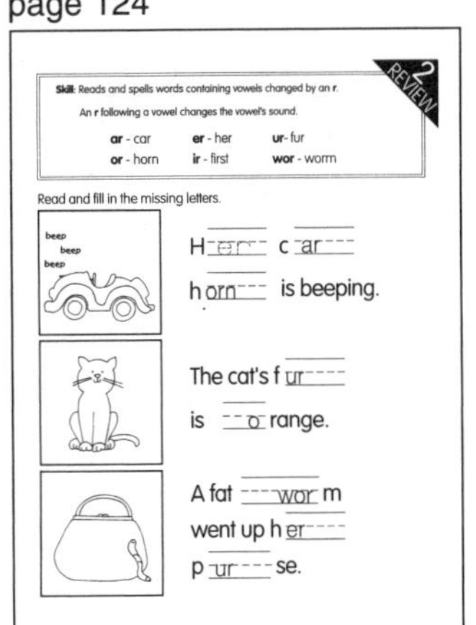

Skill: Reads and spells words containing vowels changed by an r.

An **r** following a vowel changes the vowel's sound.

ar - car er - her ur - fur
or - horn ir - first wor - worm

Read and fill in the missing letters.

Her car horn is beeping.

The cat's fur is orange.

A fat worm went up her purse.

page 125

Skill: Alphabetizes words using the second letter.

can	ten	wall
cent	the	wet
coat	top	what

a b c d e f g h i j k l m n o p q r s t u v w x y z

Put these words in alphabetical order.

big bee bag	duck dad did	help hot hill
bag bee big	dad did duck	help hill hot
run ring red	tag trick the	zoo zebra zipper
red ring run	tag the trick	zebra zipper zoo

The Busy Pond

Story Dictionary

bugs 

fish 

children 

frogs 

ducks 

2

Busy pond.
The frogs jump.
The fish swim.

3

Busy pond.
The ducks quack.
The bugs fly.

4

Busy pond.
The children play.

What Did the Story Say?

Mark the things that made the pond busy.

Draw something that might happen at the pond.

Real or Make-Believe?

Circle **yes** or **no.**

A duck can quack. yes no	A duck can fly. yes no	A duck can read. yes no
A frog can color. yes no	A frog can jump. yes no	A frog can swim. yes no
A bug can hop. yes no	A bug can paint. yes no	A bug can run. yes no

The Shortcut

Story Dictionary

butterfly 

hilltop 

woodpile 

2

Let's take a shortcut.
We'll go to the hilltop.

3

Let's take a shortcut.
We can catch a butterfly.

4

Let's take a shortcut.
We can climb the woodpile.
Then we'll go home.

What Did the Story Say?

Write and draw your answers to these questions.

Where did the shortcut go?

What did the boys catch?

What did they climb?

Working with Word Families

c + ake = ____ ____ ____ ____

r + ake = ____ ____ ____ ____

sn + ake = ____ ____ ____ ____ ____

br + ake = ____ ____ ____ ____ ____

Use the new words to finish these sentences:

I used a ____________________ to pile up the leaves.

Pull on the ____________________ to stop the sled.

Molly will have a birthday ____________________.

The little ____________________ was green.

Are You Ready?

Story Dictionary

black 

striped 

checked 

white 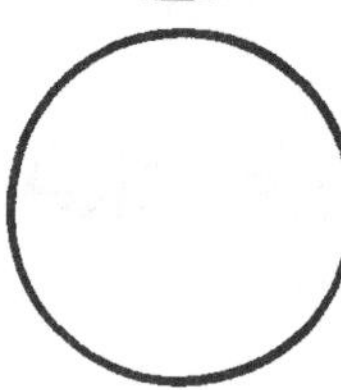

spotted 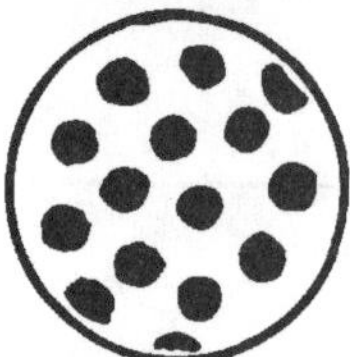

2

Black coat? No.
White coat? No.
Striped coat? Yes!

Are you ready? No.

3

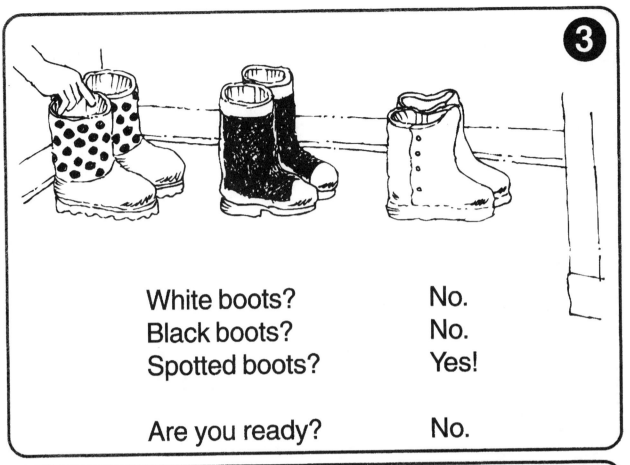

White boots?	No.
Black boots?	No.
Spotted boots?	Yes!
Are you ready?	No.

4

Black hat?	No.
White hat?	No.
Checked hat?	Yes!

Are you ready? Yes! I'm ready to go.

Reading Comprehension

What Did the Story Say?

Color the clothes to show what the girl picked.
Circle the words that tell about the clothes.

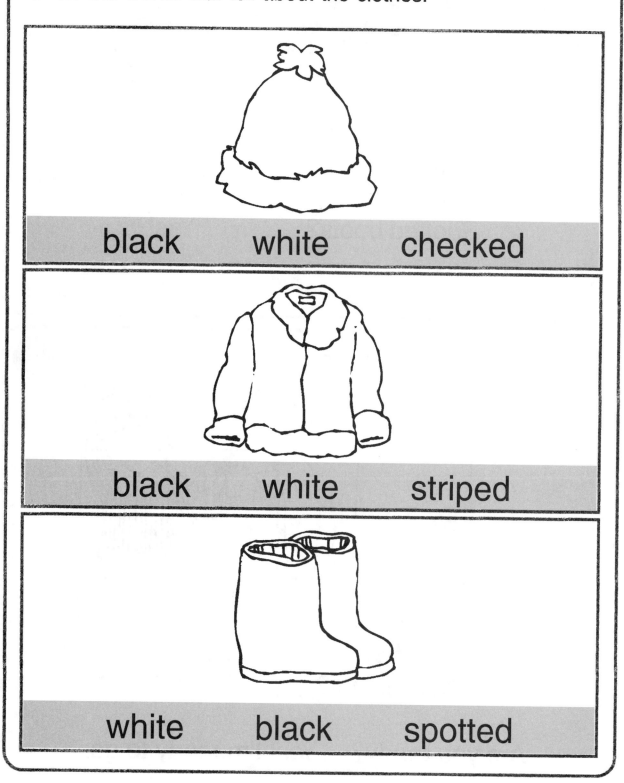

black white checked

black white striped

white black spotted

Working with Word Families

__at

c + at = ___ ___ ___

b + at = ___ ___ ___

Draw a cat with a bat.

h + at = ___ ___ ___

r + at = ___ ___ ___

Draw a rat with a hat.

fl + at = ___ ___ ___ ___

Draw something that is flat.

Star Man

Story Dictionary

cookies  Star Man 

milk  window 

2

Hey, Star Man.
I see you from my window.
You are my friend.

3

I've been thinking...
Do you have a bed?
Does your mom bring you warm milk?
Do you eat cookies, too?

4

I see you from my window.
I'm glad that you stopped by.
Good night, Star Man.

What Did the Story Say?

What questions did the boy ask Star Man?

What questions would you ask?

Rhyme Time

Circle the two pictures in each line that rhyme.

1			
2			
3	CANDY BAR		
4			
5			1 MILE

Reading Comprehension

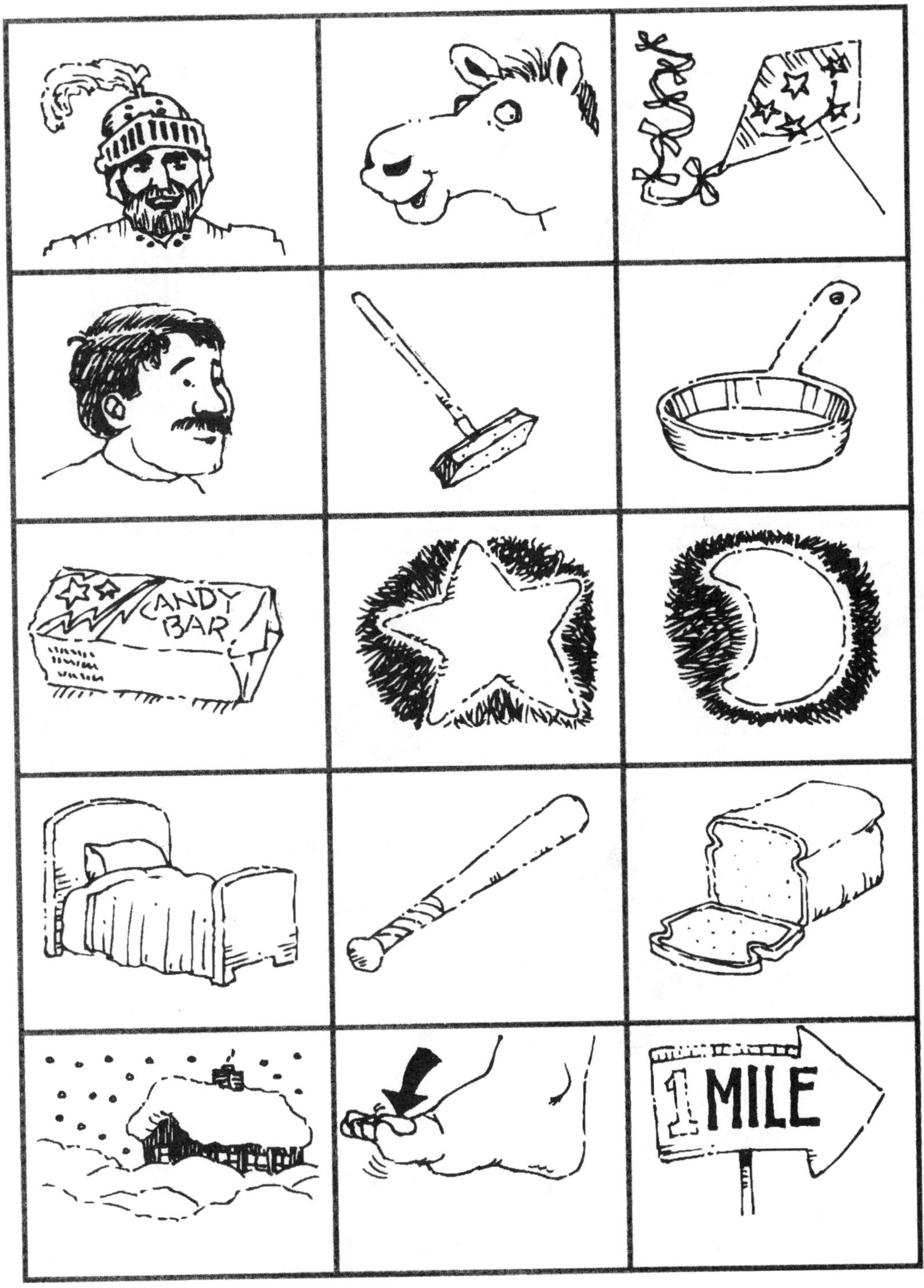

The Ticket

Story Dictionary

football 

ticket 

movies 

zoo 

2

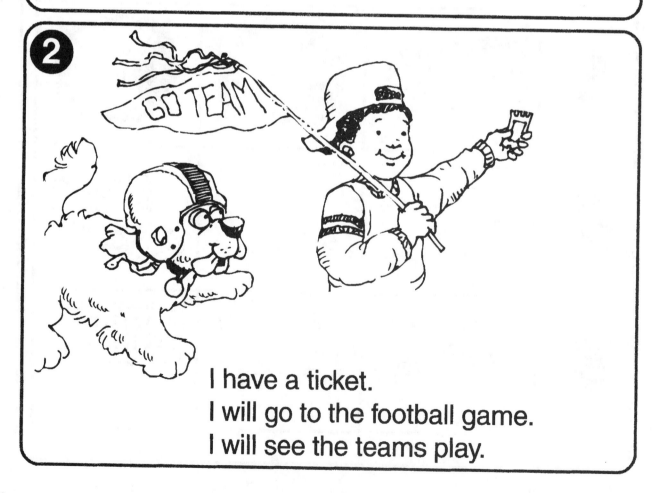

I have a ticket.
I will go to the football game.
I will see the teams play.

3

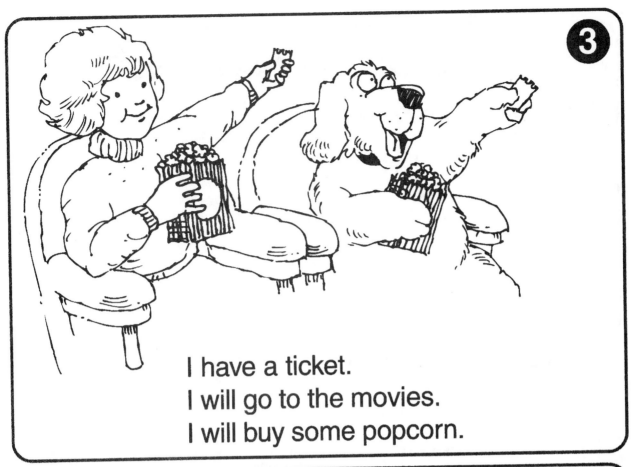

I have a ticket.
I will go to the movies.
I will buy some popcorn.

TICKETS

4

I will go to the zoo.
I will see the animals.
I have two tickets.
Will you come, too?

What Did the Story Say?

Mark the correct answers.

1. Where did the first boy go?

- [ ] to a race
- [ ] to a game
- [ ] to a pond

2. Where did the girl go?

- [ ] to ride a horse
- [ ] to get a book
- [ ] to see a movie

3. Where did the last boy go?

- [ ] to the zoo
- [ ] to the playground
- [ ] to the beach

4. Where would you go?

____

____

The Zoo

Write each animal's name under its cage.

Word Box

tiger	hippo	monkey
giraffe	bear	elephant

Reading Comprehension

1

Packing My Suitcase

Story Dictionary

blanket 

toothbrush 

dinosaur pj's 

teddy bear 

pillow 

socks 

2

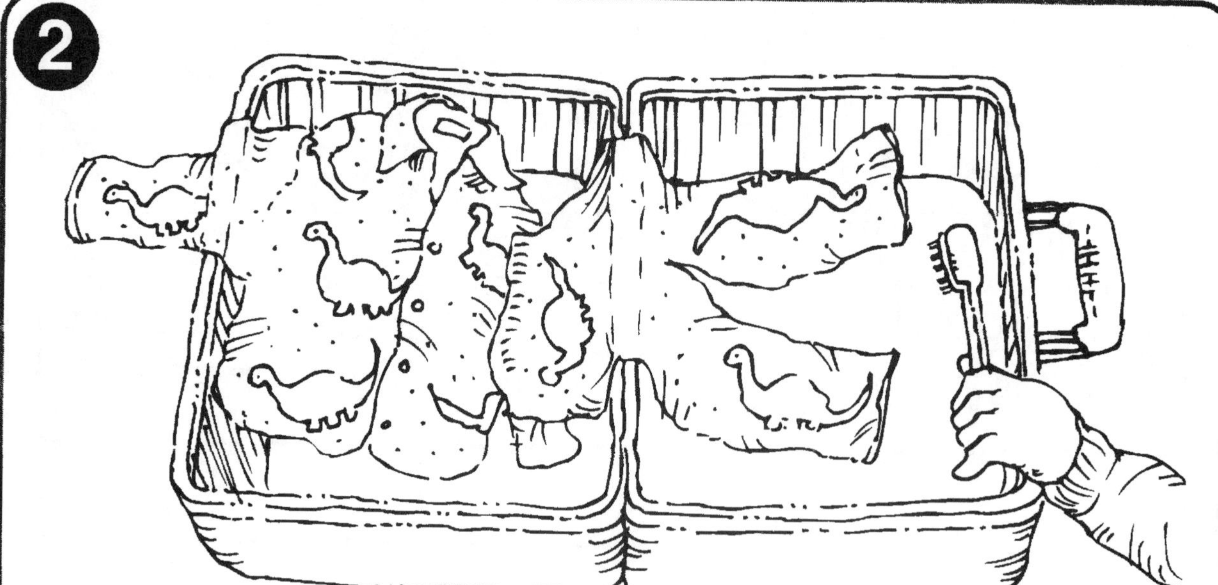

I'm going to spend the night at Grandma's.
I'll take my dinosaur pj's.
I'll take my purple toothbrush.

3

I'll take my blue blanket.
I'll take my teddy bear.
I'll take my clean socks.

4

I'll take my new book.
I'll take my soft pillow.
I'm going to spend the night at Grandma's.

What Did the Story Say?

Color the things that belong in the suitcase.

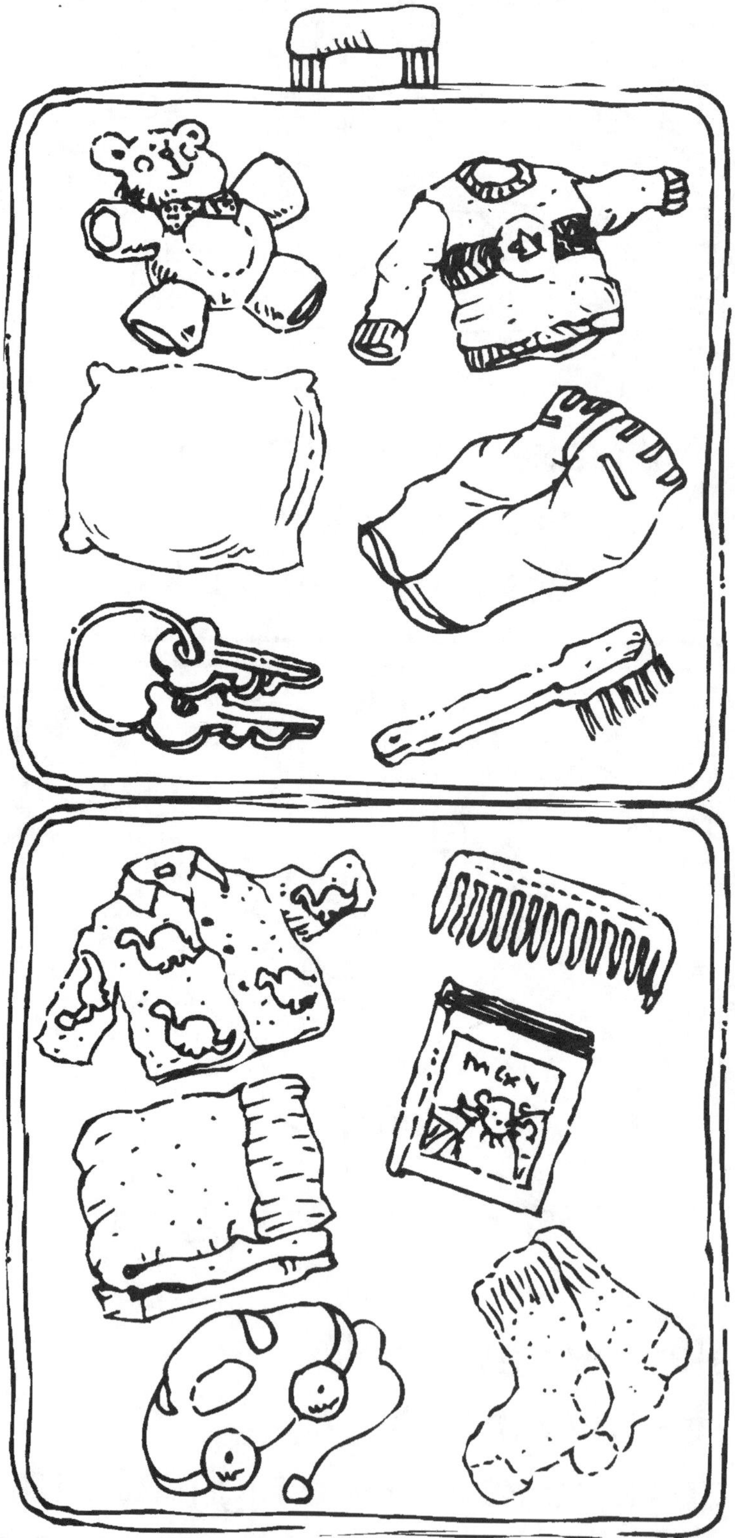

Working with Word Families

bl + ock = ____ ____ ____ ____ ____

l + ock = ____ ____ ____ ____

s + ock = ____ ____ ____ ____

cl + ock = ____ ____ ____ ____ ____

r + ock = ____ ____ ____ ____

d + ock = ____ ____ ____ ____

Write the words to label the pictures.

 ____ ____ ____ ____ ____	 ____ ____ ____ ____
 ____ ____ ____ ____ ____	 ____ ____ ____ ____

1

What Can You Put in It?

Story Dictionary

bus 

wagon 

dragon 

rocks 

truck

quacking duck 

shoe 

2

What can you put in a wagon?

A box,
a bag,
and Willy's dragon.

3

What can you put in a truck?

Some rocks,
a shoe,
and a quacking duck.

4

What can you put in a bus?

Ms. White,
Teacher,
and all of us.

What Did the Story Say?

Draw to show what went in each thing.

What's at the End?

Write the letter that stands for the sound that you hear at the end of each word.

 ba ___	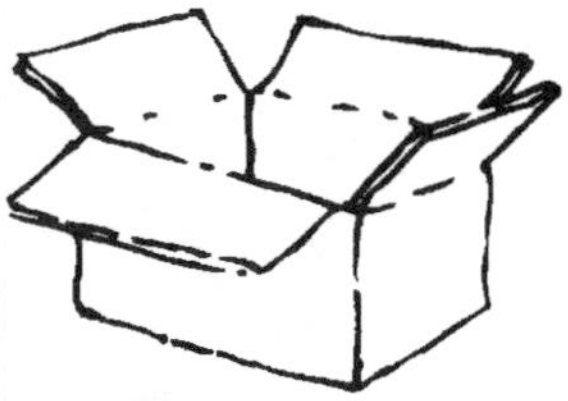 bo ___
 bu ___	 boo ___
 do ___	 ma ___
 ca ___	 cu ___
 ru ___	 ja ___
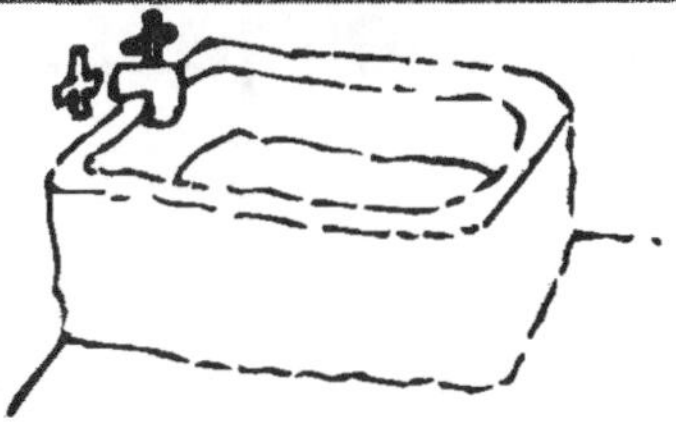 tu ___	 shi ___

Reading Comprehension

Trucks, Trucks, Trucks

Story Dictionary

animals 

blocks 

lights 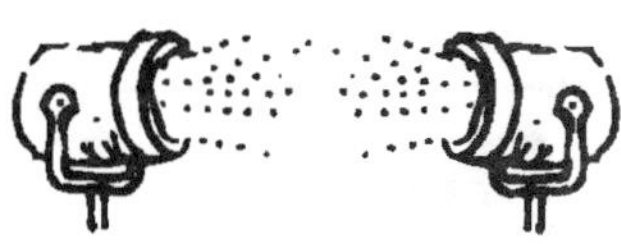

firemen 

hose 

ladders 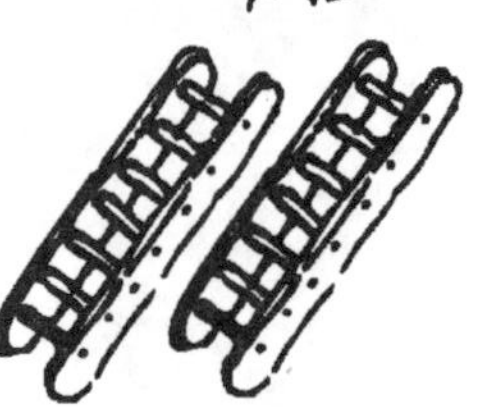

2

See the trucks, big and small.
Watch them work. They do it all.

Farm trucks help farmers to do their jobs.
They haul hay.
They haul animals.
They haul corn.

Big rig trucks help people to do their jobs.
They haul gas.
They haul food.
They haul cars.

Fire trucks help firemen to do their jobs.
They haul ladders.
They haul hoses.
They haul lights.

4

Toy trucks help kids to do their jobs.
They haul blocks.
They haul dolls.
They haul friends.

See the trucks, big and small.
Watch them work. They haul it all.

Reading Comprehension

What Did the Story Say?

Draw to show what the story said farm trucks haul.	Draw to show what the story said big rigs haul.
Draw to show what the story said toy trucks haul.	Think of one more thing that a toy truck could haul. Draw it here.

Adding -er

Add **-er** to these words. Draw a line from the new word to the picture that shows something for that person to use.

build + er =

play + er =

farm + er =

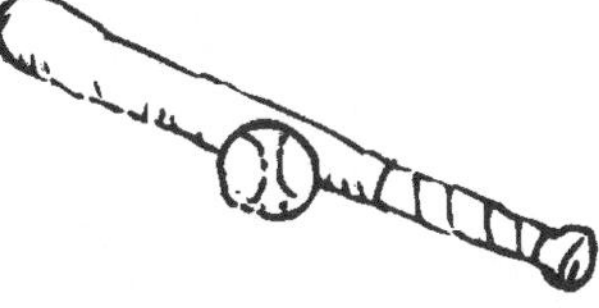

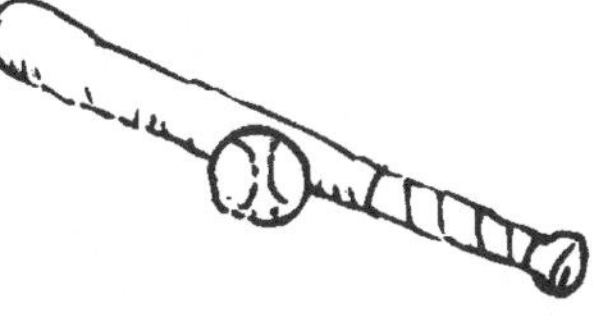

teach + er =

paint + er =

The Campfire

Story Dictionary

campfire

sleeping bag

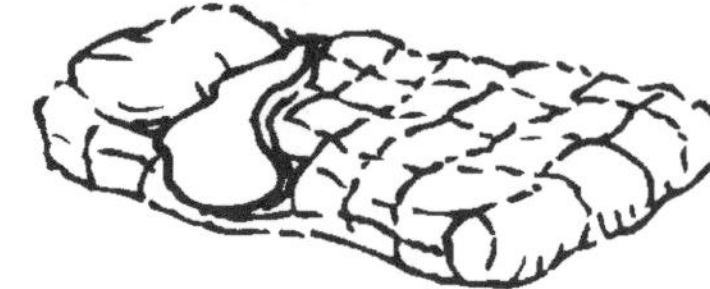

owl

2

The campfire is making a bright splash of light on the black night. The trees stand tall. I am in my sleeping bag. The sounds of the night keep me awake.

The wind whispers. The owl hoots. Something moves in the dark.

I hear the snap of the fire. I'm glad for its warm light. It makes me feel safe.

Reading Comprehension

What Did the Story Say?

Mark **Yes** or **No**.

	yes	**no**
1. The campfire went out.		
2. The trees are short.		
3. The boy is awake.		
4. The owl whispers to the boy.		
5. The fire makes the boy feel safe.		
6. The fire makes a noise.		

Draw something that might move in the dark.

Camping

Look at the picture. Draw lines to answer the questions.

Where's the boy?	in the forest
Where's the cook pot?	in the sleeping bag
Where's the sleeping bag?	in the tent
Where's the camp?	on the fire

Reading Comprehension

1

The Polar Bear

Story Dictionary

polar bear

warm fur coat

back legs

front legs

2

The polar bear lives near the North Pole. Every day it walks on the snow. It has fur on the bottom of its feet. The fur keeps its feet warm. The fur also keeps the bear from slipping on the snow.

Every day the polar bear swims in the cold water. The polar bear is a good swimmer. It paddles with its front legs. It pulls its back legs along.

After it swims, it shakes the water from its fur coat. BRRRR!

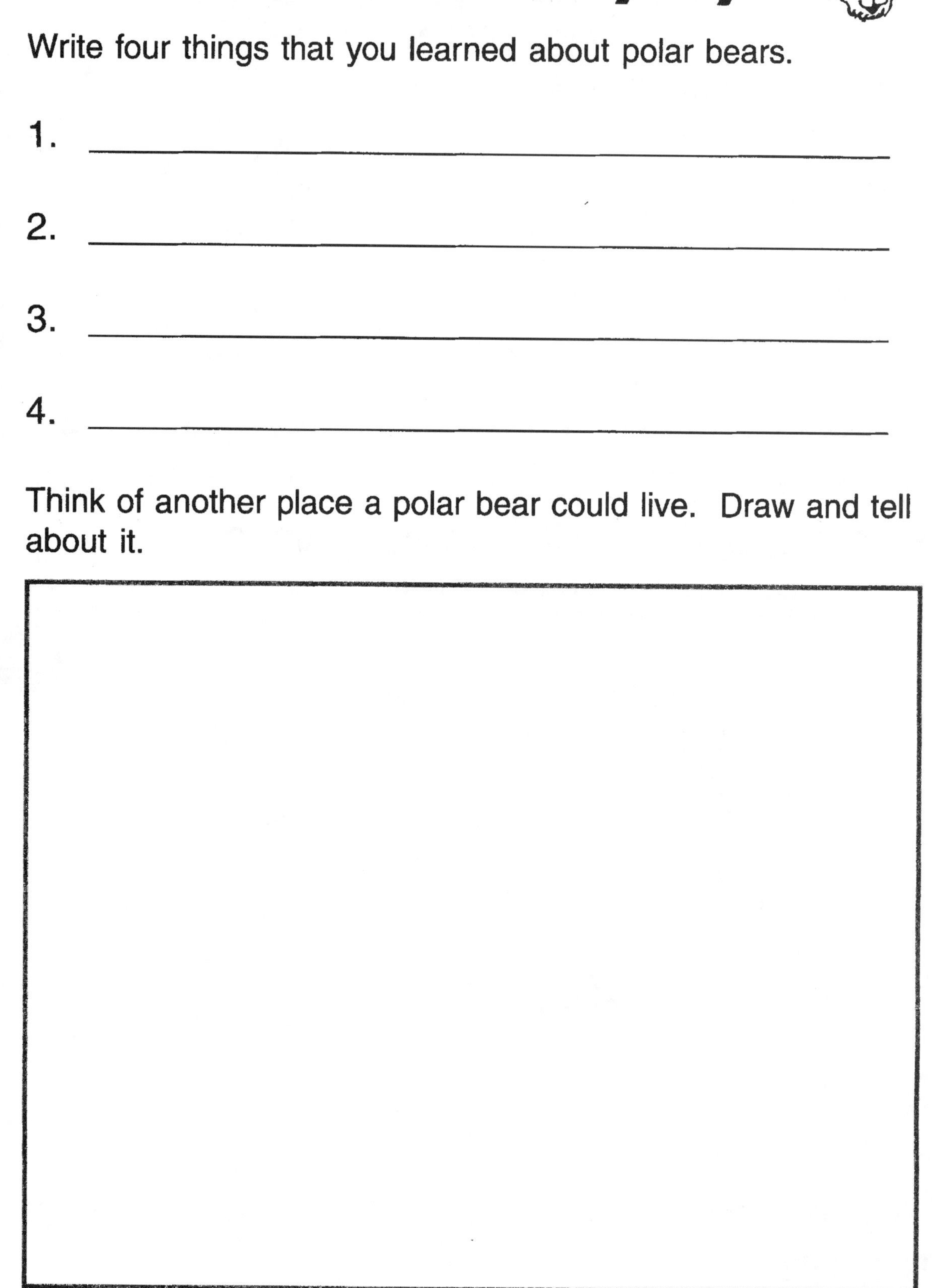

What Did the Story Say?

Write four things that you learned about polar bears.

1. ______________________________

2. ______________________________

3. ______________________________

4. ______________________________

Think of another place a polar bear could live. Draw and tell about it.

A Polar Bear Crossword Puzzle

Across

1. The polar bear has white __________.
2. The ____________ like to swim in the cold water.
4. Fur helps the bear stay ___________.

Down

1. The polar bear has four __________.
3. The polar bear can ________ in cold water.

Word Box

swim	feet	warm
fur	bears	

Reading Comprehension

Sam's Blue Hat

Story Dictionary

bunny

fox

ladybug

mouse

goat

2

One day Sam lost his hat. It was a blue hat. It was soft and warm. It had a bell on its tip.

A little mouse saw the blue hat. It looked warm and soft. The mouse moved in.

A bunny saw the blue hat. It looked warm and soft. The bunny hopped in. The blue hat got bigger.

3

A fox saw the blue hat. It looked warm and soft. The fox went in. The blue hat got bigger.

A goat saw the blue hat. It looked warm and soft. The goat crowded in. The blue hat got bigger.

A ladybug saw the blue hat.
It looked warm and soft.
The ladybug crawled in.

4

Oh, no! The blue hat ripped.
The mouse was sad.
The bunny was sad.
The fox was sad.
The goat was sad.
The ladybug was sad.
All that was left was the little bell.

What Did the Story Say?

What happened to start the story?

What happened to end the story?

Folk tales like this one have been told over and over in many different ways. Change what is lost in the story and tell it again.

When It Belongs to Someone

We use **'s** to show that something belongs to someone. The blue hat belonged to Sam, so we say it was Sam's hat. Circle the words with **'s**. Finish the sentence to tell what belongs to someone.

The bunny's ears were long.

The ears belong to the ______________________________ .

The goat's horns were sharp.

The horns belong to the ______________________________ .

The bunny stepped on the mouse's tail.

The tail belongs to the ______________________________ .

The ladybug's wings folded across her back.

The wings belong to the ______________________________ .

The ladybug's spots were black.

The spots belong to the ______________________________ .

The fox looked in the bunny's home.

The home belongs to the ______________________________ .

The goat and the mouse liked Sam's hat.

The hat belongs to ______________________________ .

Reading Comprehension

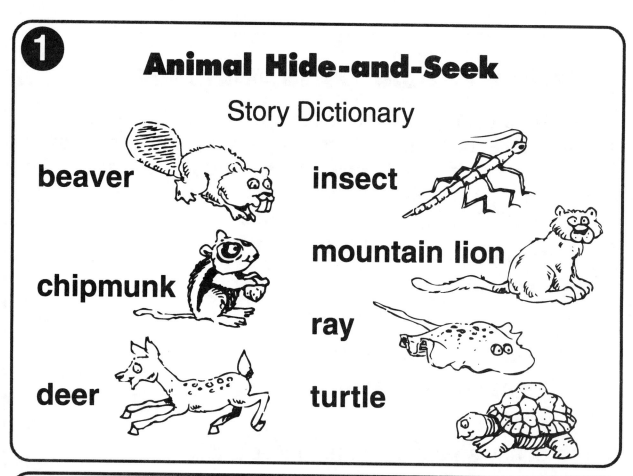

1

Animal Hide-and-Seek

Story Dictionary

beaver

insect

mountain lion

chipmunk

ray

deer

turtle

2

Have you ever played Hide-and-Seek?
For animals, hiding is more than a game.
The mountain lion can hide behind a log.
It waits for a deer to pass.
The deer will be its next meal.

3

Hiding can keep animals safe, too.
The chipmunk ducks into its hole.
The beaver swims into its home.
The ray hides in sand at the bottom of the ocean.
The turtle hides in a hard shell.

4

Other animals match the places they hide.
Think about the green frog on the green leaf.
Think about the insect that looks like a stick.
Hiding helps animals in different ways.

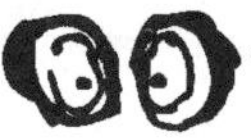

What Did the Story Say?

List two reasons why animals hide.

Draw a line to show where each animal hides.

Animals

Hiding Places

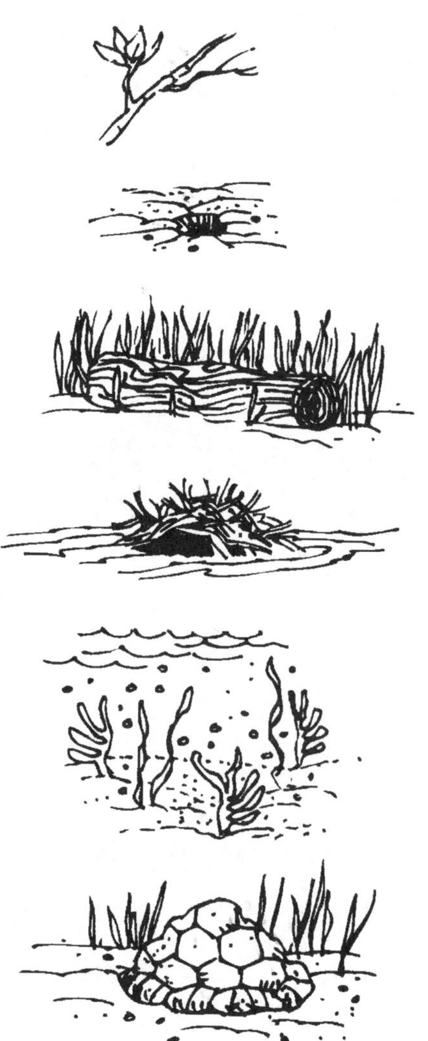

The Sound of *i*

Color the pictures that have the same vowel sound as hide.

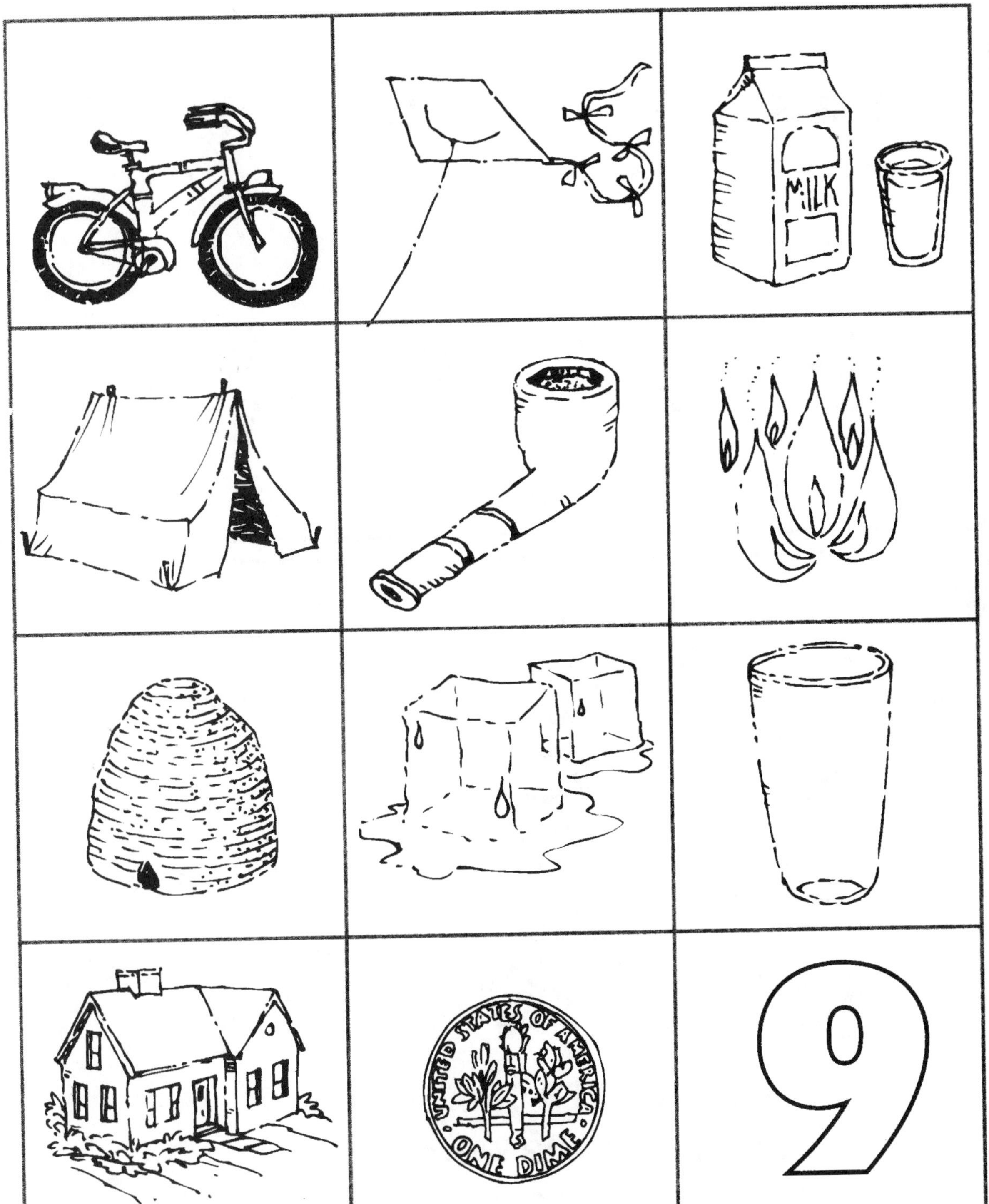

1

Ally's Garden

Story Dictionary

beets 

radishes 

lettuce 

water 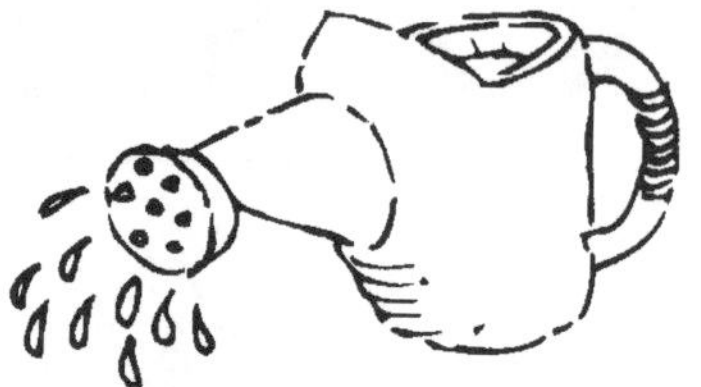

2

Ally wanted a garden.
She pulled the weeds.
She raked the soil to make it soft.
Gardens are hard work.

Ally wanted a garden.
She planted the seeds.
She watered the seeds.
She saw little plants sprout and grow.
She gave them water.
Gardens are hard work.

Ally wanted to have a garden.
She picked lettuce.
She pulled radishes and beets.

Gardens may be hard work, but they're worth it.

What Did the Story Say?

What kinds of seeds did Ally plant?

____

What did Ally do to start her garden?

____

____

Draw a garden that you might make. Show something you would do to take care of the growing plants.

Tools for Gardening

Match the tool to the job.

dig up the potatoes

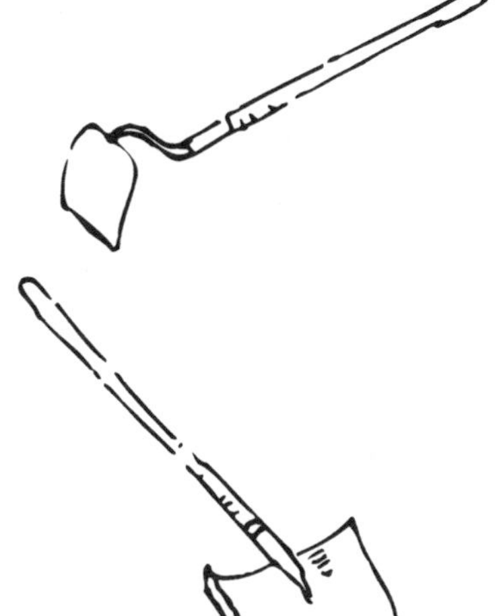

make ditches for watering

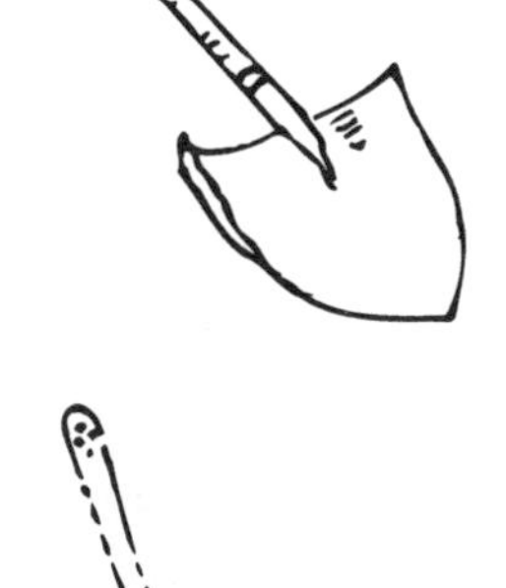

cut off the greens

smooth the soil

water the seeds

eat the salad

Reading Comprehension

Rainy Day Computer Fun

Story Dictionary

computer 

mouse 

window 

mailbox 

raining

It was quiet. Dark clouds covered the sun. Rain splashed on the window. Rhia was working at her computer. The computer beeped. A mailbox picture popped up. Rhia smiled. There was a letter in the computer mailbox. Rhia hoped that it was for her. She moved the mouse and clicked it. The e-mail came on the screen.

3

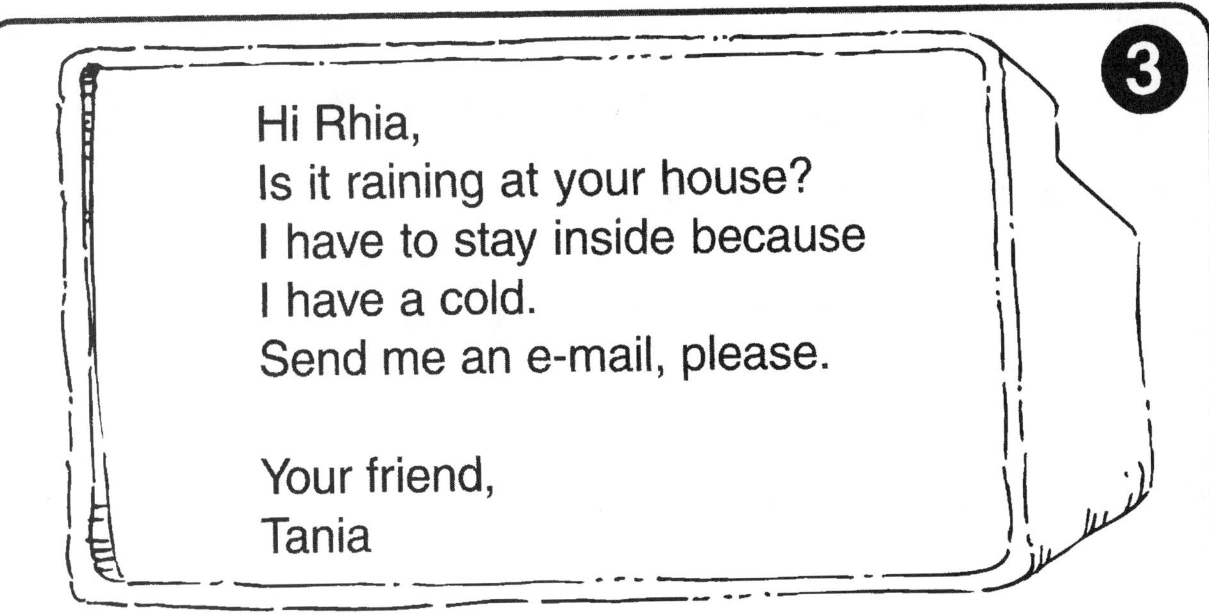
Hi Rhia,
Is it raining at your house?
I have to stay inside because
I have a cold.
Send me an e-mail, please.

Your friend,
Tania

Rhia smiled again. The letter was for her. It was from her friend Tania. It must be raining at Tania's house too. And Tania had a cold. Rhia would write her a note now.

4

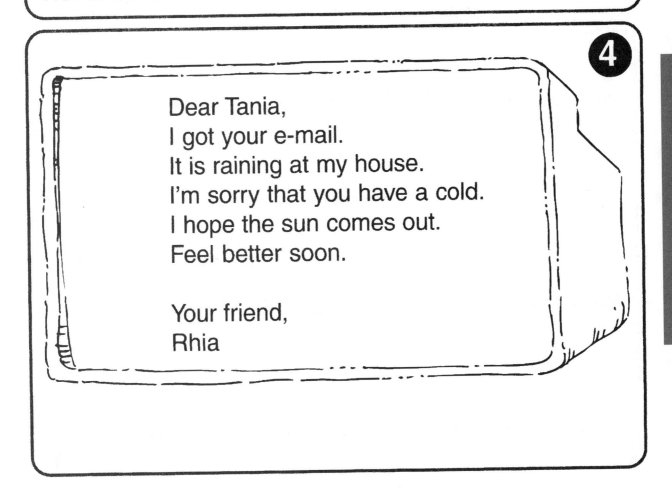

Dear Tania,
I got your e-mail.
It is raining at my house.
I'm sorry that you have a cold.
I hope the sun comes out.
Feel better soon.

Your friend,
Rhia

What Did the Story Say?

Number the parts in order.

☐ Rhia sent Tania an e-mail.

☐ The computer beeped.

☐ Tania sent Rhia an e-mail.

☐ Rhia clicked on the mailbox picture.

How do you think Tania felt when she got Rhia's e-mail?

____

____

Who would you send an e-mail to?

____

____

Working with Word Families

-ail

h + ail = ___ ___ ___ ___   j + ail = ___ ___ ___ ___

m + ail = ___ ___ ___ ___   n + ail = ___ ___ ___ ___

t + ail = ___ ___ ___ ___   tr + ail = ___ ___ ___ ___ ___

Draw a line from the picture to the word that names it.

nail

jail

mail

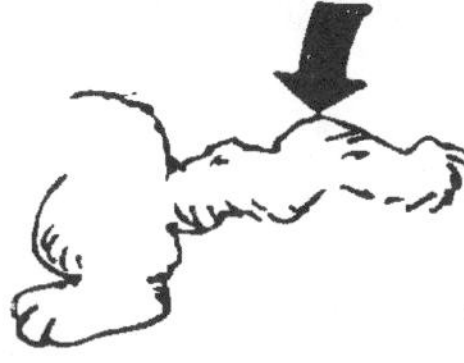

hail

quail

snail

tail

trail

1

Zack's Sandwich

Story Dictionary

ham 

lettuce leaf 

pickle 

sandwich 

slice of bread 

2

This is Zack.

Here is a slice of bread
that started the sandwich that
Zack made.

This is the pickle
on top of a slice of bread
that started the sandwich that
Zack made.

3

This is the ham that
covers the pickle
on top of a slice of bread
that started the sandwich that Zack made.

This is the lettuce leaf
on the ham that
covers the pickle
on top of a slice of bread
that started the sandwich that Zack made.

4

This is another slice of bread, a lid for the lettuce leaf on the ham that covers the pickle on top of the slice of bread that started the sandwich that Zack made.

This is the sandwich that Zack made.

What Did the Story Say?

Write a recipe for making Zack's sandwich.

Recipe for a Sandwich
From Zack's Kitchen

Ingredients:

____

____

What to do:

1. ____________________________

2. ____________________________

3. ____________________________

4. ____________________________

5. ____________________________

Answer Key

Please take time to go over the work your child has completed. Ask your child to explain what he/she has done. Praise both success and effort. If mistakes have been made, explain what the answer should have been and how to find it. Let your child know that mistakes are a part of learning. The time you spend with your child helps let him/her know you feel learning is important.

page 132

What Did the Story Say?

Mark the things that made the pond busy.

Draw something that might happen at the pond.

page 133

Real or Make-Believe?

Circle **yes** or **no**.

A duck can quack.	A duck can fly.	A duck can read.
(yes) no	(yes) no	yes (no)
A frog can color.	**A frog can jump.**	**A frog can swim.**
yes (no)	(yes) no	(yes) no
A bug can hop.	**A bug can paint.**	**A bug can run.**
(yes) no	yes (no)	(yes) no

page 136

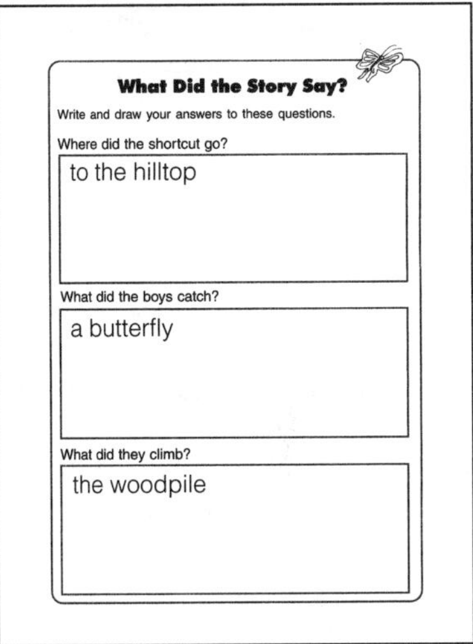

What Did the Story Say?

Write and draw your answers to these questions.

Where did the shortcut go?

to the hilltop

What did the boys catch?

a butterfly

What did they climb?

the woodpile

page 137

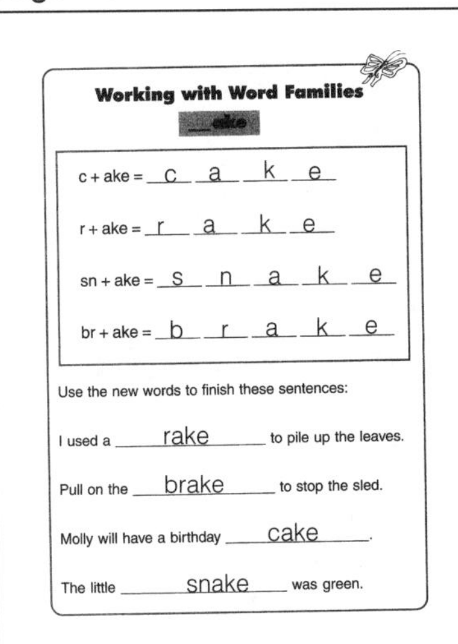

Working with Word Families

___ake

c + ake = c a k e

r + ake = r a k e

sn + ake = s n a k e

br + ake = b r a k e

Use the new words to finish these sentences:

I used a rake to pile up the leaves.

Pull on the brake to stop the sled.

Molly will have a birthday cake.

The little snake was green.

page 140

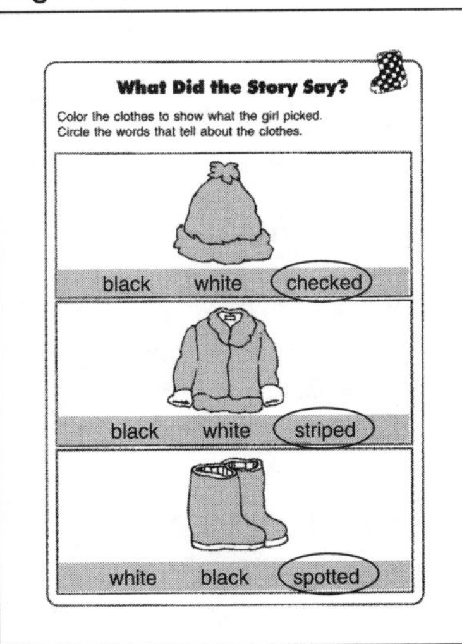

What Did the Story Say?

Color the clothes to show what the girl picked.
Circle the words that tell about the clothes.

black white (checked)

black white (striped)

white black (spotted)

page 144

What Did the Story Say?

What questions did the boy ask Star Man?

Do you have a bed?

Does your mom bring you warm milk?

Do you eat cookies too?

What questions would you ask?

page 145

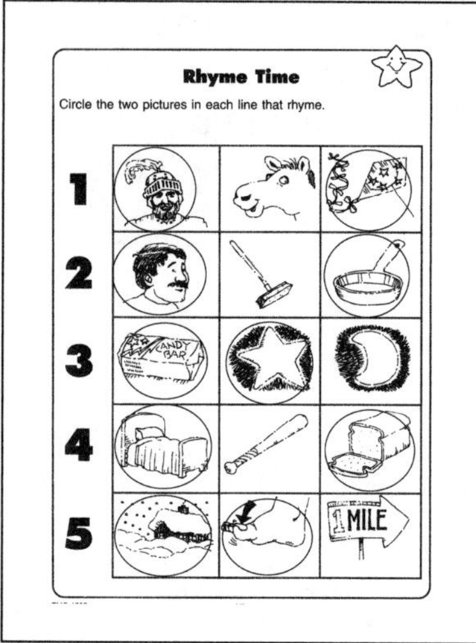

Rhyme Time

Circle the two pictures in each line that rhyme.

1

2

3

4

5

page 148

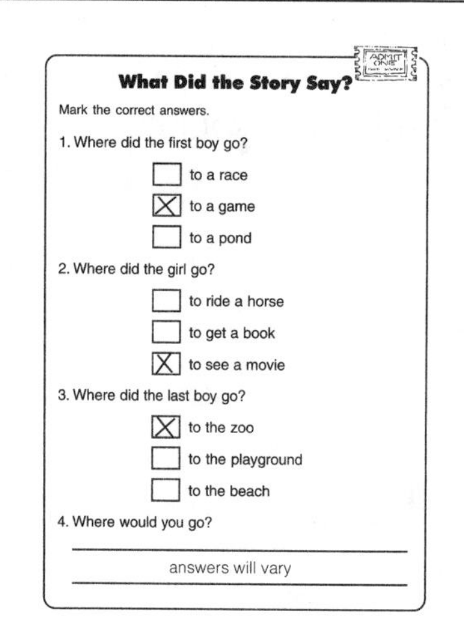

What Did the Story Say?

Mark the correct answers.

1. Where did the first boy go?
   - [ ] to a race
   - [x] to a game
   - [ ] to a pond
2. Where did the girl go?
   - [ ] to ride a horse
   - [ ] to get a book
   - [x] to see a movie
3. Where did the last boy go?
   - [x] to the zoo
   - [ ] to the playground
   - [ ] to the beach
4. Where would you go?

answers will vary

page 149

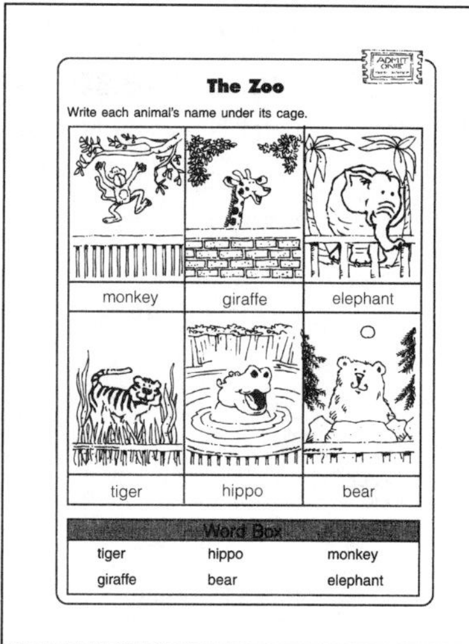

The Zoo

Write each animal's name under its cage.

monkey	giraffe	elephant
tiger	hippo	bear

Word Box		
tiger	hippo	monkey
giraffe	bear	elephant

page 152

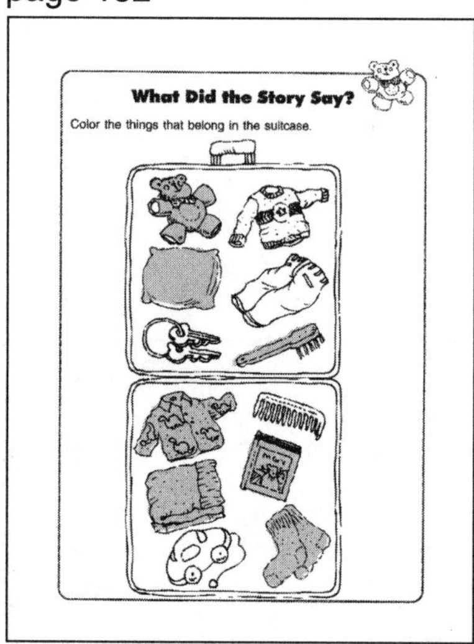

What Did the Story Say?

Color the things that belong in the suitcase.

page 153

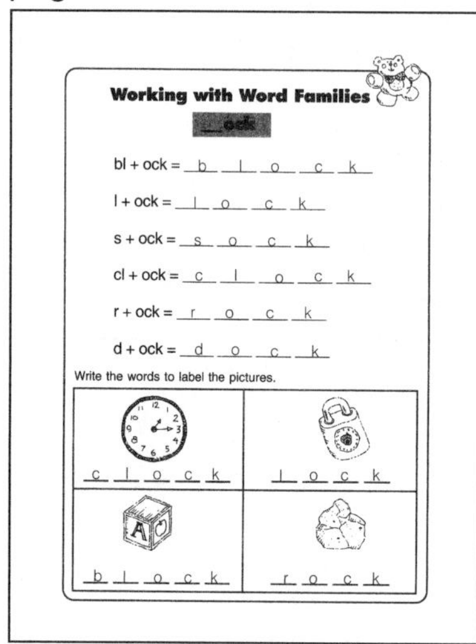

Working with Word Families

_ock

bl + ock = b l o c k

l + ock = l o c k

s + ock = s o c k

cl + ock = c l o c k

r + ock = r o c k

d + ock = d o c k

Write the words to label the pictures.

c l o c k	l o c k
b l o c k	r o c k

page 156

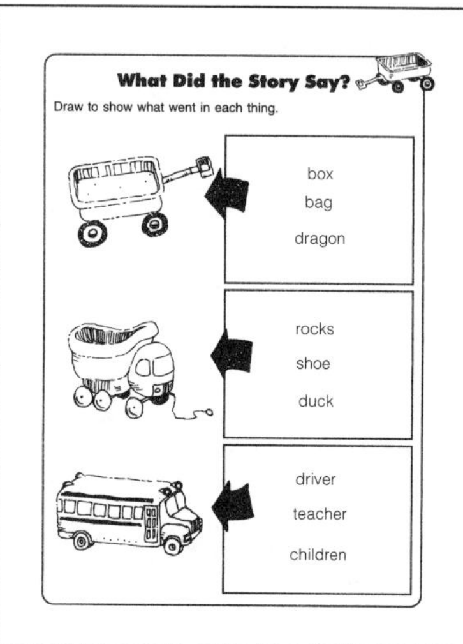

What Did the Story Say?

Draw to show what went in each thing.

box
bag
dragon

rocks
shoe
duck

driver
teacher
children

page 157

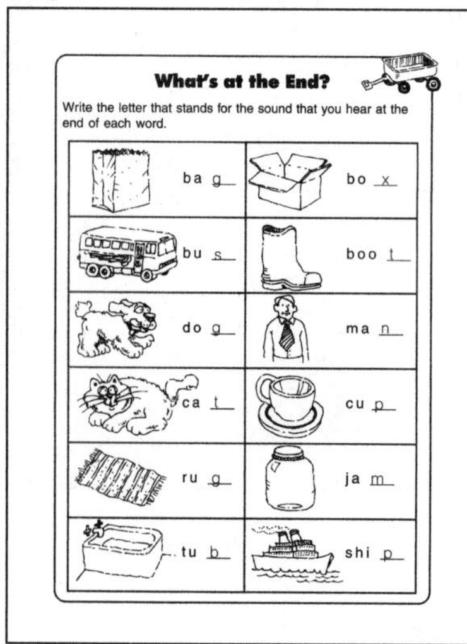

What's at the End?

Write the letter that stands for the sound that you hear at the end of each word.

ba g	bo x
bu s	boo t
do g	ma n
ca t	cu p
ru g	ja m
tu b	shi p

page 160

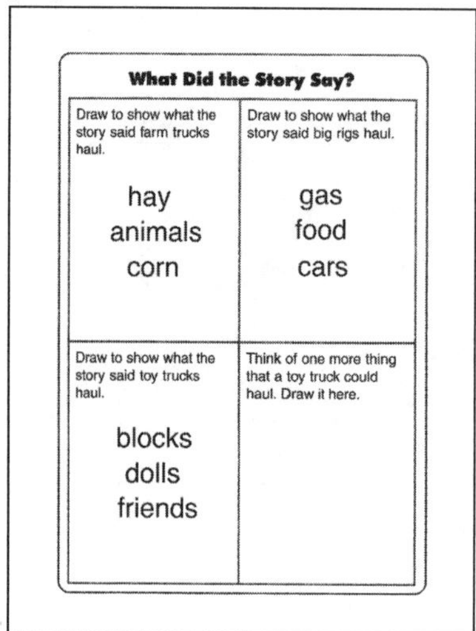

What Did the Story Say?

Draw to show what the story said farm trucks haul. hay animals corn	Draw to show what the story said big rigs haul. gas food cars
Draw to show what the story said toy trucks haul. blocks dolls friends	Think of one more thing that a toy truck could haul. Draw it here.

page 161

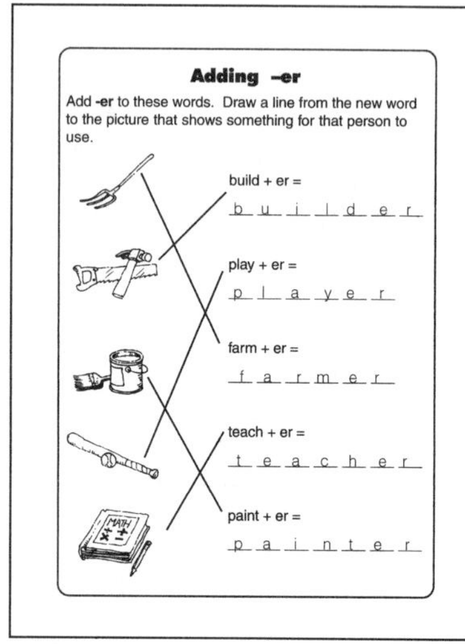

Adding -er

Add **-er** to these words. Draw a line from the new word to the picture that shows something for that person to use.

build + er = b u i l d e r

play + er = p l a y e r

farm + er = f a r m e r

teach + er = t e a c h e r

paint + er = p a i n t e r

page 164

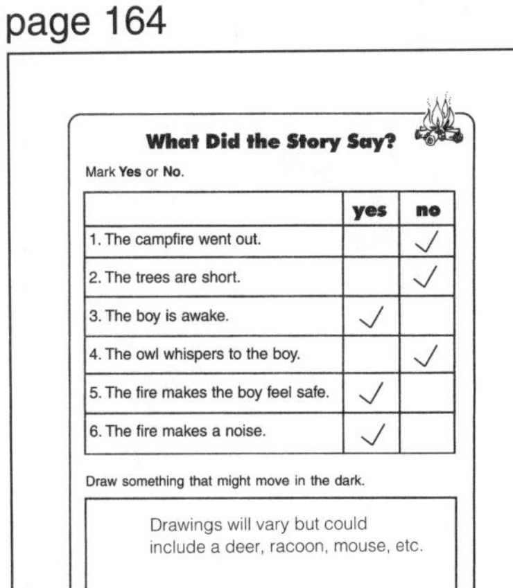

What Did the Story Say?

Mark **Yes** or **No**.

	yes	no
1. The campfire went out.		✓
2. The trees are short.		✓
3. The boy is awake.	✓	
4. The owl whispers to the boy.		✓
5. The fire makes the boy feel safe.	✓	
6. The fire makes a noise.	✓	

Draw something that might move in the dark.

Drawings will vary but could include a deer, racoon, mouse, etc.

page 165

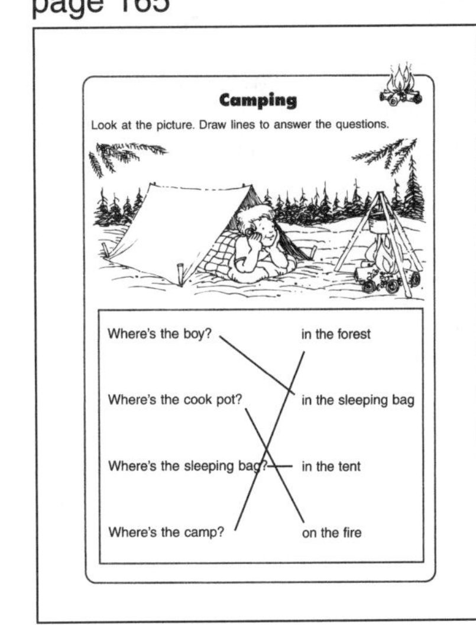

Camping

Look at the picture. Draw lines to answer the questions.

Where's the boy? — in the sleeping bag

Where's the cook pot? — on the fire

Where's the sleeping bag? — in the tent

Where's the camp? — in the forest

page 168

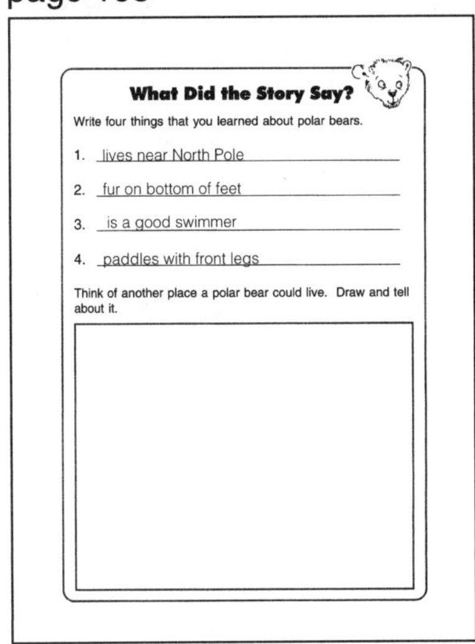

What Did the Story Say?

Write four things that you learned about polar bears.

1. lives near North Pole
2. fur on bottom of feet
3. is a good swimmer
4. paddles with front legs

Think of another place a polar bear could live. Draw and tell about it.

page 169

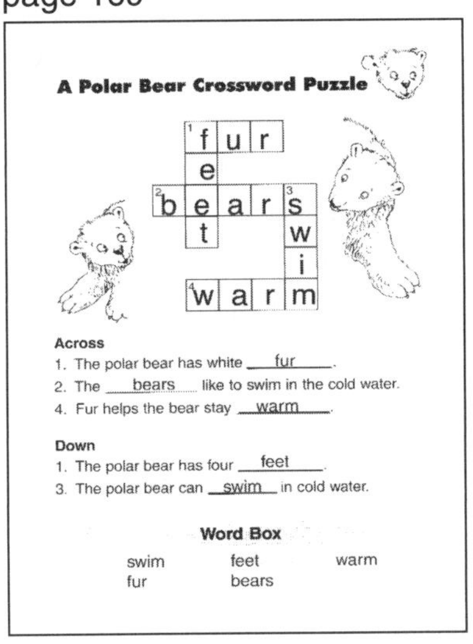

A Polar Bear Crossword Puzzle

Across

1. The polar bear has white fur.
2. The bears like to swim in the cold water.
4. Fur helps the bear stay warm.

Down

1. The polar bear has four feet.
3. The polar bear can swim in cold water.

Word Box

swim feet warm fur bears

page 172

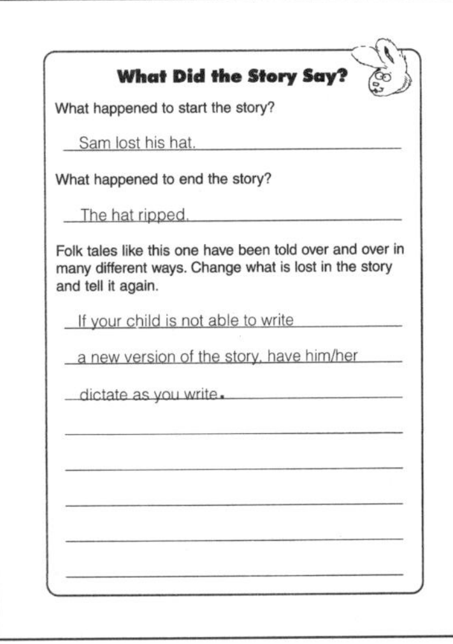

What Did the Story Say?

What happened to start the story?

Sam lost his hat.

What happened to end the story?

The hat ripped.

Folk tales like this one have been told over and over in many different ways. Change what is lost in the story and tell it again.

If your child is not able to write a new version of the story, have him/her dictate as you write.

page 173

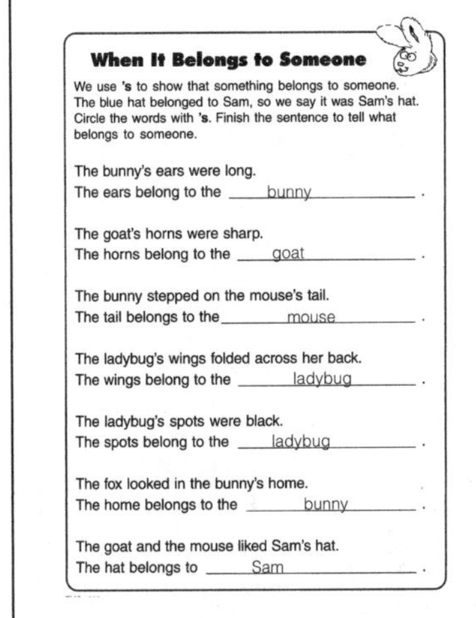

When It Belongs to Someone

We use **'s** to show that something belongs to someone. The blue hat belonged to Sam, so we say it was Sam's hat. Circle the words with **'s**. Finish the sentence to tell what belongs to someone.

The bunny's ears were long.
The ears belong to the bunny.

The goat's horns were sharp.
The horns belong to the goat.

The bunny stepped on the mouse's tail.
The tail belongs to the mouse.

The ladybug's wings folded across her back.
The wings belong to the ladybug.

The ladybug's spots were black.
The spots belong to the ladybug.

The fox looked in the bunny's home.
The home belongs to the bunny.

The goat and the mouse liked Sam's hat.
The hat belongs to Sam.

page 176

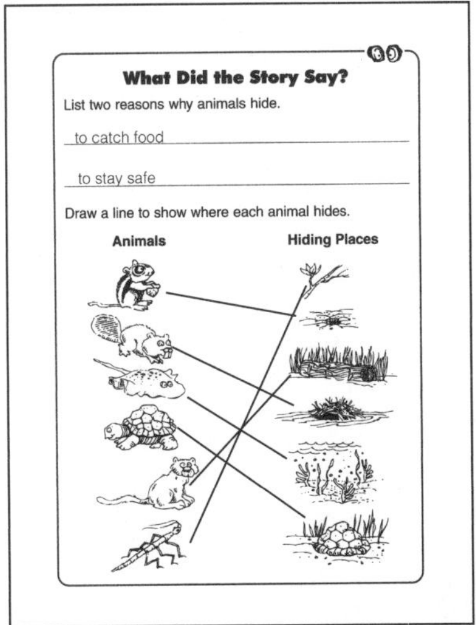

What Did the Story Say?

List two reasons why animals hide.

to catch food

to stay safe

Draw a line to show where each animal hides.

page 177

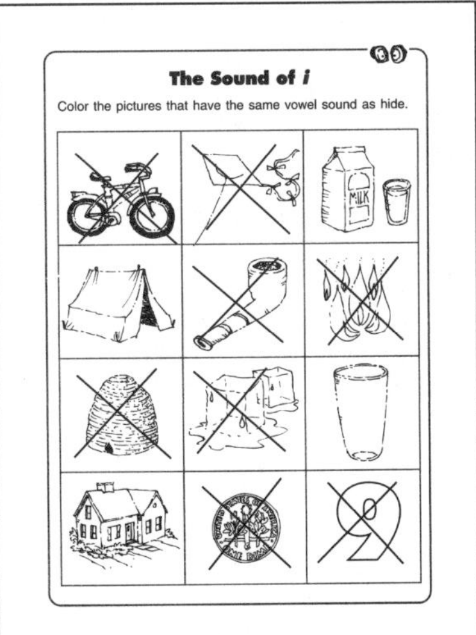

The Sound of *i*

Color the pictures that have the same vowel sound as hide.

page 180

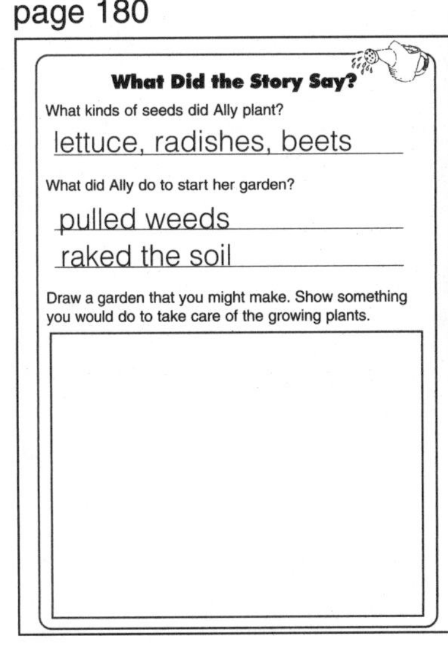

What Did the Story Say?

What kinds of seeds did Ally plant?

lettuce, radishes, beets

What did Ally do to start her garden?

pulled weeds

raked the soil

Draw a garden that you might make. Show something you would do to take care of the growing plants.

Reading Comprehension

page 181

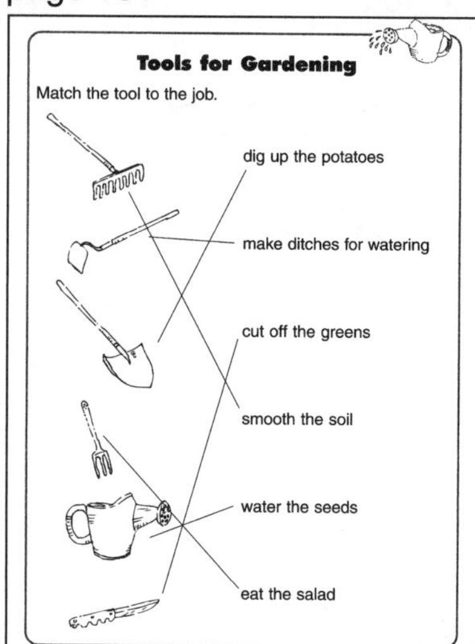

Tools for Gardening

Match the tool to the job.

dig up the potatoes

make ditches for watering

cut off the greens

smooth the soil

water the seeds

eat the salad

page 184

What Did the Story Say?

Number the parts in order.

4 Rhia sent Tania an e-mail.

2 The computer beeped.

1 Tania sent Rhia an e-mail.

3 Rhia clicked on the mailbox picture.

How do you think Tania felt when she got Rhia's e-mail?

Tania will feel happy, feel better, etc.

Who would you send an e-mail to?

Answers to last question will vary.

page 185

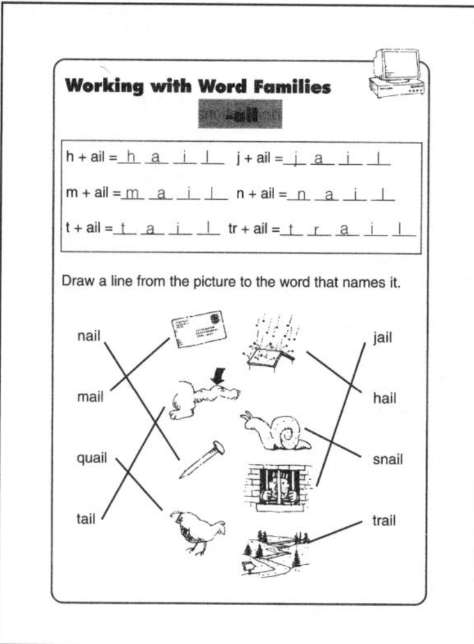

Working with Word Families

-ail

h + ail = h a i l j + ail = j a i l

m + ail = m a i l n + ail = n a i l

t + ail = t a i l tr + ail = t r a i l

Draw a line from the picture to the word that names it.

nail, mail, quail, tail, jail, hail, snail, trail

page 188

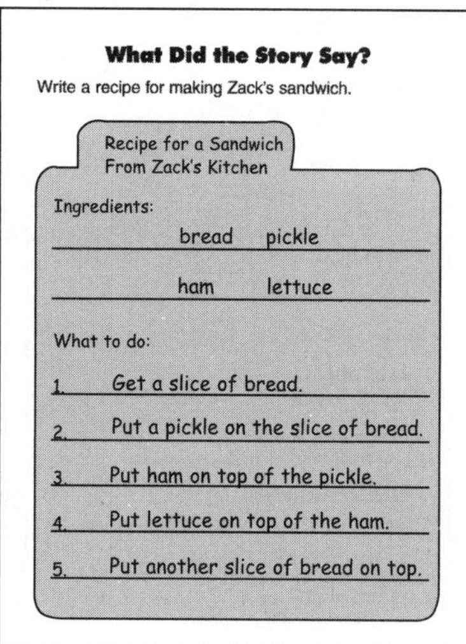

What Did the Story Say?

Write a recipe for making Zack's sandwich.

Recipe for a Sandwich From Zack's Kitchen

Ingredients:

bread pickle

ham lettuce

What to do:

1. Get a slice of bread.
2. Put a pickle on the slice of bread.
3. Put ham on top of the pickle.
4. Put lettuce on top of the ham.
5. Put another slice of bread on top.

How many carrots?

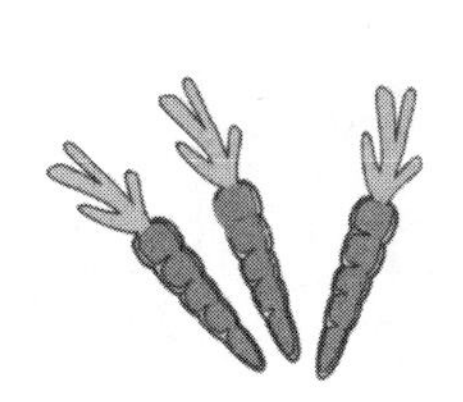 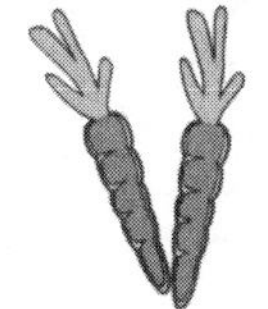 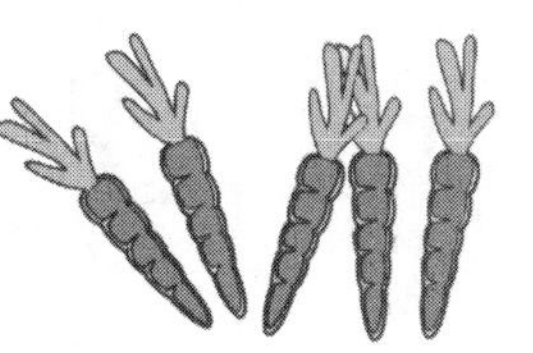

3 + 2 = 5

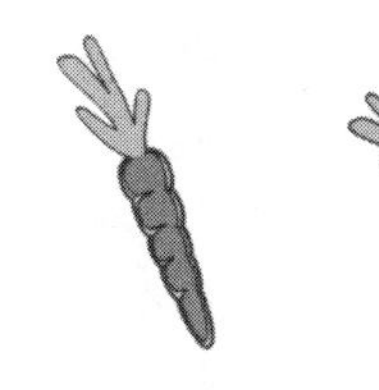

___ + ___ = ___

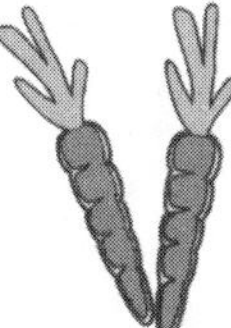 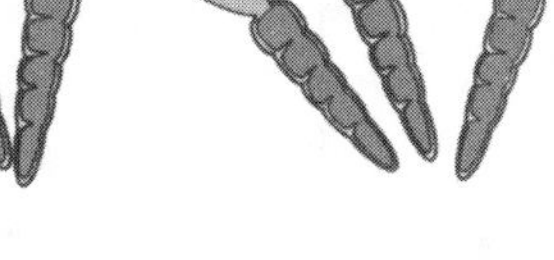

___ + ___ = ___

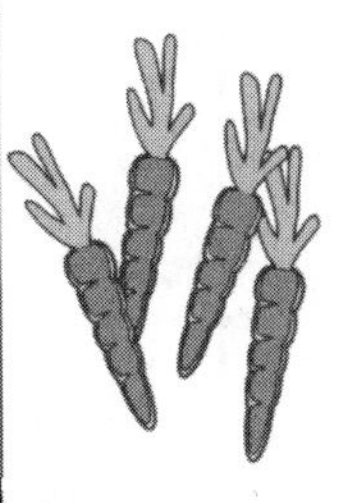   

___ + ___ = ___

  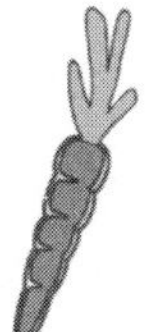

___ + ___ = ___

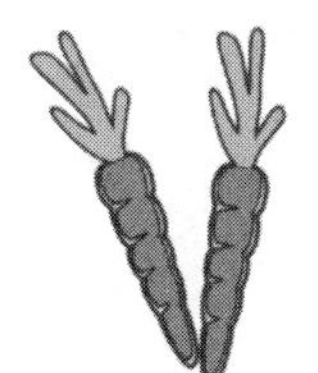  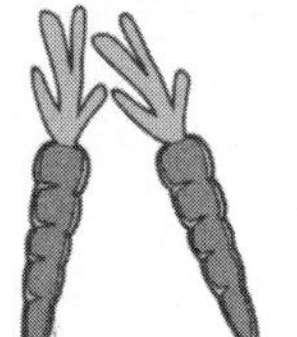

___ + ___ = ___

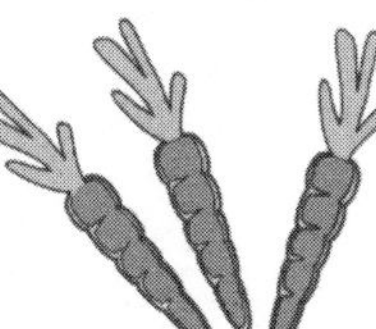  

___ + ___ = ___

Find my pet.

1 0 + 5	4 + 1	5 + 0	1 + 1	2 + 2	1 + 4	2 + 3	3 + 2 1
2 + 3	3 + 2	5 + 0			3 + 2	4 + 1	0 + 5
2 + 0	1 + 3	3 + 2		5 + 0		2 + 1	3 + 1
1 + 2	4 + 0	3 + 1	4 + 1 =	2	1 + 0	2 + 2	3 + 0

- Add
- Color

0-	black	3-	red
1-	red	4-	red
2-	red	5-	brown

Note: Give your child small objects to use as counters if he/she needs help on these pages.

How many bones?

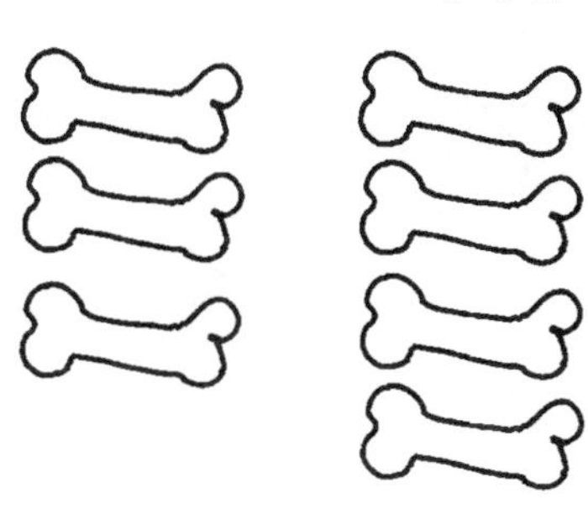

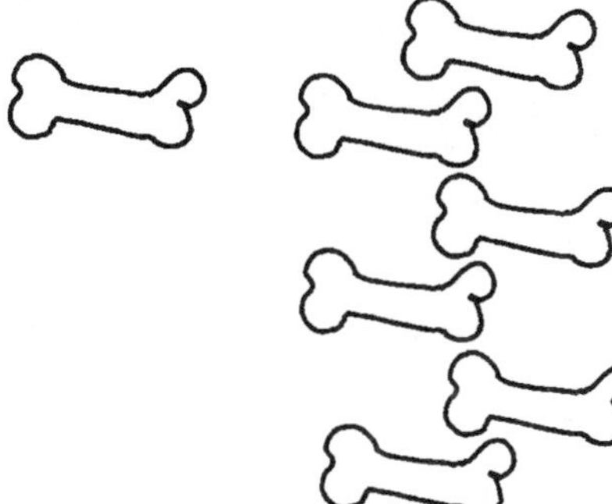

3 + 4 = 7

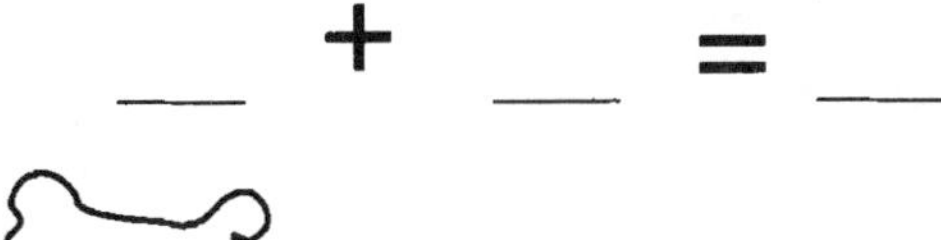

___ + ___ = ___

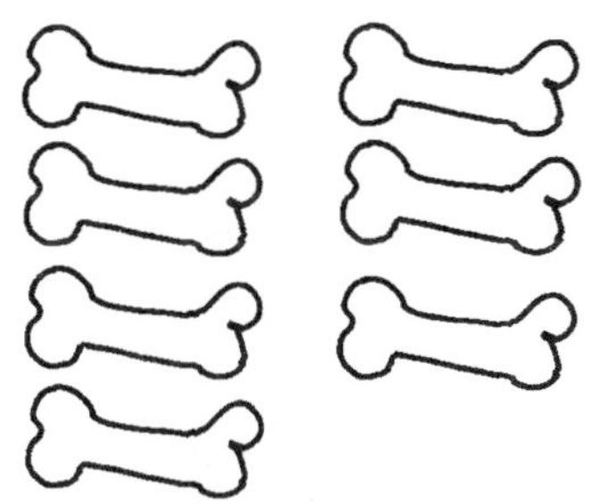

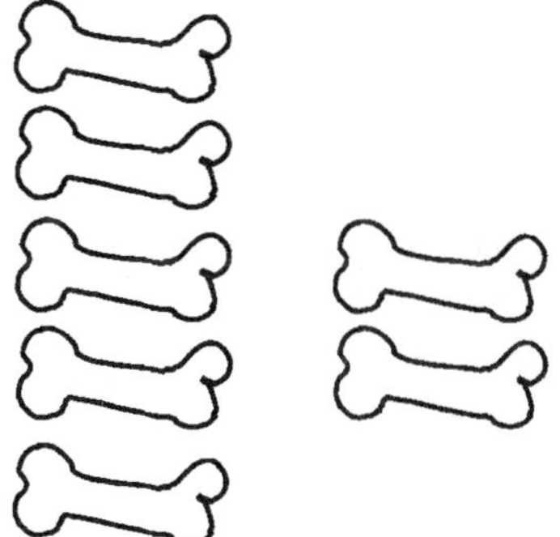

___ + ___ = ___   ___ + ___ = ___

5	6	5	4	3
+ 2	+ 1	+ 1	+ 2	+ 3
___	___	___	___	___

3	2	2	0	7
+ 4	+ 4	+ 2	+ 5	+ 0
___	___	___	___	___

Put the fish in their bowls.

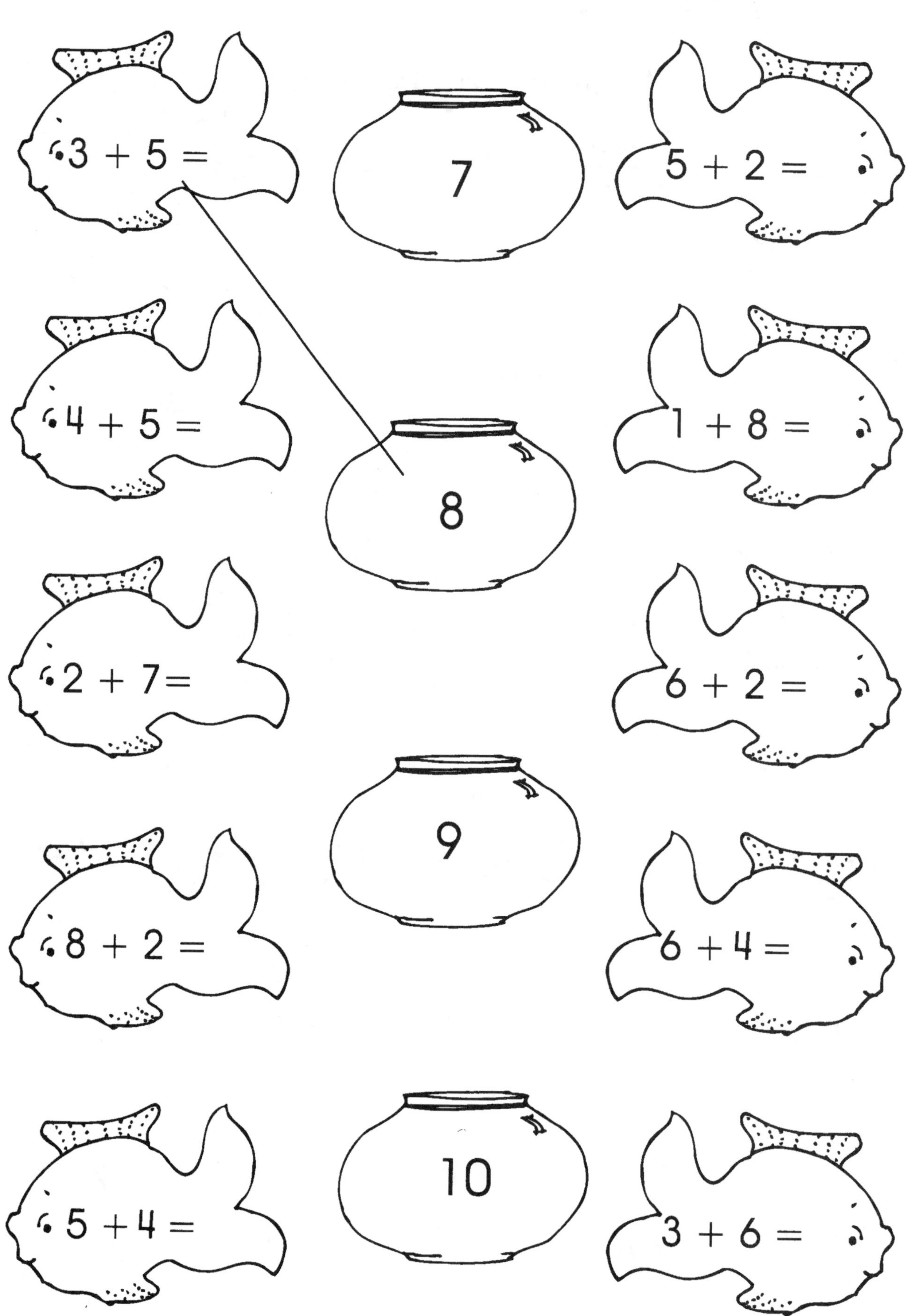

My Favorite Fruit

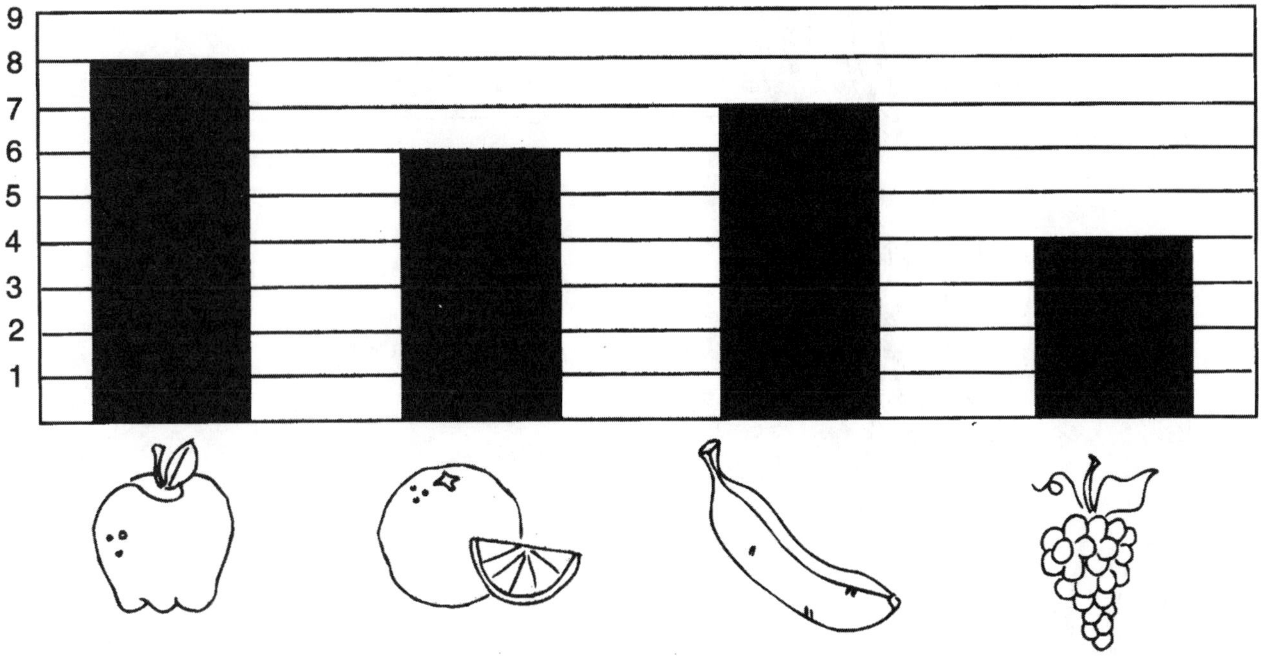

1. How many picked...?

 apples ______  grapes ______

 oranges ______  bananas ______

2. What was picked most? ______________

3. How many picked  oranges and  grapes together? ______________

How many bananas are left?

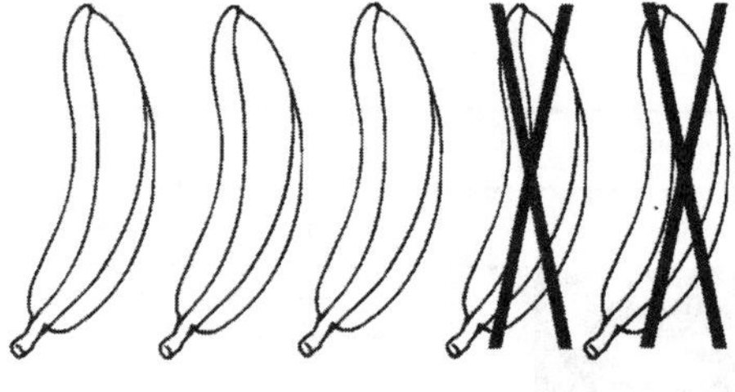

5 - 2 = 3

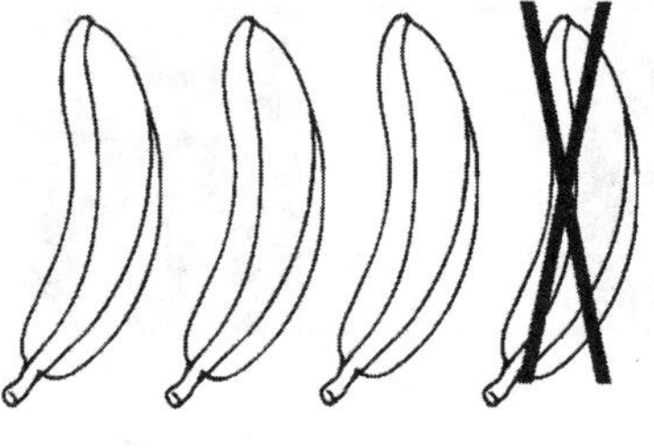

_____ - _____ = _____

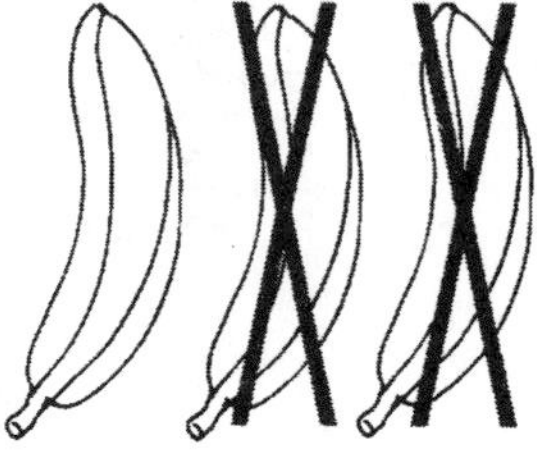

_____ - _____ = _____

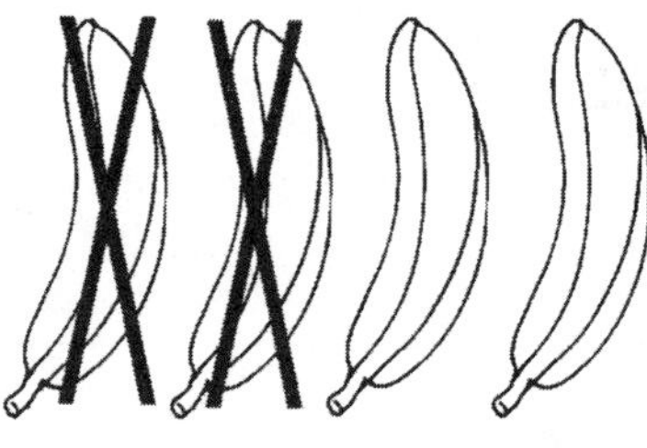

_____ - _____ = _____

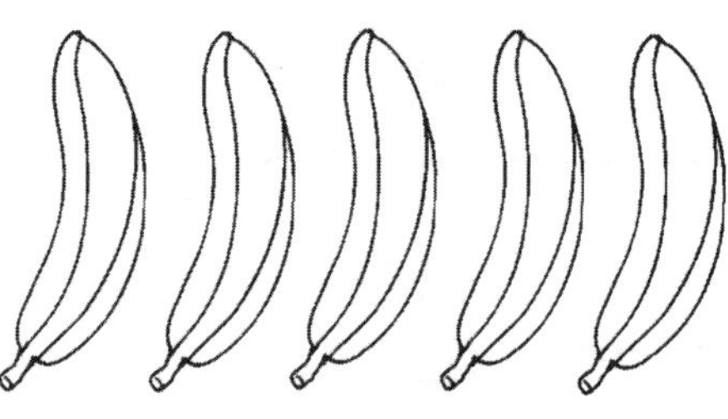

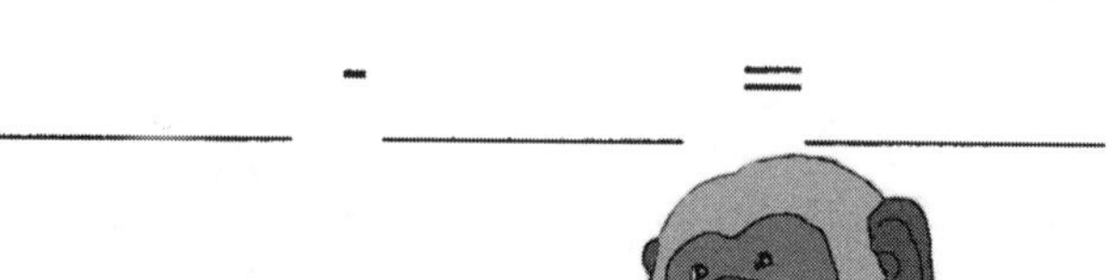

Connect the dots in order.
Start at 0.

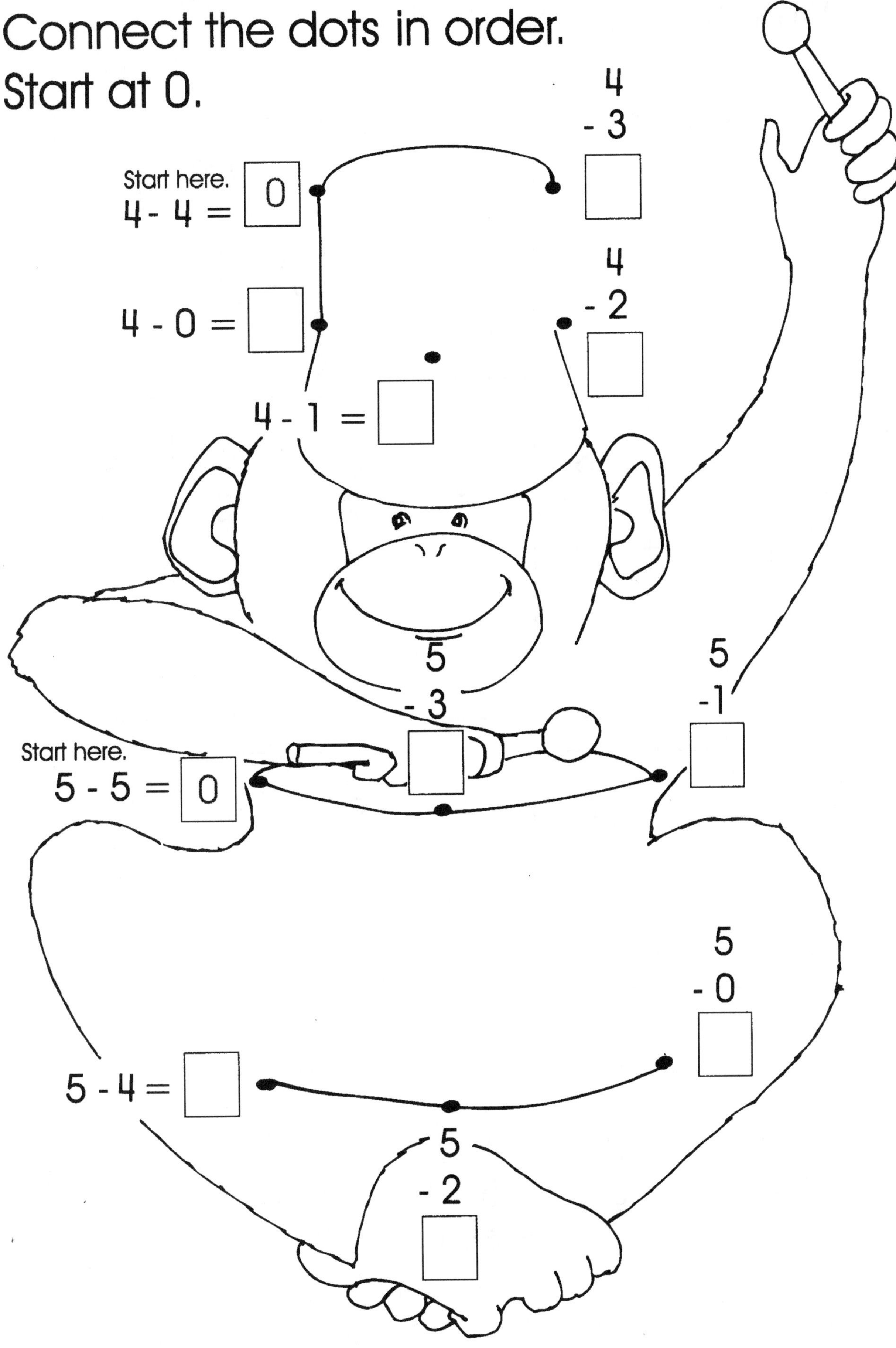

What has 4 wheels and flies?

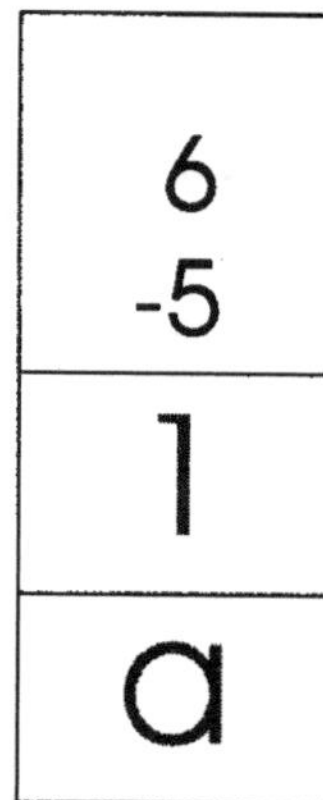

6 -5
1
a

9 -7	8 -7	6 -3	9 -5	3 -2	4 -2	9 -4

7 -1	8 -5	9 -2	9 -1	9 -0

1 - a	4 - b	7 - u
2 - g	5 - e	8 - c
3 - r	6 - t	9 - k

What is the rule?

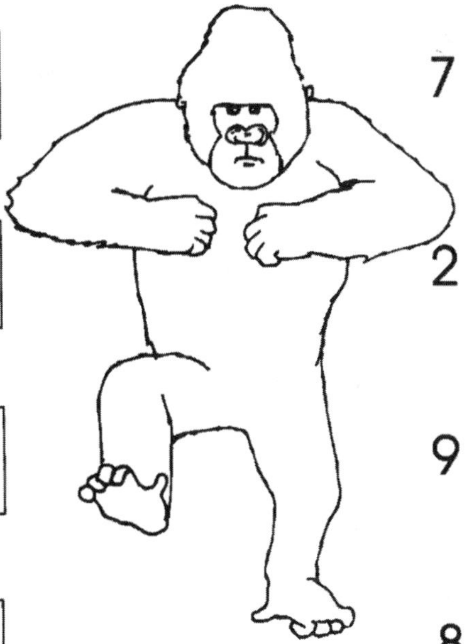

9 - 9 = ☐	1 - 0 = ☐
7 - 7 = ☐	7 - 0 = ☐
3 - 3 = ☐	2 - 0 = ☐
5 - 5 = ☐	9 - 0 = ☐
8 - 8 = ☐	8 - 0 = ☐
1 - 1 = ☐	6 - 0 = ☐
4 - 4 = ☐	3 - 0 = ☐
2 - 2 = ☐	5 - 0 = ☐
6 - 6 = ☐	4 - 0 = ☐

A number minus itself is always zero.
A number minus zero stays the same.

Take 1 Away

9	6	5	2
-1	-1	-1	-1
___	___	___	___

8	4	7	3
-1	-1	-1	-1
___	___	___	___

One less.

8 9 ___4 ___1 ___5

___ 3 ___8 ___6 ___2

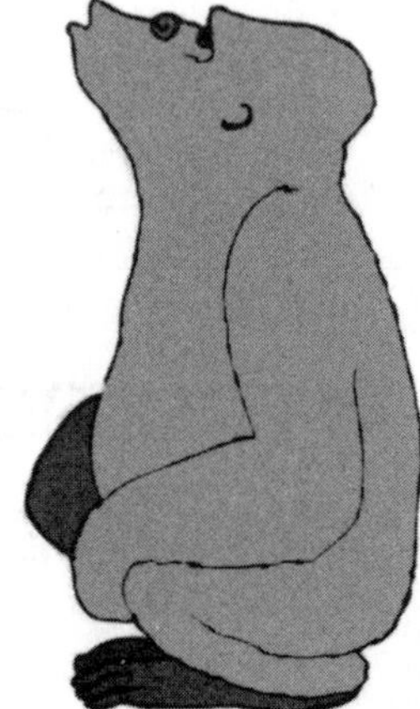

Subtract to Check Addition

3 + 4 = 7	7 − 3 = 4	7 − 4 = 3
1 + 3 = 4	4 − 1 = 3	4 − 3 = 1
2 + 7 = ___	___	___
4 + 2 = ___	___	___
7 + 1 = ___	___	___
3 + 5 = ___	___	___
6 + 3 = ___	___	___
2 + 6 = ___	___	___

Color 5 blue.
Color 3 red.
Color 2 yellow.

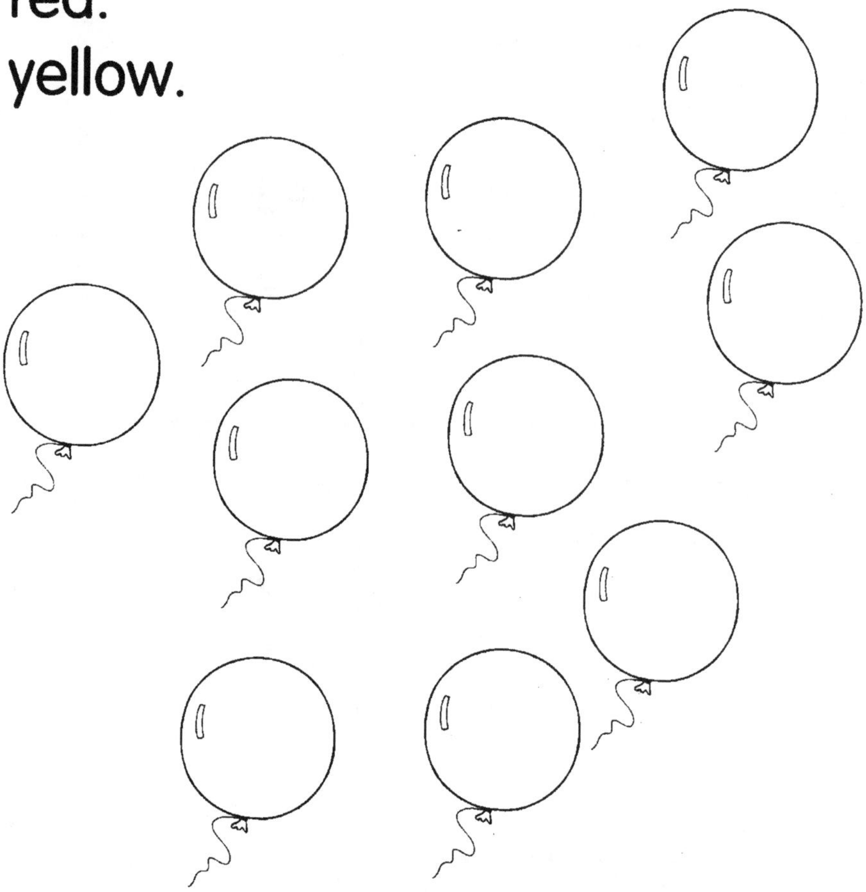

1. How many are there?

blue	red	yellow

2. How many more blue than yellow?

3. How many more red than yellow?

5. If 3 balloons broke, how many
would you have?

Fill in the missing numbers.

Help Electro find his bone.

56	57	58	59		61	62	63	64
55	30	31	32	33		35	36	65
	29	12		14	15	16	37	66
53		11	2	3		17	38	
52	27	10	1		5	18	39	68
51	26		8	7	6		40	69
50	25	24		22	21	20	41	70
	48	47	46	45	44	43		
80		78	77		75	74	73	72
81	82	83		85	86	87		89
98	97	96		94	93		91	90
99	100							

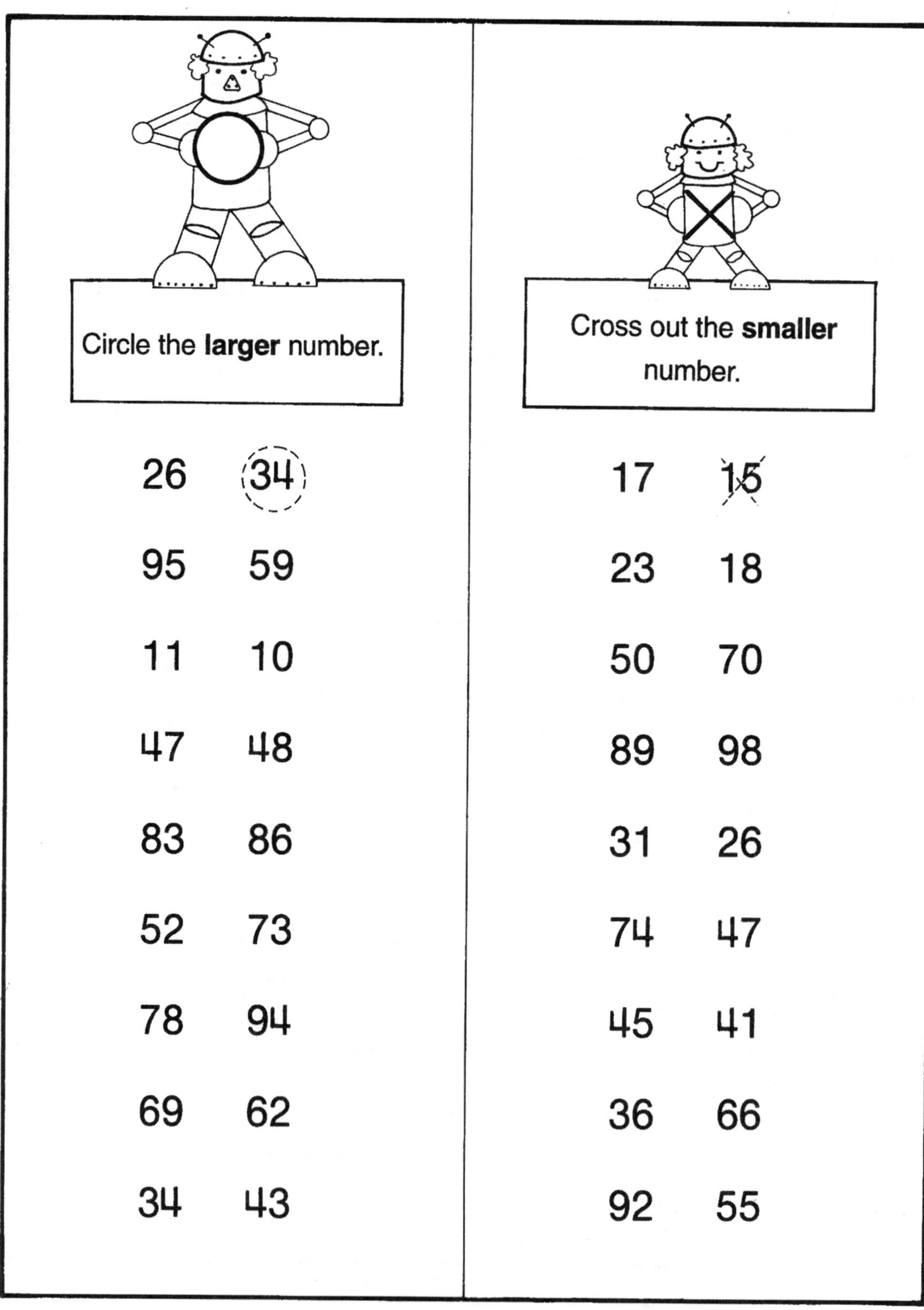
Circle the **larger** number.
26 34
95 59
11 10
47 48
83 86
52 73
78 94
69 62
34 43
Cross out the **smaller** number.
17 15
23 18
50 70
89 98
31 26
74 47
45 41
36 66
92 55

Fill in the numbers.

10	20								

Color...

red	green	purple
10	40	80
20	50	90
30	60	100
	70	

Color the empty boxes blue.

	70	40						
	50	60				80	100	
	40	60				90	80	
40	50	70	40			100	90	
		10			90	80	100	90
	20						10	
		30				20		

Off zoom the rockets.

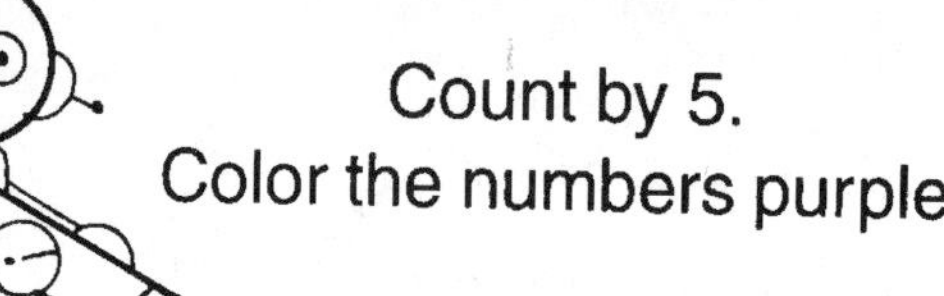

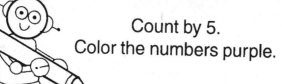

Count by 5.
Color the numbers purple.

1	2	3	4	5	6	7	8	9	10
11	12	13	14	15	16	17	18	19	20
21	22	23	24	25	26	27	28	29	30
31	32	33	34	35	36	37	38	39	40
41	42	43	44	45	46	47	48	49	50
51	52	53	54	55	56	57	58	59	60
61	62	63	64	65	66	67	68	69	70
71	72	73	74	75	76	77	78	79	80
81	82	83	84	85	86	87	88	89	90
91	92	93	94	95	96	97	98	99	100

Now count by 5.

5	10	15							

Count by 5s to 100.

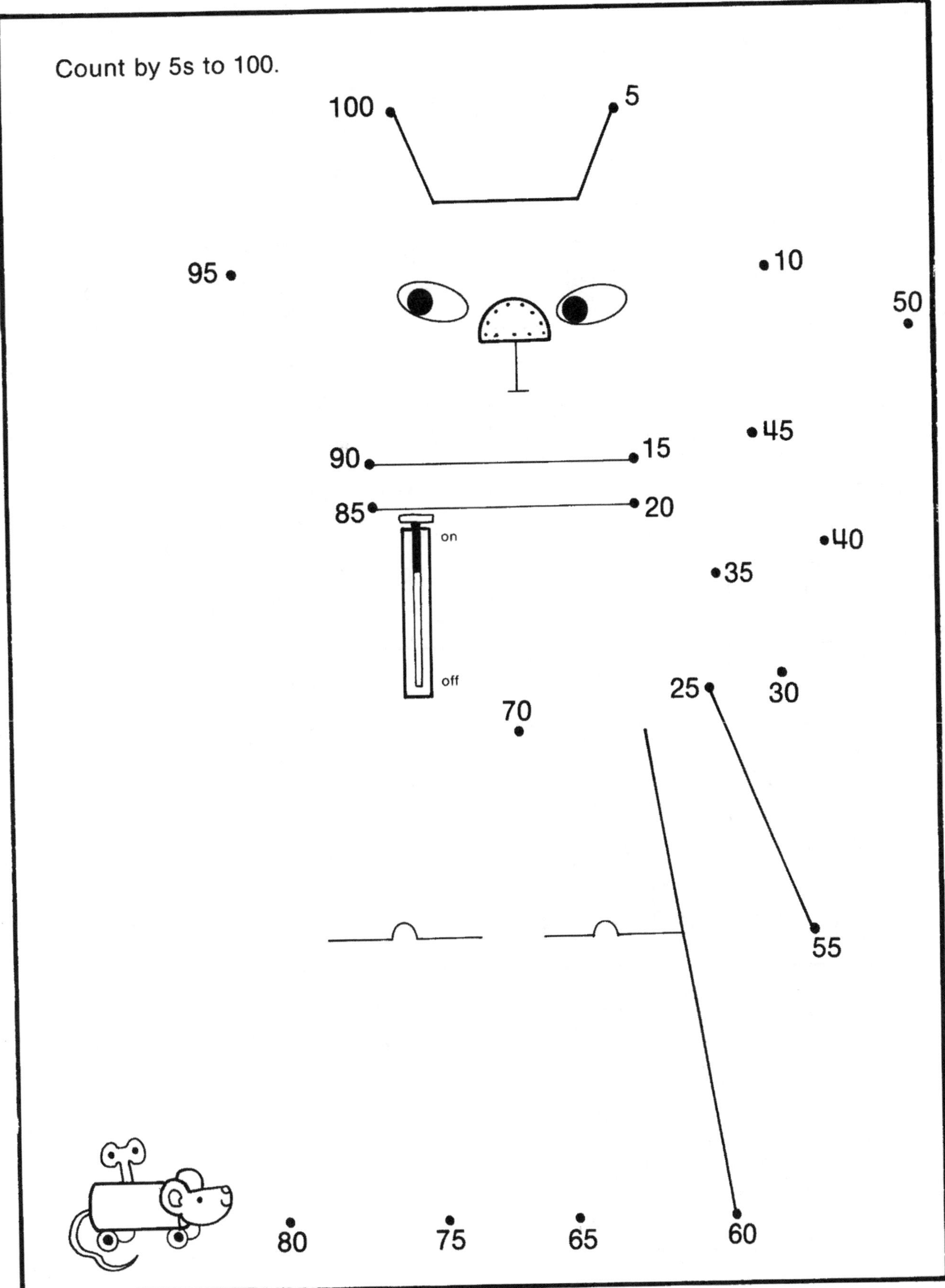

Count by 2.
Color the numbers **red**.

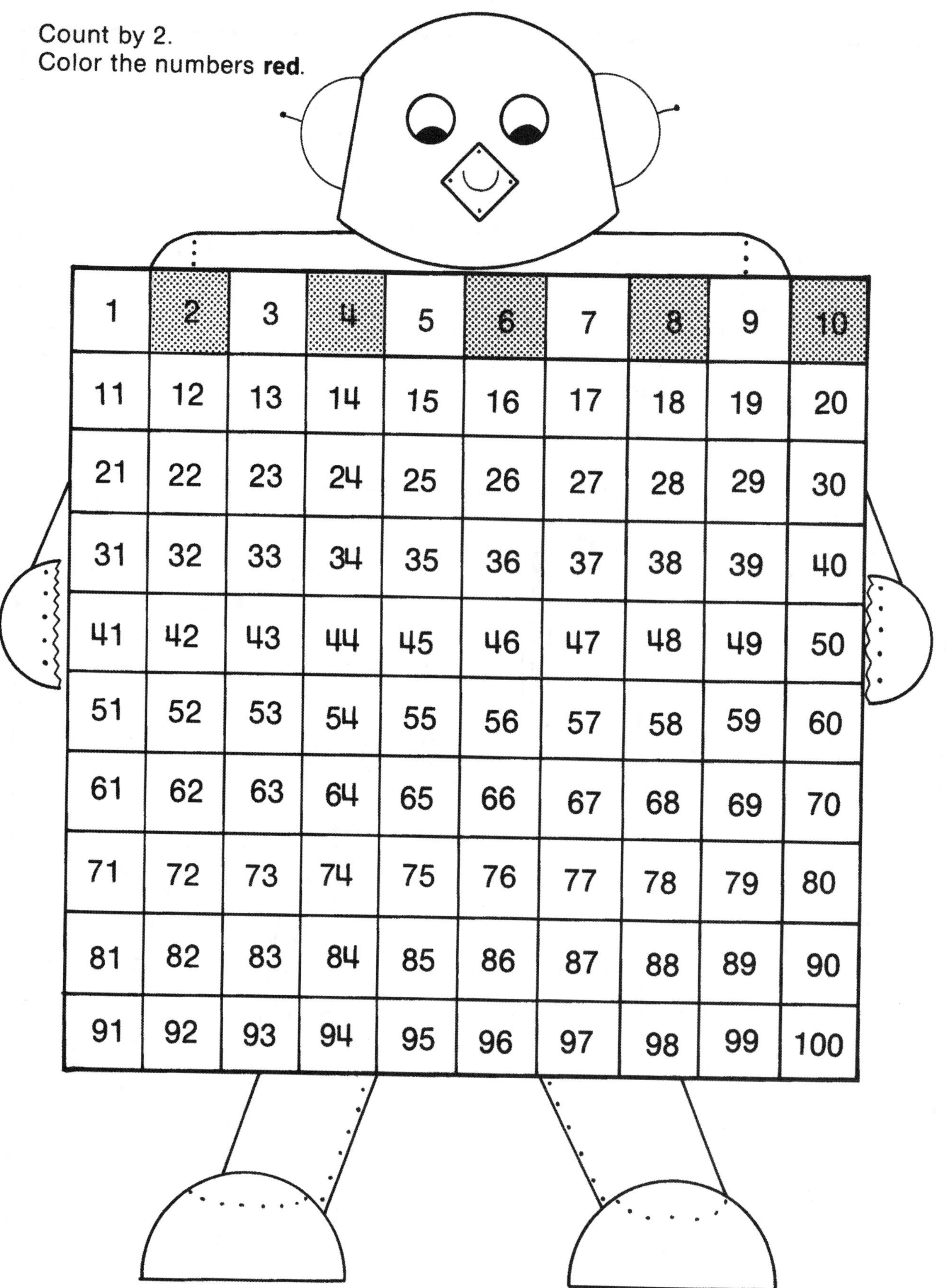

1	2	3	4	5	6	7	8	9	10
11	12	13	14	15	16	17	18	19	20
21	22	23	24	25	26	27	28	29	30
31	32	33	34	35	36	37	38	39	40
41	42	43	44	45	46	47	48	49	50
51	52	53	54	55	56	57	58	59	60
61	62	63	64	65	66	67	68	69	70
71	72	73	74	75	76	77	78	79	80
81	82	83	84	85	86	87	88	89	90
91	92	93	94	95	96	97	98	99	100

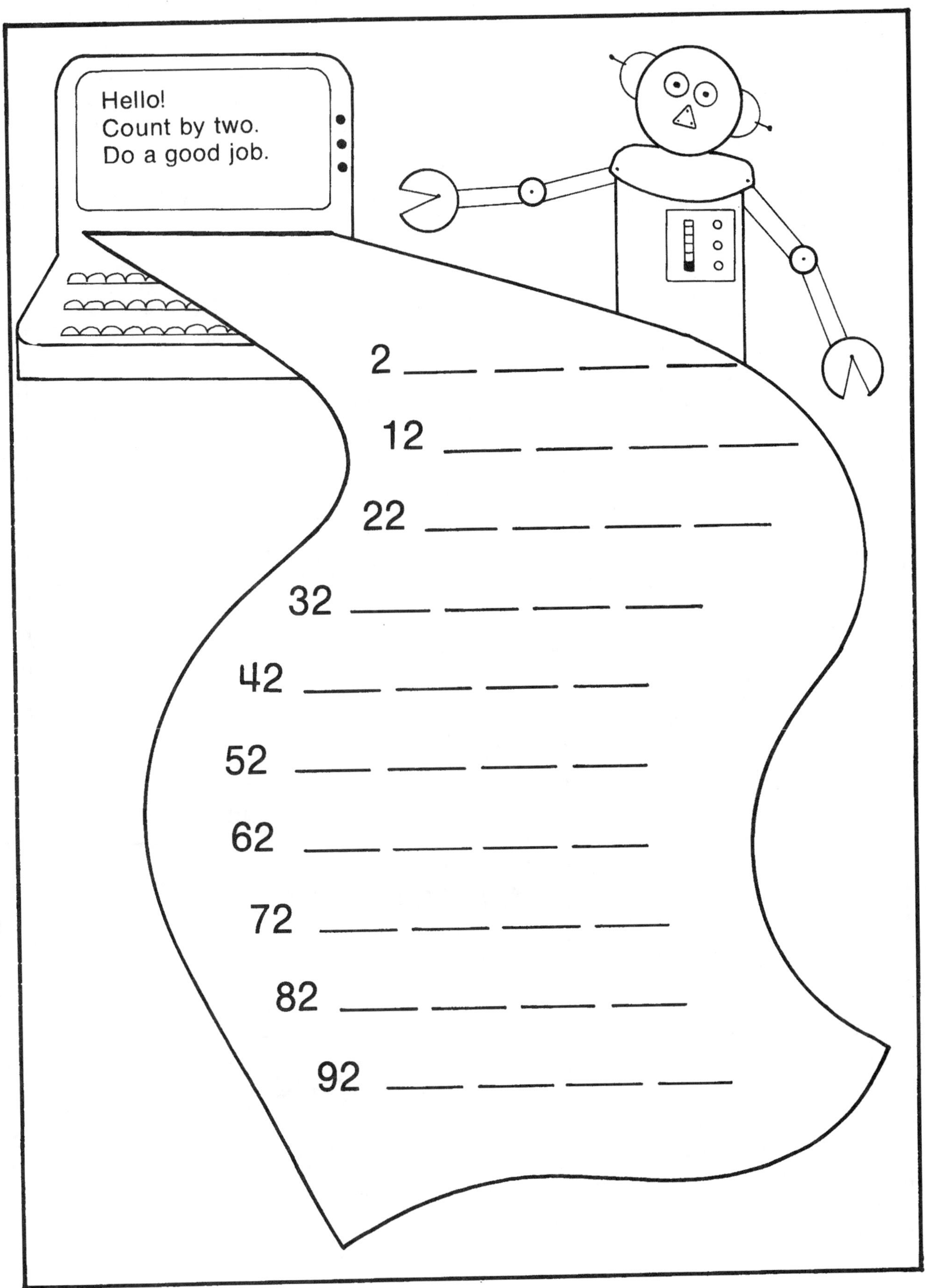
Hello!
Count by two.
Do a good job.
2 ___ ___ ___ ___
12 ___ ___ ___ ___
22 ___ ___ ___ ___
32 ___ ___ ___ ___
42 ___ ___ ___ ___
52 ___ ___ ___ ___
62 ___ ___ ___ ___
72 ___ ___ ___ ___
82 ___ ___ ___ ___
92 ___ ___ ___ ___

The Pets

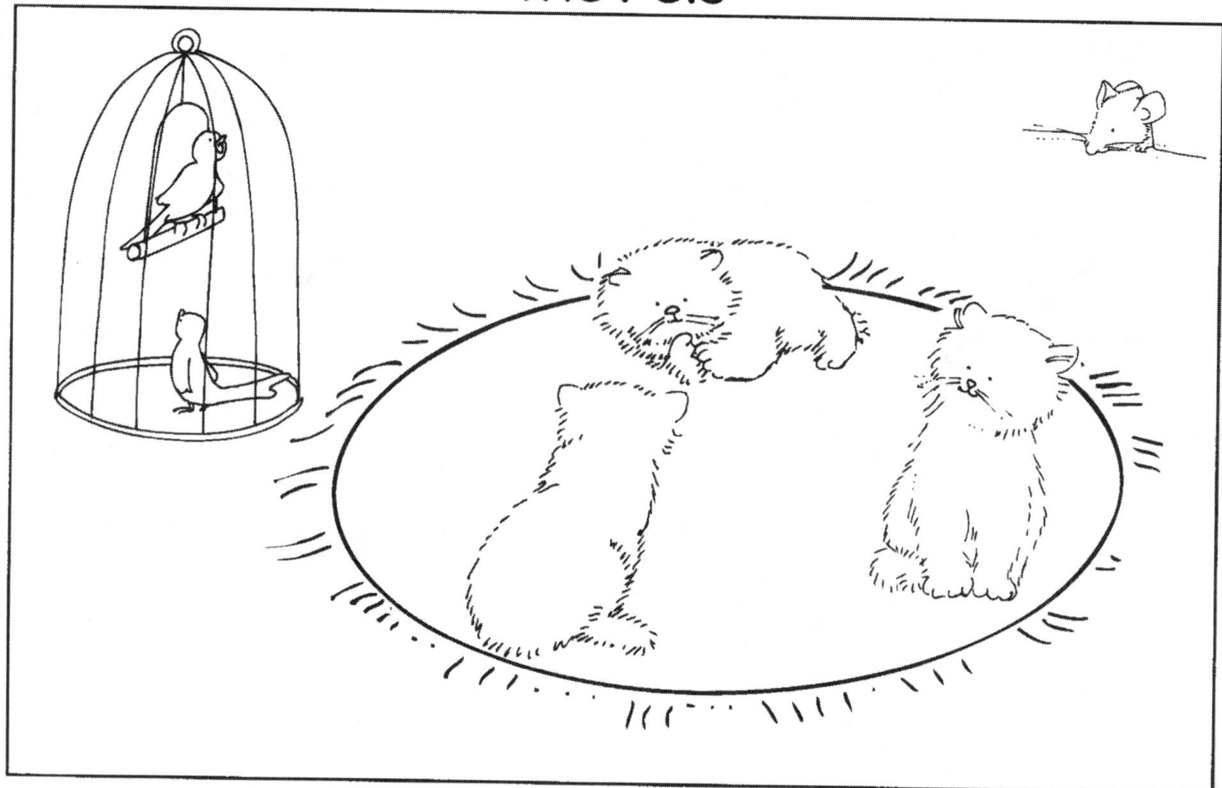

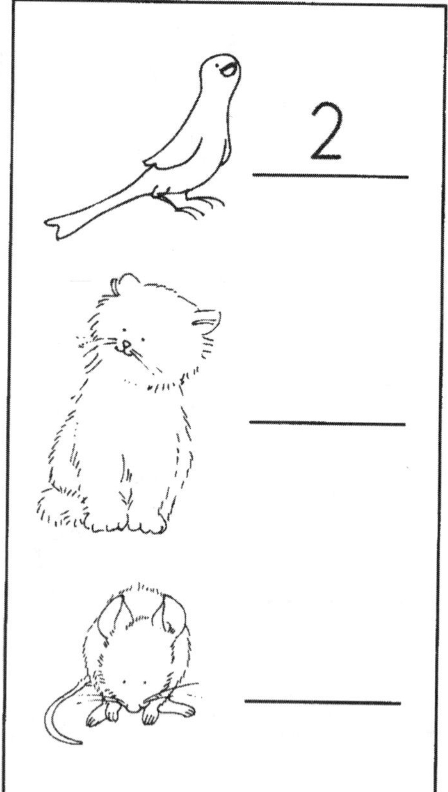
2

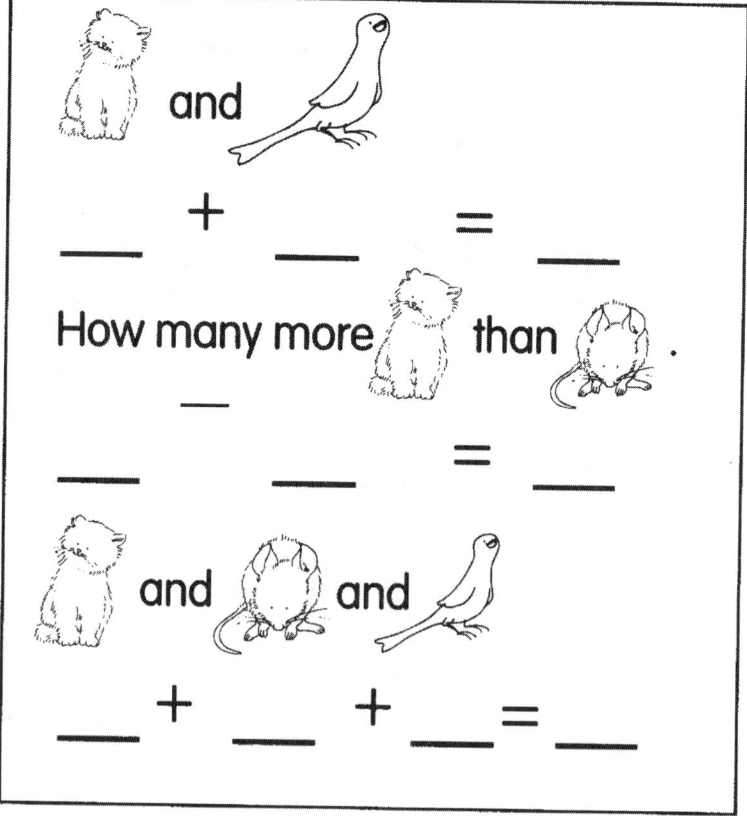
and
+
=
How many more than .
−
=
and
and
+
+
=

The Piggybank

How much?

1 ¢

____ ¢

____ ¢

How much is in the ? ____ ¢

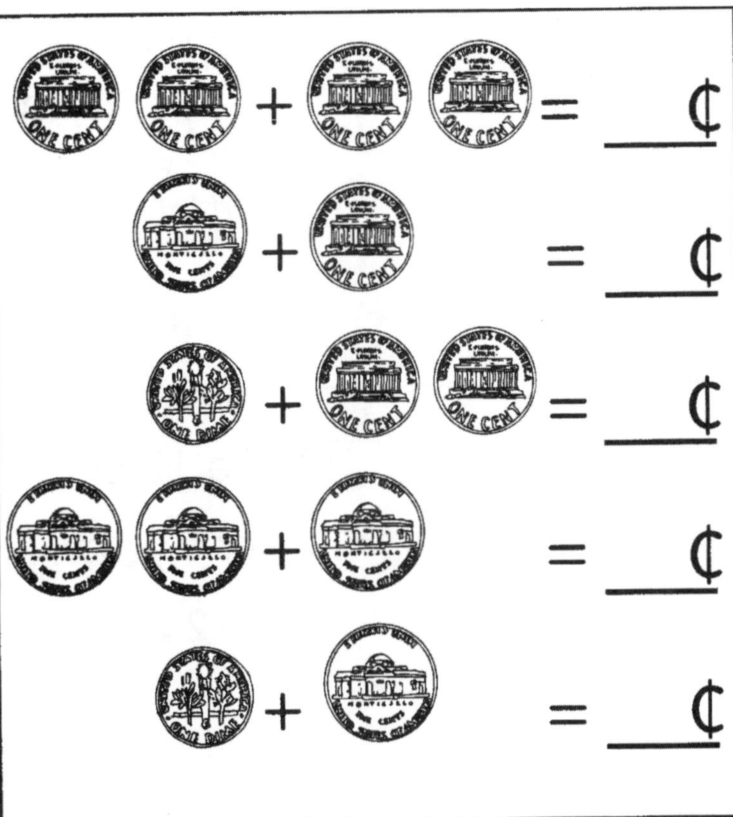

Blow Bubbles

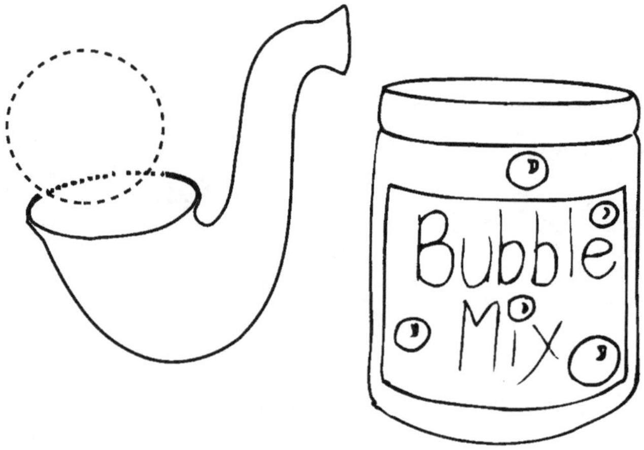

Make 12 big .

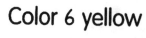

Color 6 yellow

2 blue

4 white

How many yellow ◯ and white ◯? ___ + ___ = ___	How many more yellow ◯ than blue ◯? ___ − ___ = ___
How many blue ◯ and yellow ◯? ___ + ___ = ___	How many more white ◯ than blue ◯? ___ − ___ = ___
If 4 ◯ pop, I will have ______ ◯ left.	If I blow 2 more ◯, I will have ______ ◯ in all.

Parents: You may need to read these directions to your child. If your child has trouble finding the answer, encourage him/her to draw pictures as a way to solve the problem.

Pairs

There are 2 mittens in a pair.
How many mittens are in 3 pairs?

_______ mittens

There are 2 socks in a pair.
If I have 10 socks, how many pairs do I have?

_______ pairs

There are 2 shoes in a pair.
Lee has 3 pairs of shoes.
Ann had 3 pairs of shoes.
How many shoes do they have in all?

_______ shoes

Parents: You may need to help your child read these problems.

My Garden

I got six packs of seeds for my garden.
A pack of seeds costs 10 cents.
How much did I spend for seeds?

_______ ¢

I planted 4 rows of squash.
I planted 2 rows of tomatoes.
I planted 7 rows of corn.
How many rows did I plant?

_______ rows

I picked vegetables from my garden.
I filled 2 baskets with vegetables.
Each basket had 3 ears of corn,
2 tomatoes, and 1 squash.
How many vegetables did I pick?

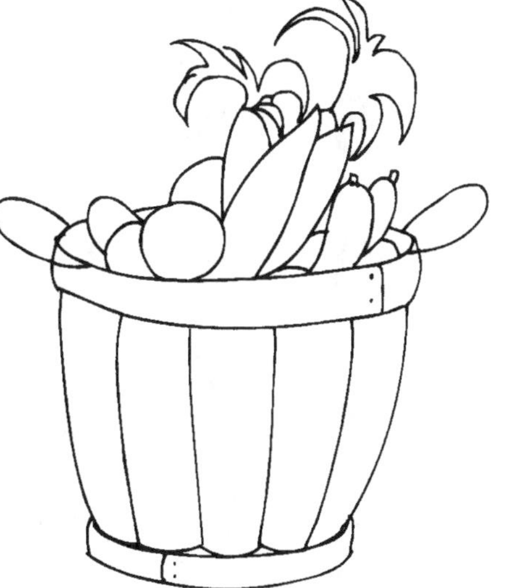

_______ vegetables

Make 4			
0	4	2	3
1	3	1	1
2	3	1	4
2	0	1	0

Make 6				
0	6	4	1	1
3	2	2	0	4
3	2	3	6	2
0	2	1	5	1

Make 8				
7	6	2	3	2
1	5	4	4	3
8	3	4	2	6
5	2	1	2	2
2	2	2	2	2

Make 10				
3	3	1	9	8
2	2	8	4	1
5	5	2	6	1
5	7	2	1	0
4	1	6	2	2

Color the blanket.

10	yellow
11	orange
12	blue

<table>
<tr><td>5
3
+4</td><td>9
1
+1</td><td>9
2
+1</td><td>5
5
+0</td><td>6
0
+6</td><td>4
3
+4</td></tr>
<tr><td>5
6
+0</td><td>4
4
+4</td><td>0
2
+8</td><td>3
3
+6</td><td>6
2
+3</td><td>8
2
+2</td></tr>
<tr><td>8
1
+3</td><td>2
6
+2</td><td>4
7
+1</td><td>7
3
+1</td><td>2
6
+4</td><td>3
4
+3</td></tr>
<tr><td>3
6
+1</td><td>5
3
+4</td><td>5
3
+3</td><td>8
2
+2</td><td>5
1
+4</td><td>5
1
+5</td></tr>
</table>

Why did the elephant sit on a marshmallow?

2-i	9-s
3-f	10-n
4-d	11-e
5-u	12-l
6-w	13-o
7-c	14-t
8-a	15-h

6 + 3	9 + 4
9	13
s	o

4 + 5	8 + 7	9 + 2
9	15	11
s	h	e

2 + 4	8 + 5	5 + 0	9 + 3	1 + 3	8 + 2	5 + 9
6	13	5	12	4	10	14
w	o	u	l	d	n'	t

2 + 1	3 + 5	8 + 4	6 + 6
3	8	12	12
f	a	l	l

2 + 0	3 + 7	6 + 8	7 + 6
2	10	14	13
i	n	t	o

7 + 7	9 + 6	5 + 6
14	15	11
t	h	e

6 + 9	4 + 9	8 + 6
15	13	14
h	o	t

5 + 2	7 + 8	6 + 7	1 + 6	5 + 8	7 + 5	4 + 4	9 + 5	4 + 7
7	15	13	7	13	12	8	14	11
c	h	o	c	o	l	a	t	e

Up, Up, and Away

5 + 4 = [9]

3 + 7 = [10]

2 + 6 = [8]

3 + 4 = [7]

5 + 6 = [11]

6 + 0 = [6]

3 + 9 = [12]

2 + 3 = [5]

6 + 7 = [13]

3 + 1 = [4]

0 + 1 = [1] ★

5 + 9 = [14]

9 + 9 = [18]

8 + 7 = [15]

1 + 2 = [3]

1 + 1 = [2]

9 + 8 = [17]

7 + 9 = [16]

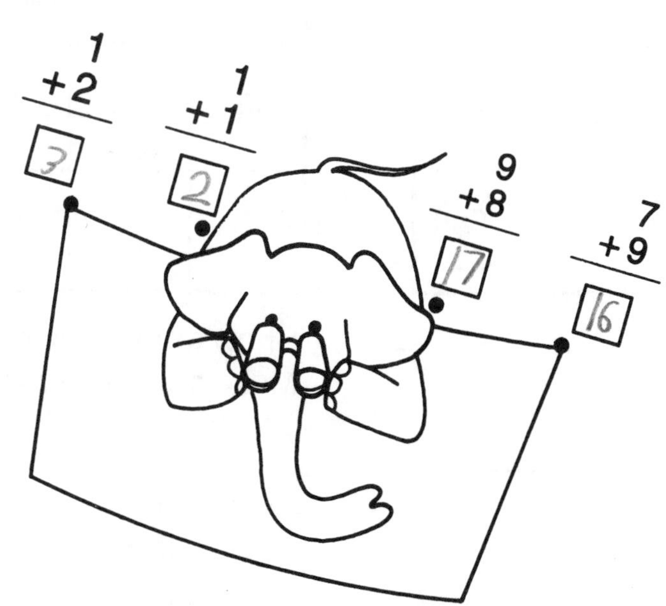

Ring Toss

1. score 10

7	8	9
4	5	6
1	2	3

2. score 18

7	8	9
4	5	6
1	2	3

3. score 18

7	8	9
4	5	6
1	2	3

4. score 14

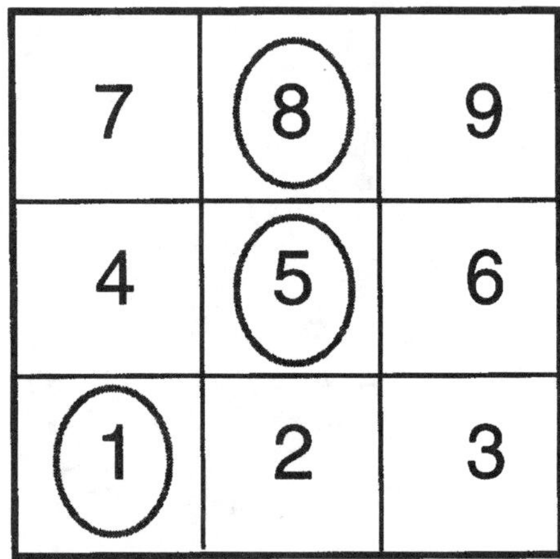

7	8	9
4	5	6
1	2	3

5. Ralph

7	8	9
4	5	6
1	2	3

Alfred

7	8	9
4	5	6
1	2	3

a. Who has the highest score? Alfred

b. How higher is his score? 2

6.

7	8	9
4	5	6
1	2	3

Show three throws. Make the highest score you can.

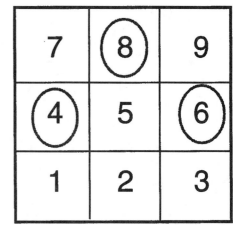

What is gray, has big ears, and carries a trunk?

6-r	11-s	15-g
7-t	12-u	16-n
8-v	13-m	17-a
9-c	14-i	18-o
10-e		

6
3
+8
17
a

4	6	5	3	2
7	3	5	4	5
+2	+9	+2	+4	+3
13	18	12	11	10
m	o	u	s	e

5	3	7	4	6
5	7	3	9	8
+5	+8	+4	+3	+1
15	18	14	16	15
g	o	i	n	g

7	8
6	2
+5	+6
18	16
o	n

9	4	9	5	4	1
1	0	1	3	4	2
+1	+8	+3	+5	+2	+3
11	12	13	13	10	6
s	u	m	m	e	r

7	9	4	5	2	8	5	8
0	6	3	7	3	2	9	3
+1	+2	+2	+5	+2	+4	+4	+5
8	17	9	17	7	14	18	16
v	a	c	a	t	i	o	n

.

What did the elephant say when he sat on the box of cookies?

46	73	25	54	65
+ 23	+ 14	+ 33	+ 15	+ 31
69	87	58	69	96
t	h	a	t	s

37	44	52
+ 32	+ 43	+ 22
69	87	74
t	h	e

36	40	12
+ 63	+ 18	+ 24
99	58	36
w	a	y

28	65	41
+ 41	+ 22	+ 33
69	87	74
t	h	e

24	33	42	19	20	12
+ 24	+ 33	+ 24	+ 40	+ 11	+ 62
48	66	66	59	31	74
c	o	o	k	i	e

31	61	35	26	14	45	44	72
+ 17	+ 34	+ 12	+ 13	+ 41	+ 32	+ 30	+ 24
48	95	47	39	55	77	74	96
c	r	u	m	b	l	e	s

!

31-i
36-y
39-m
47-u
48-c
55-b
58-a
59-k
66-o
69-t
74-e
77-l
87-h
95-r
96-s
99-w

Skill: shows an understanding of patterns of objects and numbers

Finish the pattern.
Draw what comes next.

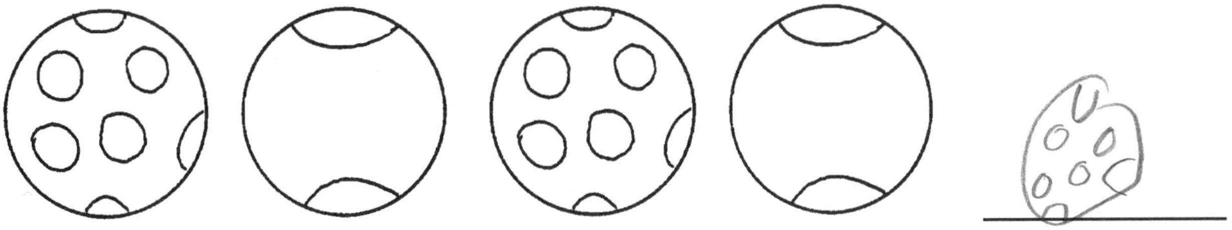

1 2 3 1 2 3 1 2 3

Skill: identifies which numbers come between, after, or before given numbers to 20

Write the missing numerals.

in between	after	before
8 __9__ 10	6 __7__	__6__ 7
3 __4__ 5	11 __12__	__8__ 9
12 __13__ 14	9 __10__	__10__ 11
6 __7__ 8	15 __16__	__19__ 20
10 __11__ 12	0 __1__	__12__ 13
18 __19__ 20	4 __5__	__6__ 7
15 __16__ 17	19 __20__	__16__ 17
12 __13__ 14	14 __15__	__1__ 2

Parents: Have your child count aloud from 1 to 100, then read each of the numbers aloud to you.

Skill: reads numerals to 100

25	31	40	59
30	62	44	27
50	73	60	83
90	86	38	80
77	23	9	100

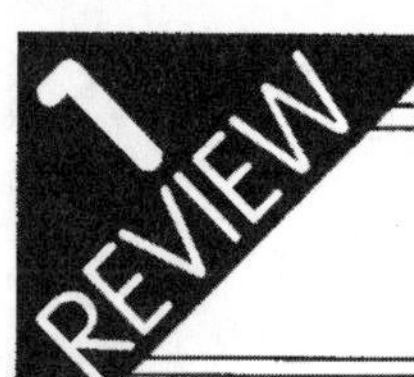

Skill: writes numerals in sequence from 1 to 100

Write from 1 to 100.

1	2	3	4	5	6	7	8	9	10
11	12	13	14	15	16	17	18	19	20
21	22	23	24	25	26	27	28	29	30
31	32	33	34	35	36	37	38	39	40
41	42	43	44	45	46	47	48	49	50
51	52	53	54	55	56	57	58	59	60
61	62	63	64	65	66	67	68	69	70
71	72	73	74	75	76	77	78	79	80
81	82	83	84	85	86	87	88	89	90
91	92	93	94	95	96	97	98	99	100

Skill: identifies which numbers come between, after, or before given numbers to 100

Write the missing numerals.

after	before	in between
21 22	46 47	29 30 31
39 40	49 50	43 44 45
45 46	35 36	38 39 40
50 51	63 64	51 52 53
64 65	20 21	67 68 69
77 78	91 92	80 81 82
99 100	62 63	87 88 89

Skill: can tell which of two numbers is less and which is greater

Circle the larger number.	
26	34
95	59
11	10
47	48
83	86
52	73

Cross out the smaller number.	
17	15
23	18
50	70
89	98
31	26
74	47

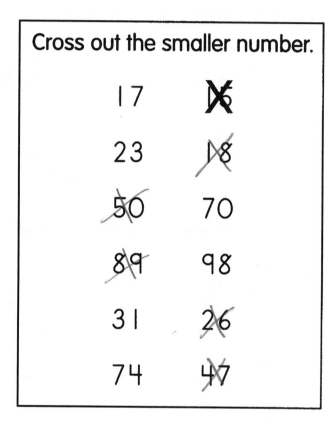

Skill: counts by 10s to 100

Count by 10s to 100

10	20	30	40	50
60	70	80	90	100

Count by 10s to connect the dots.

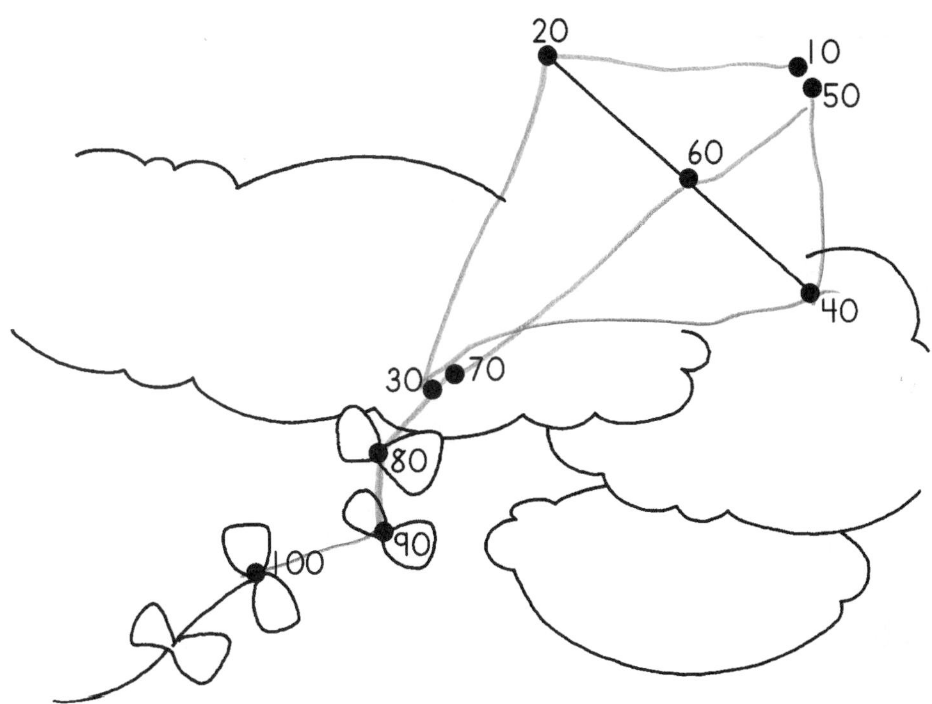

1 REVIEW

Skill: counts by 5s to 100

Count by 5s to 100

5	10	15	20	25
30	35	40	45	50
55	60	65	70	75
80	85	90	95	100

Count by 5s to connect the dots.

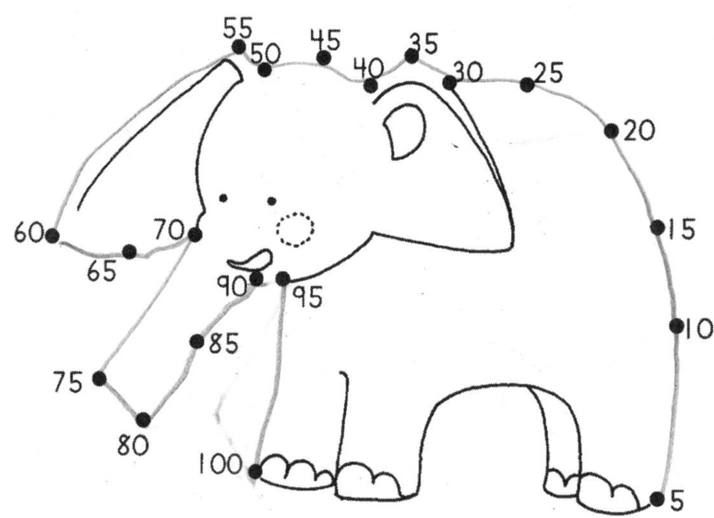

Skill: identifies number words to ten

Read the word.
Write the numeral on the line.

ten 10 nine 9

six 6 three 3

eight 8 one 1

four 4 two 2

seven 7 five 5

Write the number word.

6 Six 10 Ten 7 Seven

1 REVIEW

Skill: • identifies ordinal numbers through 10
• identifies first and last

first	second	third	fourth	fifth
sixth	seventh	eighth	ninth	tenth

Draw a line.

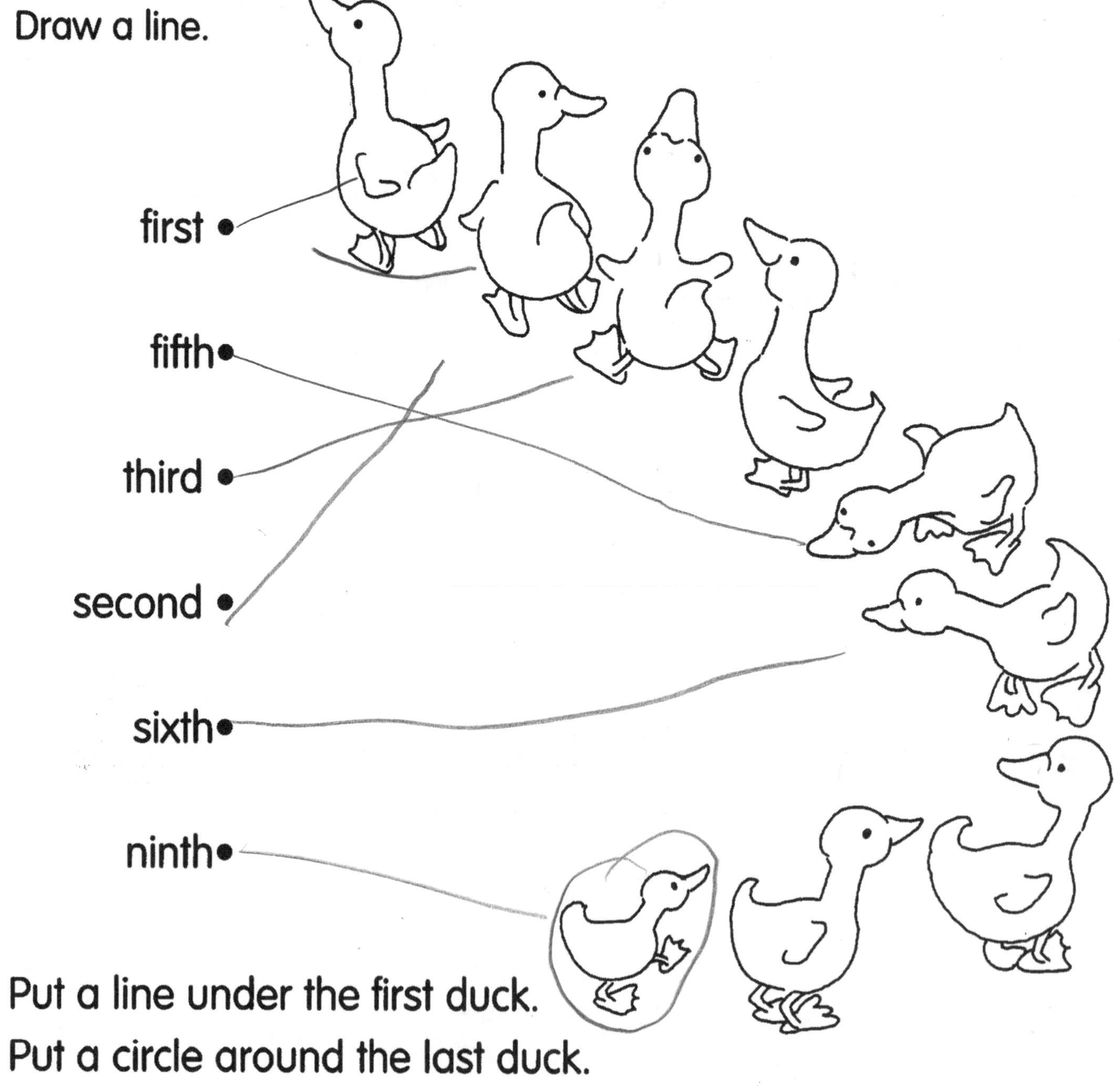

Put a line under the first duck.

Put a circle around the last duck.

Skill: • recalls basic addition facts
• recognizes the symbol +

Add.

$8 + 1 = 9$ $5 + 3 = 8$ $2 + 6 = 8$ $2 + 7 = 9$ $4 + 5 = 9$ $2 + 3 =$

$0 + 7 = 7$ $1 + 5 = 6$ $4 + 4 = 8$ $3 + 6 = 9$ $7 + 2 = 9$ $8 + 0 = 8$

$3 + 5 = 8$ $6 + 3 = 9$ $5 + 4 = 9$ $1 + 7 = 8$ $1 + 8 = 9$ $3 + 4 = 7$

$3 + 3 = 6$ $4 + 2 = 6$ $9 + 0 = 9$ $4 + 5 = 9$ $2 + 5 = 7$ $7 + 1 = 8$

$0 + 9 = 9$ $6 + 2 = 8$ $6 + 3 = 9$ $8 + 1 = 9$ $3 + 5 = 8$ $1 + 8 = 9$

Skill: • recalls basic subtraction facts

Subtract.

7	8	6	7	8	3
−2	−2	−2	−5	−4	−0
5	6	6	2	4	3
5	10	9	8	7	6
−1	−5	−7	−7	−3	−3
4	5	2	1	4	3
9	5	6	9	9	5
−2	−2	−1	−6	−4	−3
7	3	5	3	5	2
9	7	7	9	5	8
−3	−7	−4	−1	−4	−3
6	0	3	8	1	5
8	9	7	8	9	8
−6	−5	−6	−8	−8	−5
2	4	1	0	1	3

Skill: adds numbers in a series to sums of 10 or less

Add.

2	3	6	4	8	1
3	5	1	3	0	7
+4	+1	+2	+1	+2	+1
9	9	9	8	10	9

1	2	3	4	5	6
6	5	4	3	2	1
+3	+2	+3	+2	+3	+2
10	9	10	9	10	9

3	5	7	2	9	6
4	2	0	6	1	3
+2	+1	+2	+1	+0	+0
9	8	9	9	10	9

1 REVIEW

Skill: solves word problems involving addition and subtraction

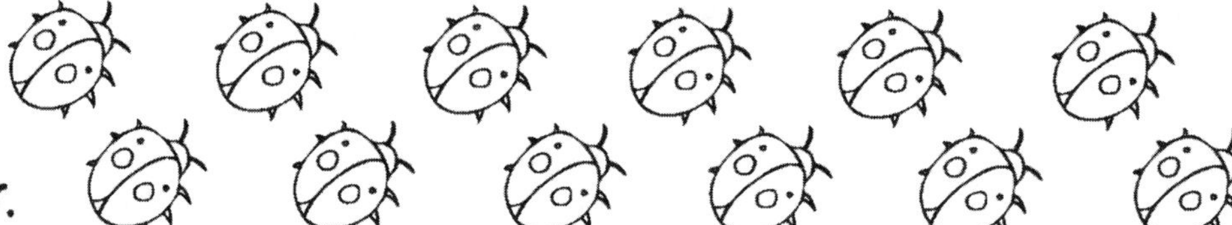

Find the answer.

1. 5 red bugs.
   3 yellow bugs.
   How many bugs in all?

   8

2. 8 black bugs.
   4 green bugs.
   How many more black bugs than green bugs?

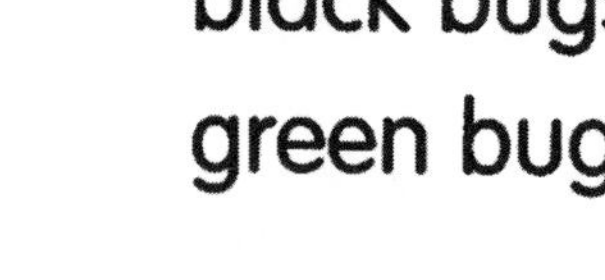

   4

3. I see 6 bugs.
   4 more come.
   How many bugs in all?

4. I see 9 bugs.
   3 bugs go away
   How many bugs are left?

   6

5. I see 3 bugs and 5 bugs and 1 bug. How many bugs in all?

6. I see 10 bugs.
   5 bugs go away.
   How many bugs are left?

   5

Skill: understands the meaning of and can use terms of comparison

Color the longer snake.
Put an X on the shorter snake.

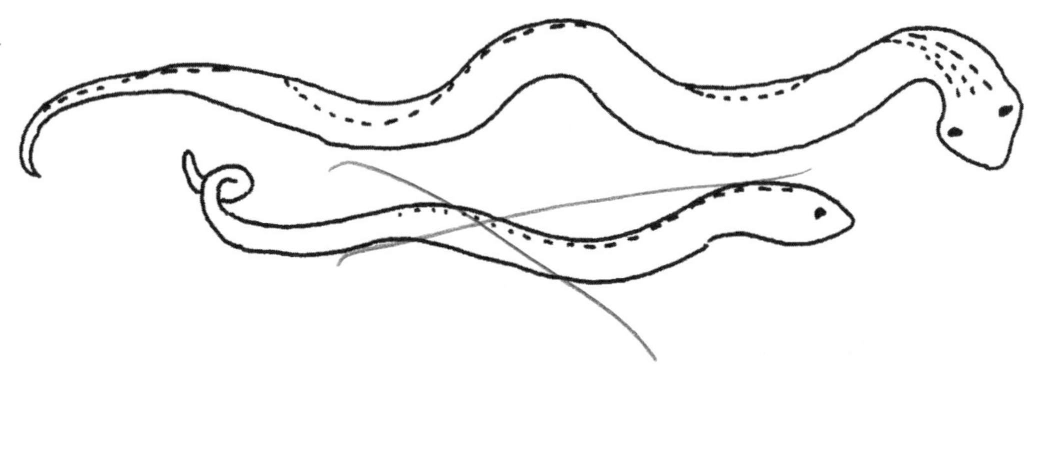

Color the smallest ball.
Put an X on the largest ball.

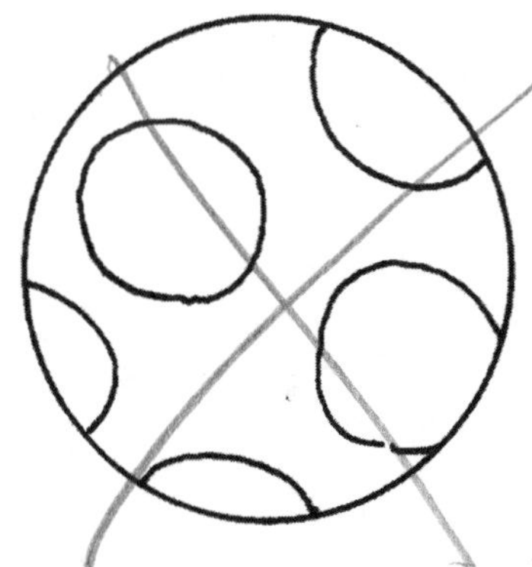

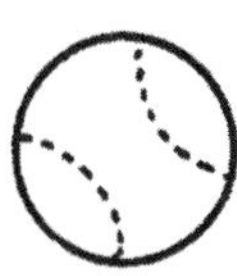

1 REVIEW

Skill: identifies equivalent sets

Are these the same amount? yes no

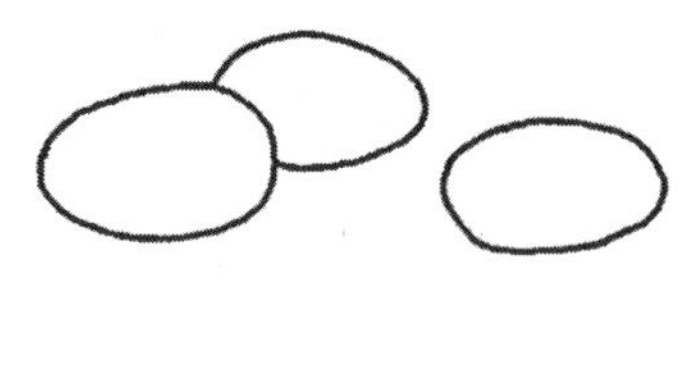

Are these the same amount? yes no

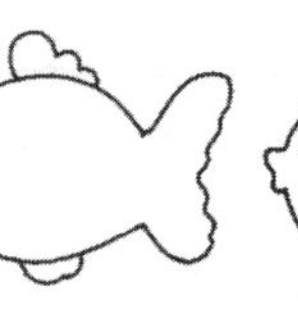
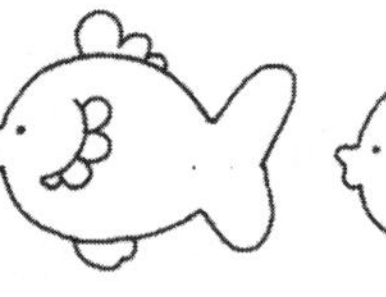

Are these the same amount? yes no

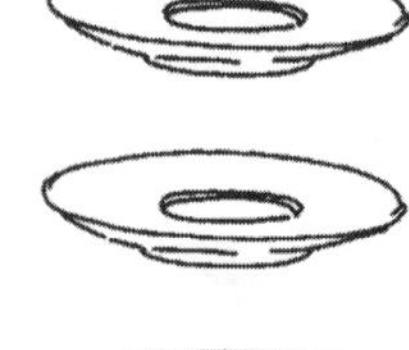
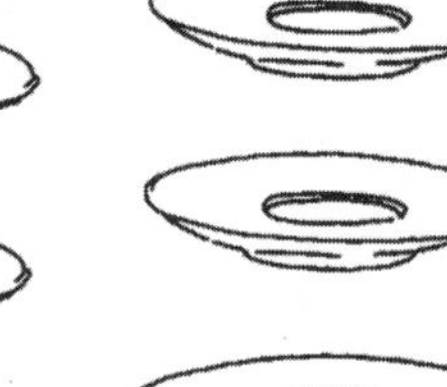

Parents: Point to each coin. Ask your child to name it and tell how much it is worth. Then have him/her do the matching activity.

Skill: identifies and gives the value in cents for penny, nickel, dime and quarter

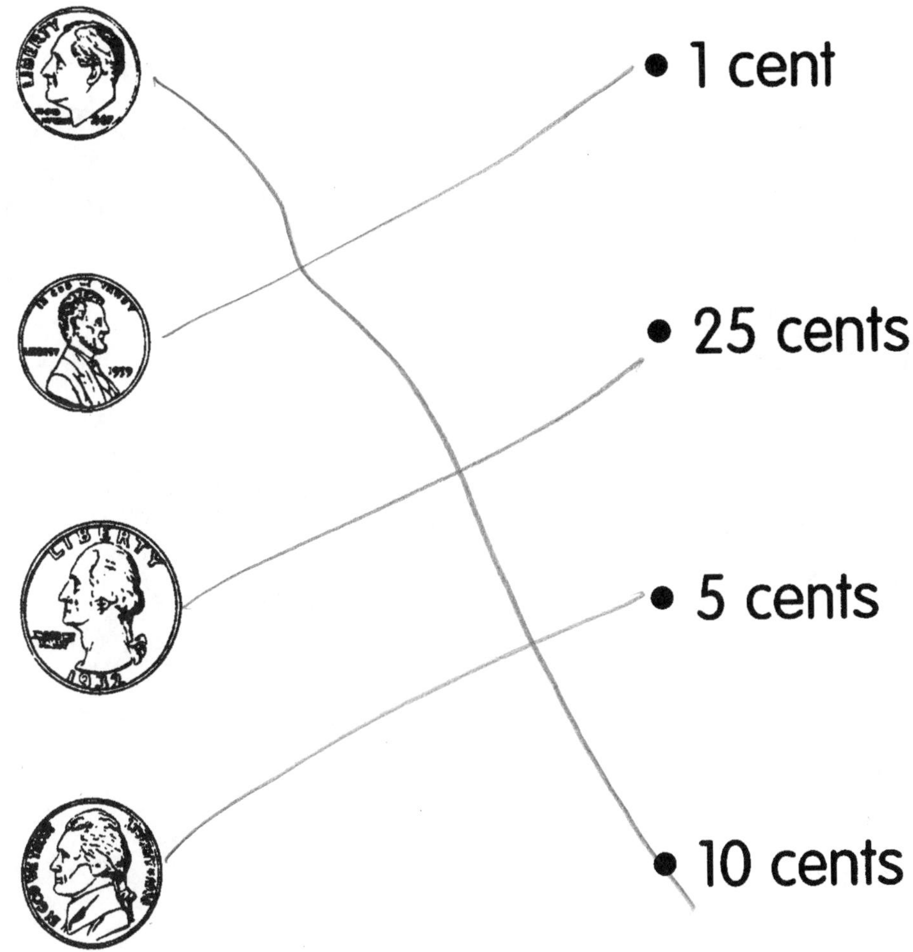

Skill: gives the value for groups of coins

Count the money.
How much is it?

Skill: shows the ability to tell time to the nearest half-hour

Write the time.

1 REVIEW

Parents: Ask your child to say the days of the week in order. Help him/her read the questions.

Skill: • names days of the week in sequence
• locates days and dates on a calendar

Sunday	Monday	Tuesday	Wednesday	Thursday	Friday	Saturday
				1	2	3
4	5	6	7	8	9	10
11	12	13	14	15	16	17
18	19	20	21	22	23	24
25	26	27	28	29	30	

1. What day of the week is the 9th? Friday

2. How many days are in this month? 30

3. What is the date of the first Sunday? 4th

4. What day of the week is the last day? Friday

Parents: Help your child cut out the ruler at the bottom of the page. One edge shows inches, the other centimeters. Show your child the appropriate side to use.

Skill: uses a ruler to measure a line segment to the nearest whole unit

Measure the snakes.

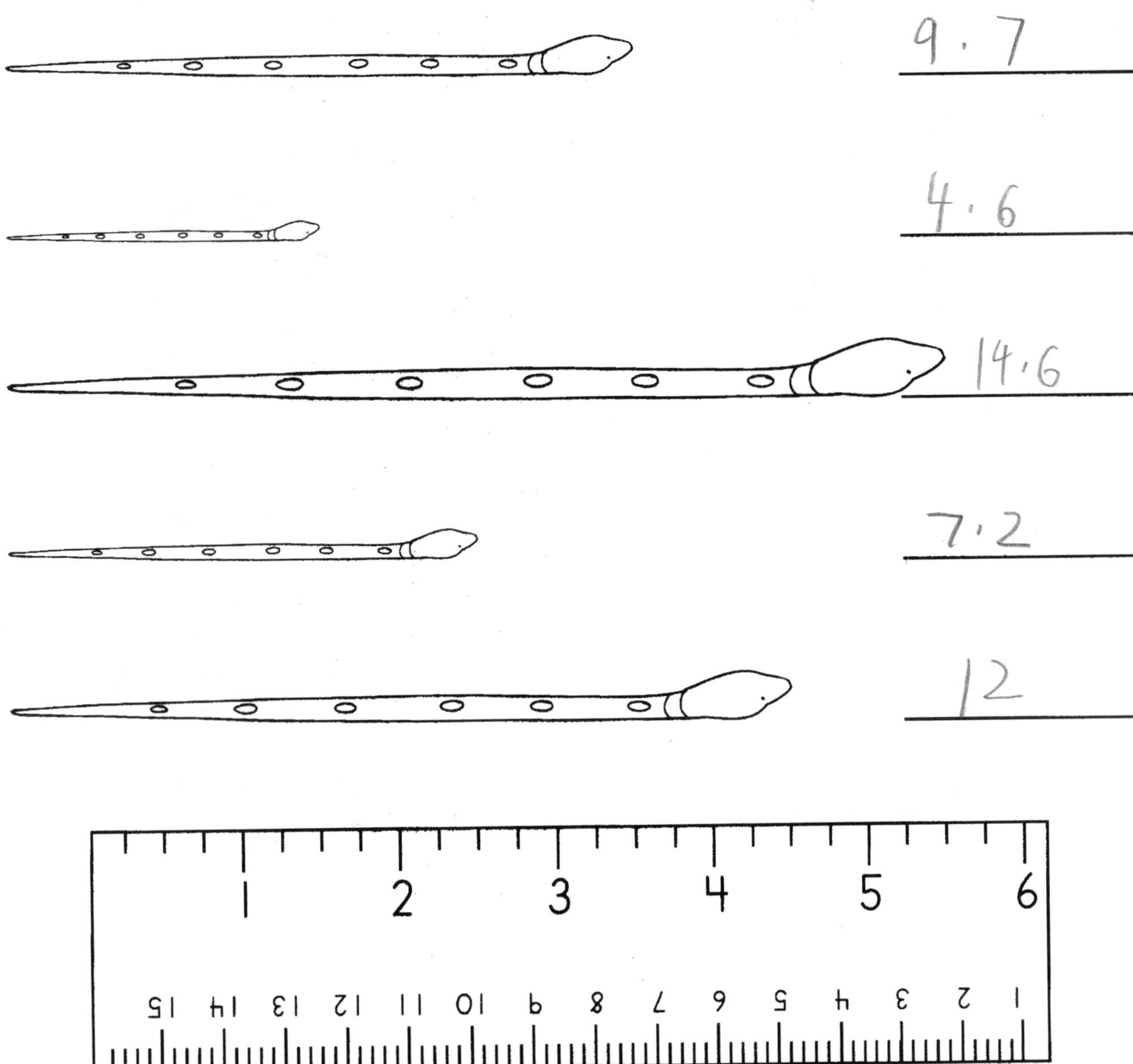

1 REVIEW

Point to each shape and ask your child to name it.

Skill: recognizes and matches geometric shapes

circle	triangle
square	rectangle

Match.

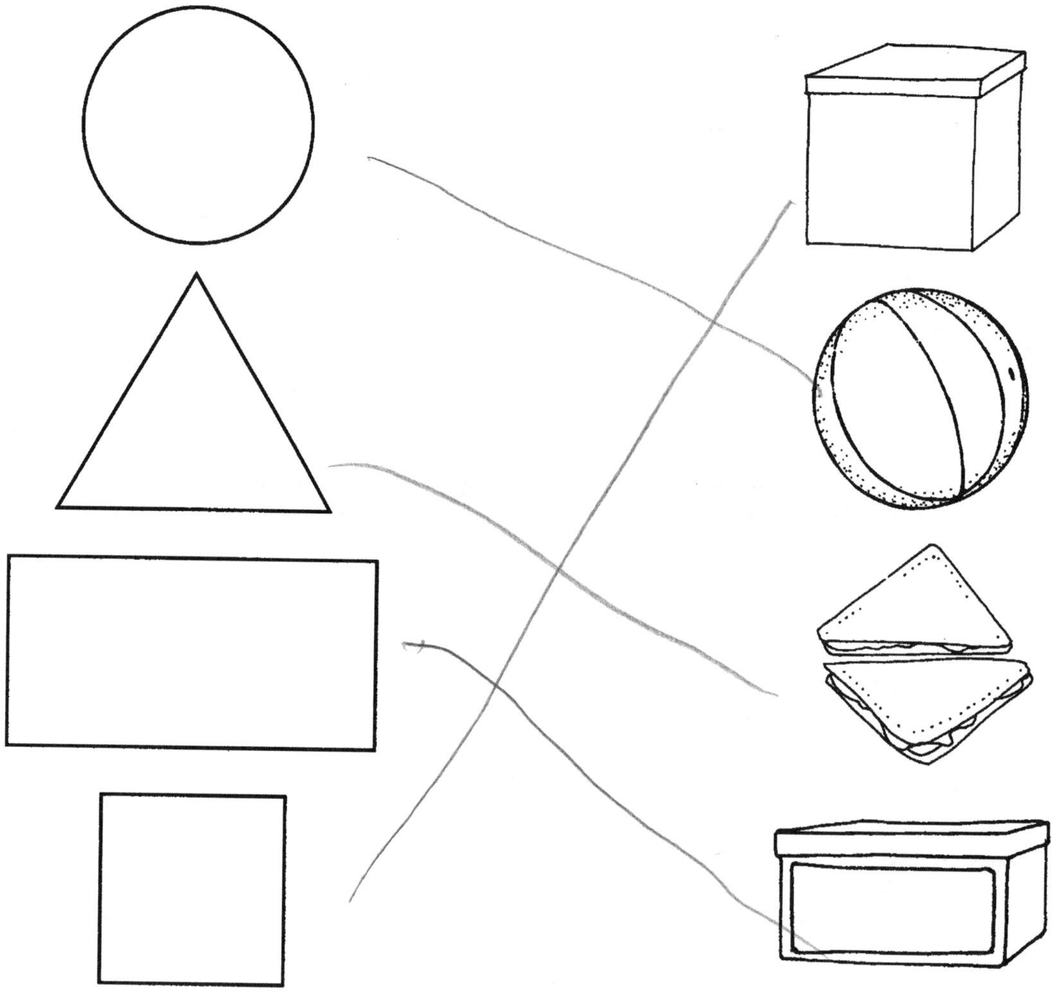

Skill: adds 2-digit numbers without regrouping

Add.

12 + 23	34 + 45	56 + 32	17 + 81	33 + 22
45 + 52	37 + 61	82 + 17	97 + 2	51 + 48
62 + 36	71 + 18	82 + 15	93 + 3	25 + 24

Skill: subtracts 2-digit numbers without regrouping

Subtract.

98	76	54	32	66
−23	−45	−31	−20	−51
75	31	23	12	15

99	88	77	66	55
−78	−67	−56	−45	−34
21	21	21	21	21

57	35	24	91	86
−25	−12	−13	−60	−42
32	23	11	31	44

Skill: reads a simple bar graph

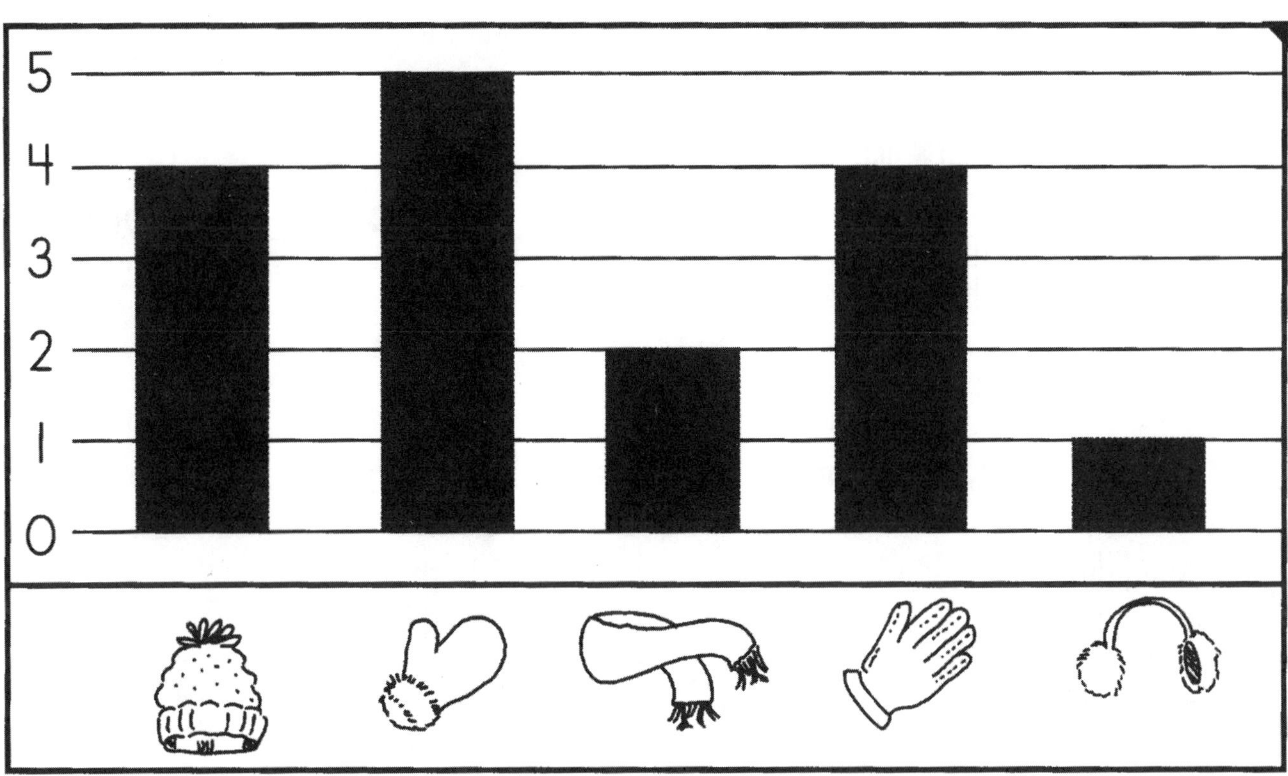

1. How many?

hat 4 glove 4 scarf 2

earmuffs 1 mitten 5

2. How many hat and glove in all? 9

4. How many mitten and earmuffs in all? 6

3. How many scarf and mitten in all? 7

5. How many glove, scarf, and hat in all? 10

1 REVIEW

Skill: identifies place value of numerals to 99

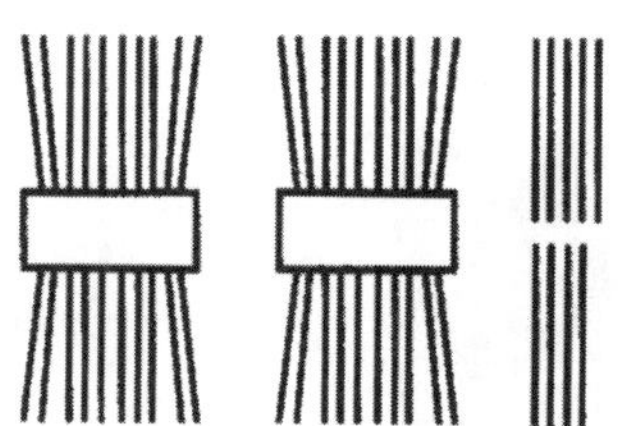

29 = __2__ tens and __9__ ones

How many tens and ones in these numbers?

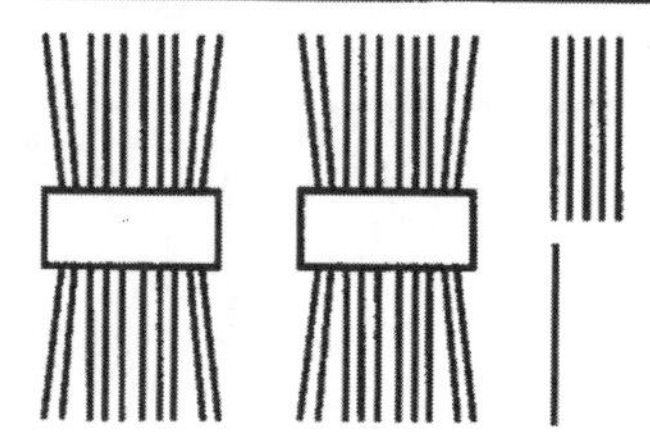 26 = __2__ tens and __6__ ones	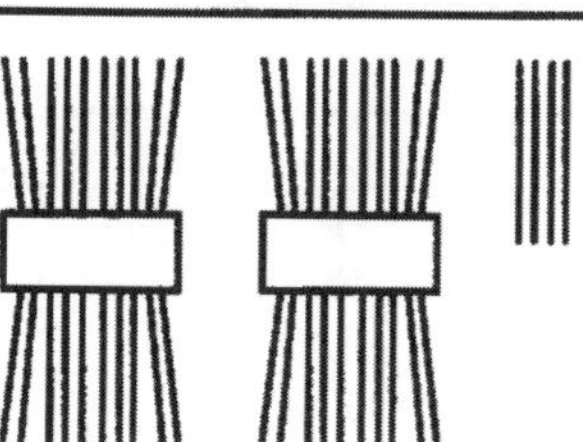 24 = __2__ tens and __4__ ones
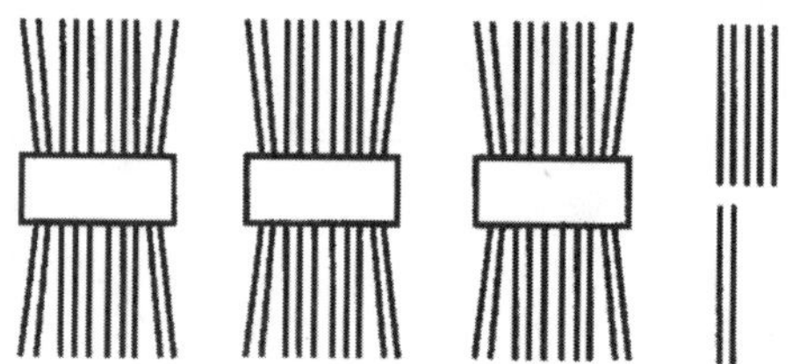 37 = __3__ tens and __7__ ones	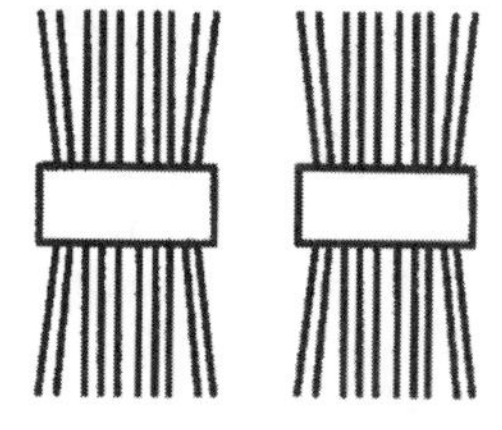 22 = __2__ tens and __2__ ones
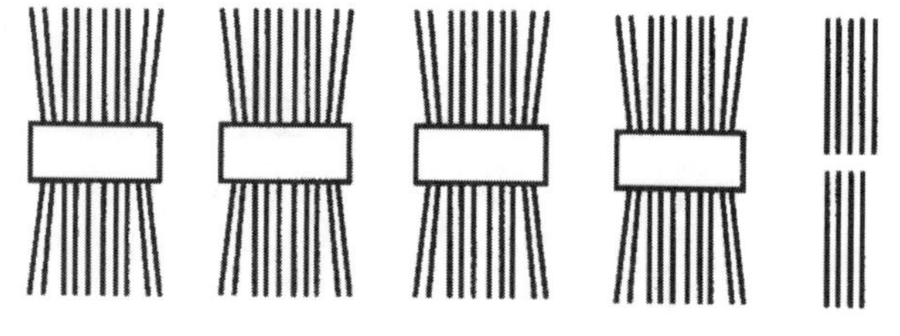 49 = __4__ tens and __9__ ones	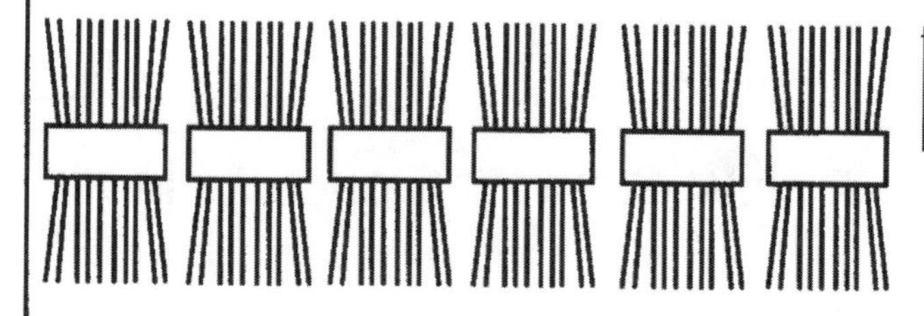 61 = __6__ tens and __1__ ones

Skill: identifies fractional parts of a shape

Circle.

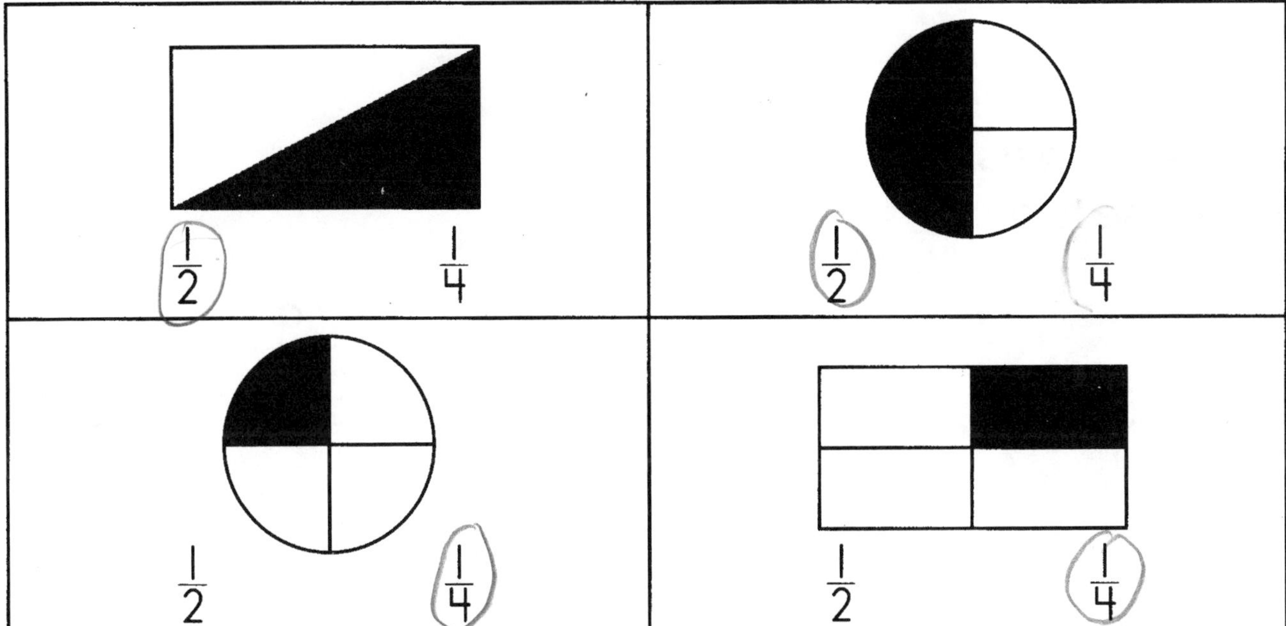

Color.

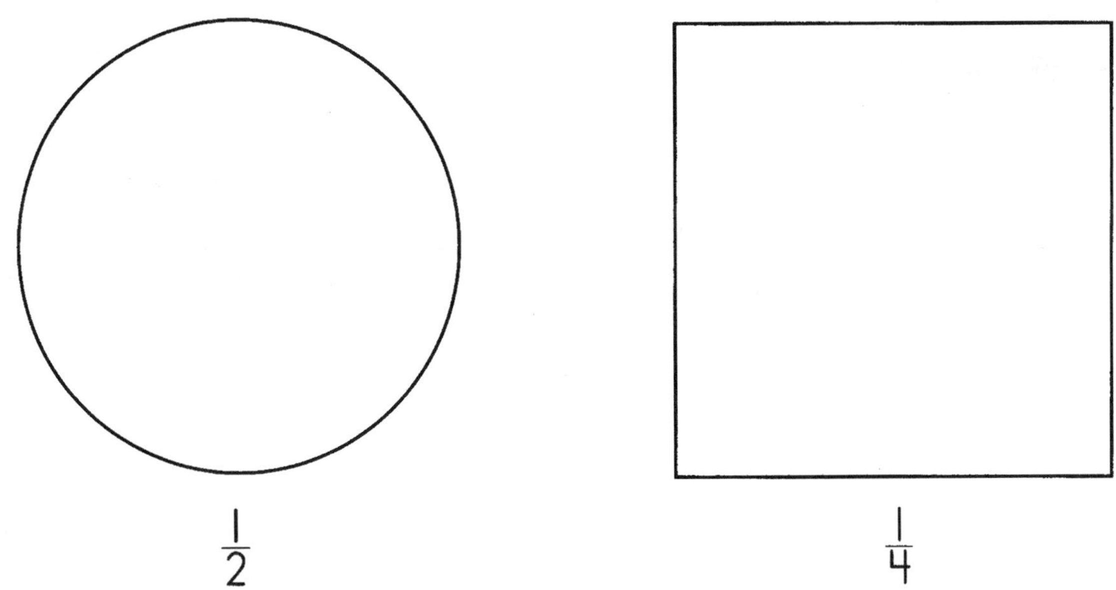

Parents: Ask your child to explain what happens when a zero is added to or taken away from another number.

Skill: • communicates math understandings to others
• demonstrates an understanding of what happens when 0 is added to or subtracted from any number

Find the answers.
Explain the rule.

$2 + 0$	$3 + 0$	$5 + 0$	$8 + 0$	$9 + 0$	$6 + 0$
2	3	5	8	9	6

Find the answers.
Explain the rule.

$7 - 0$	$4 - 0$	$5 - 0$	$8 - 0$	$2 - 0$	$9 - 0$
7	4	5	8	2	9

Answer Key

Please take time to go over the work your child has completed. Ask your child to explain what he/she has done. Praise both success and effort. If mistakes have been made, explain what the answer should have been and how to find it. Let your child know that mistakes are a part of learning. The time you spend with your child helps let him/her know you feel learning is important.

page 193

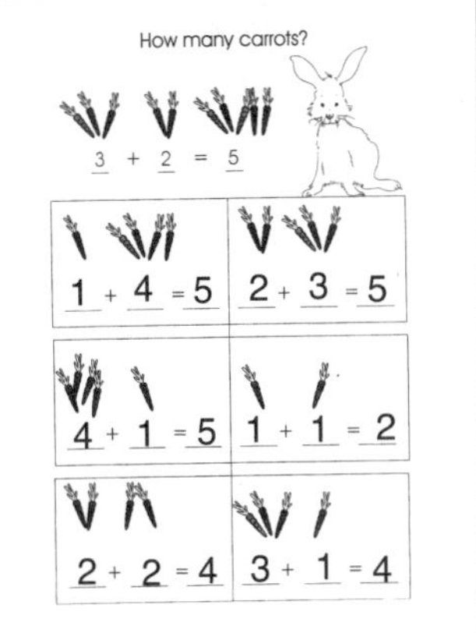
How many carrots?

3 + 2 = 5

1 + 4 = 5 2 + 3 = 5

4 + 1 = 5 1 + 1 = 2

2 + 2 = 4 3 + 1 = 4

page 194

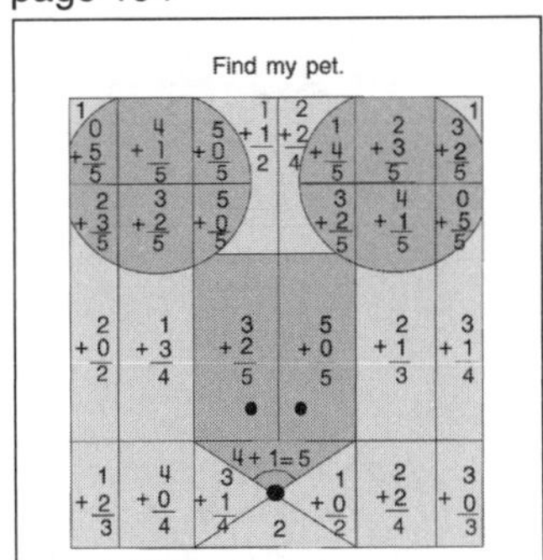
Find my pet.

• Add
• Color

0- black 3- red
1- red 4- red
2- red 5- brown

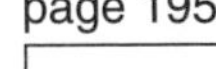
page 195

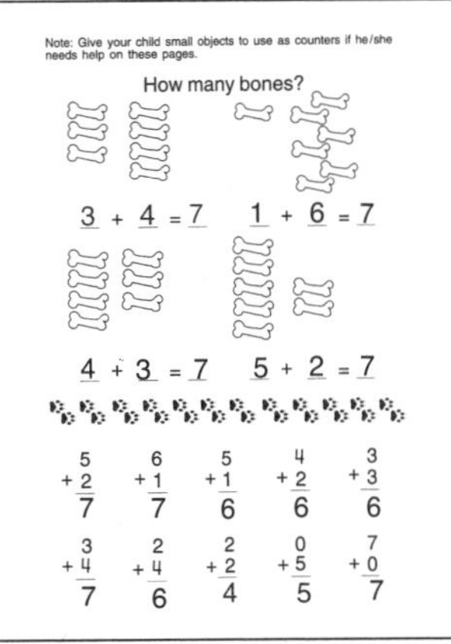
Note: Give your child small objects to use as counters if he/she needs help on these pages.

How many bones?

3 + 4 = 7 1 + 6 = 7

4 + 3 = 7 5 + 2 = 7

page 196

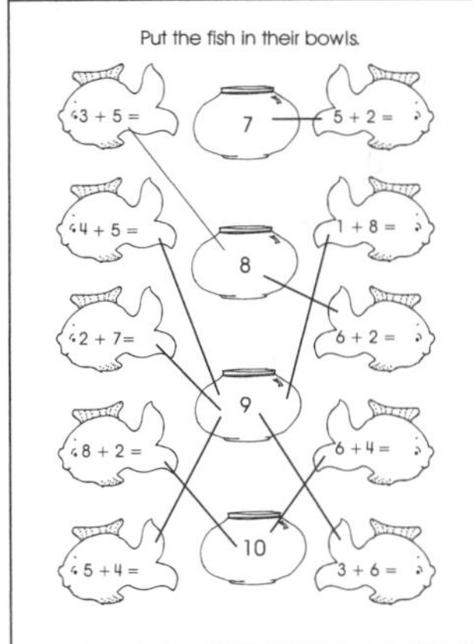
Put the fish in their bowls.

page 197

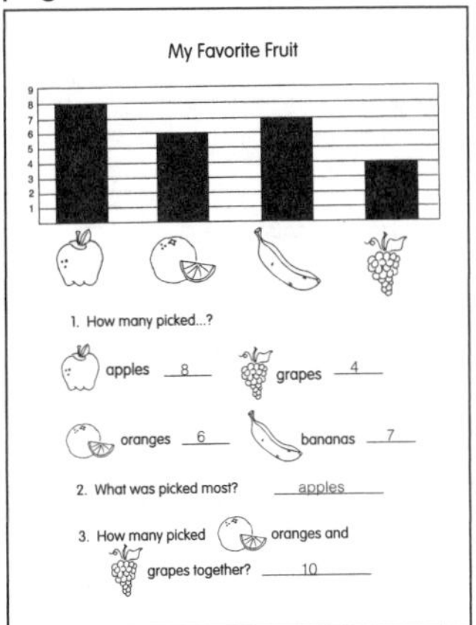
My Favorite Fruit

1. How many picked...?

apples 8 grapes 4

oranges 6 bananas 7

2. What was picked most? apples

3. How many picked oranges and grapes together? 10

page 198

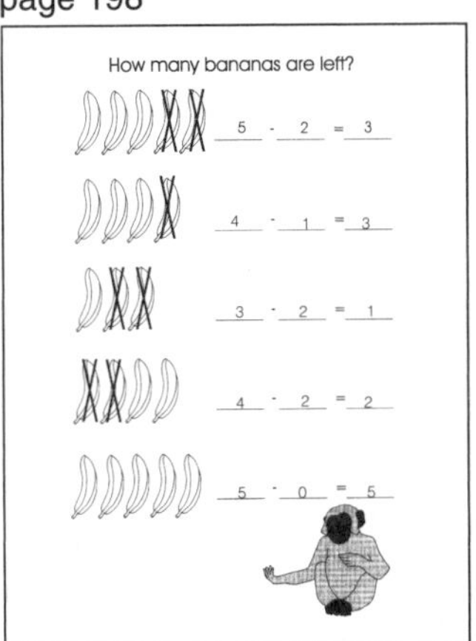
How many bananas are left?

5 - 2 = 3

4 - 1 = 3

3 - 2 = 1

4 - 2 = 2

5 - 0 = 5

page 199

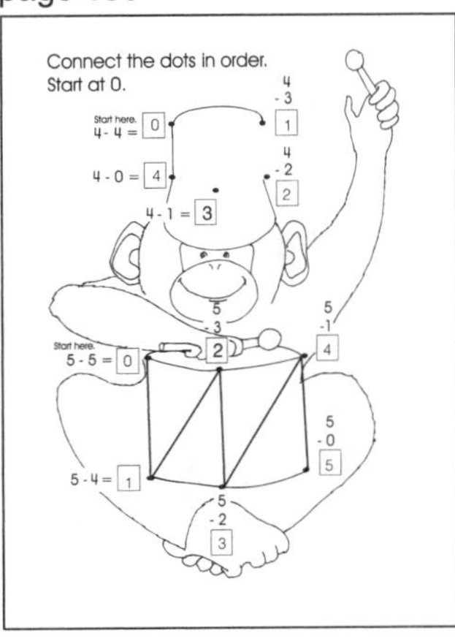
Connect the dots in order.
Start at 0.

page 200

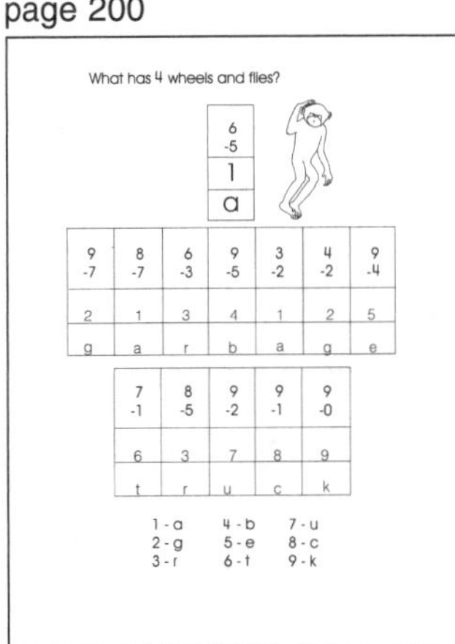
What has 4 wheels and flies?

1 - a 4 - b 7 - u
2 - g 5 - e 8 - c
3 - r 6 - t 9 - k

page 201

What is the rule?

A number minus itself is always zero.
A number minus zero stays the same.

page 202

Take 1 Away

One less.

page 203

Subtract to Check Addition

page 204

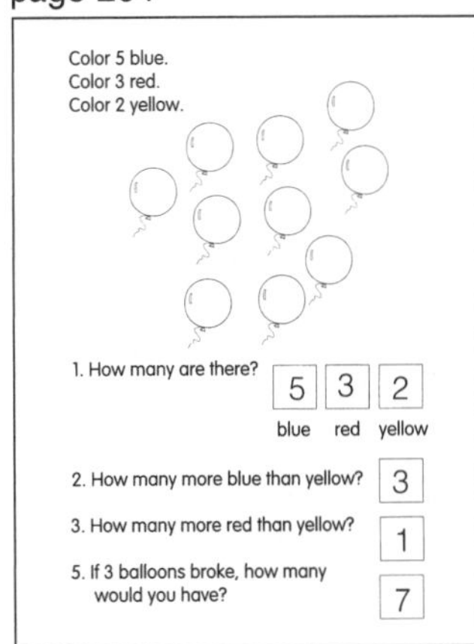
Color 5 blue.
Color 3 red.
Color 2 yellow.

1. How many are there? 5 blue 3 red 2 yellow

2. How many more blue than yellow? 3

3. How many more red than yellow? 1

5. If 3 balloons broke, how many would you have? 7

page 205

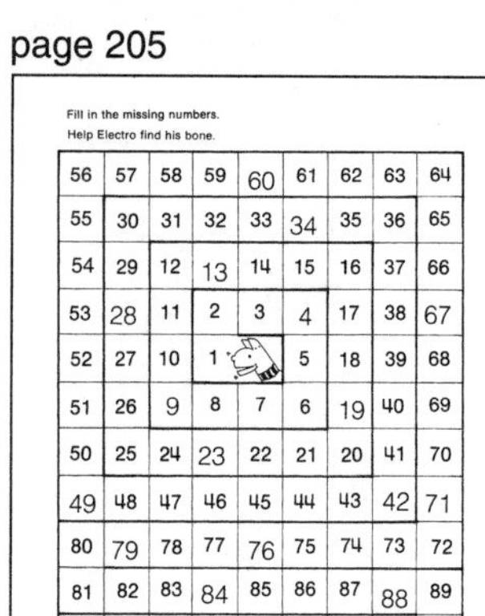

page 206

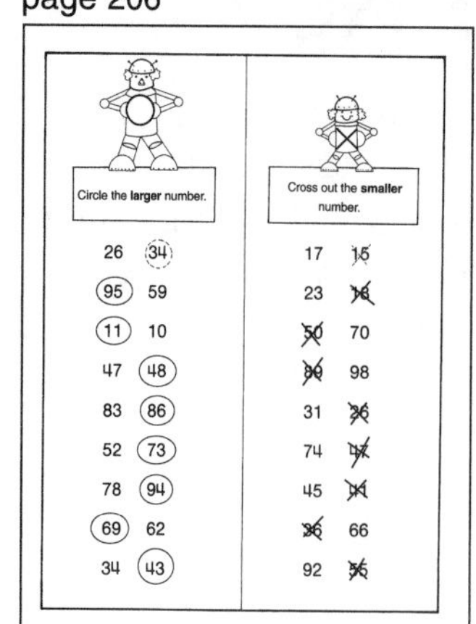

page 207

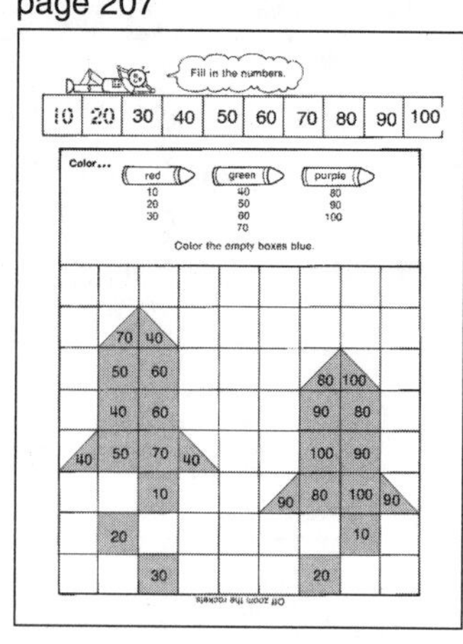

page 208

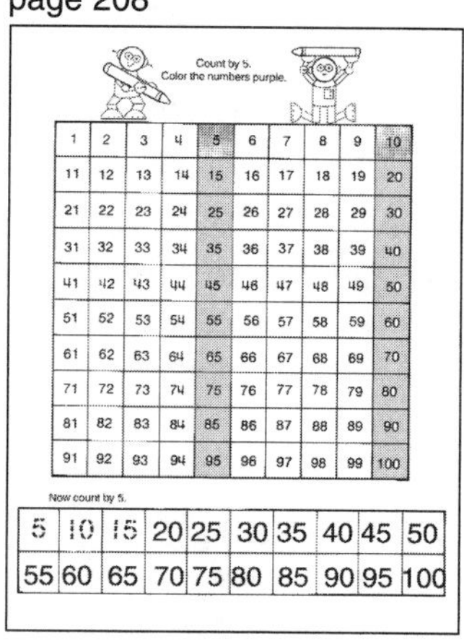

page 209

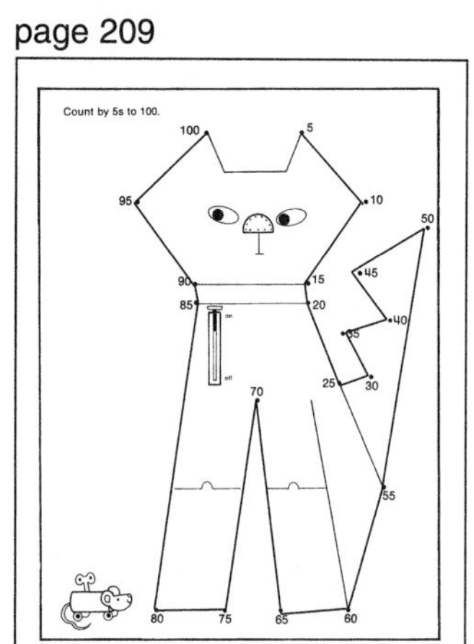

page 210

page 211

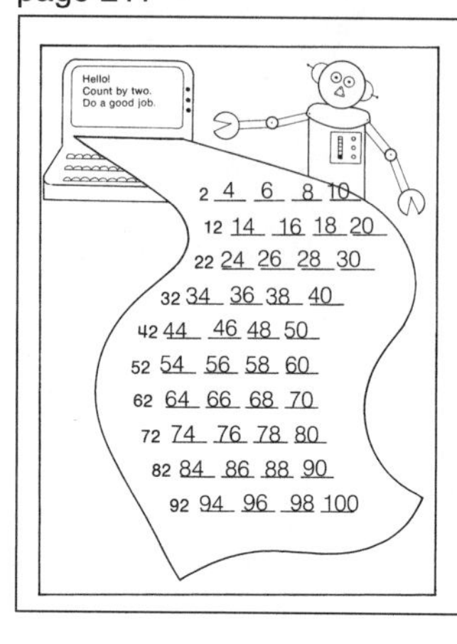

page 212

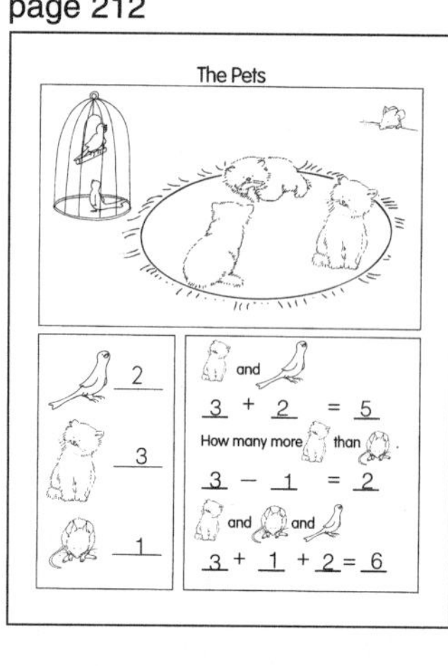

page 213

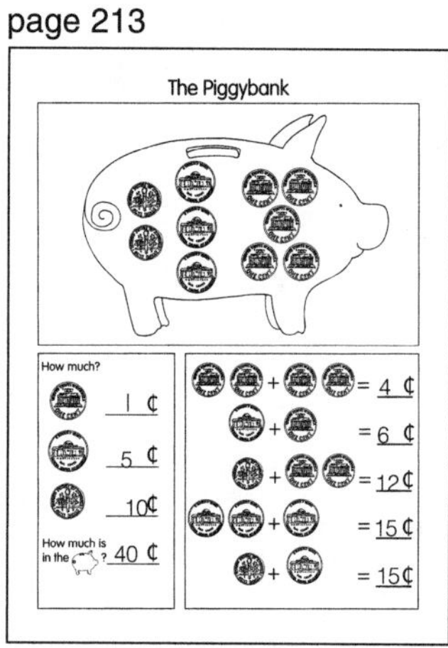

page 214

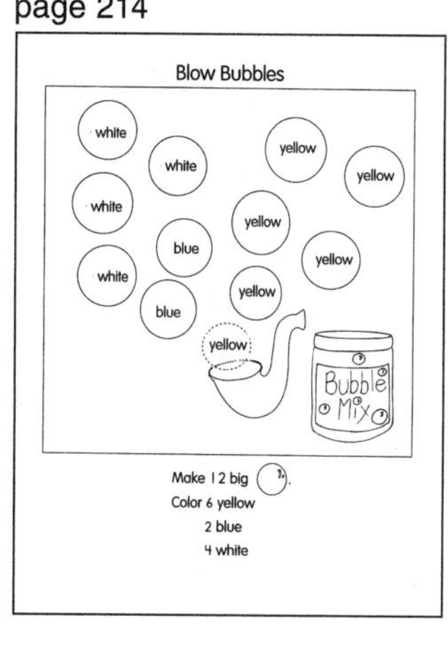

page 215

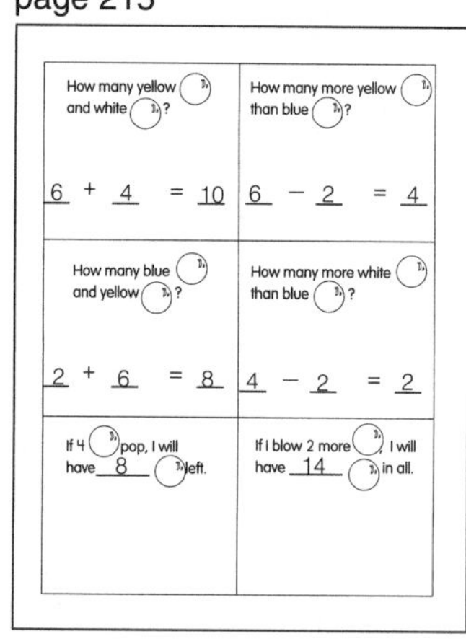

page 216

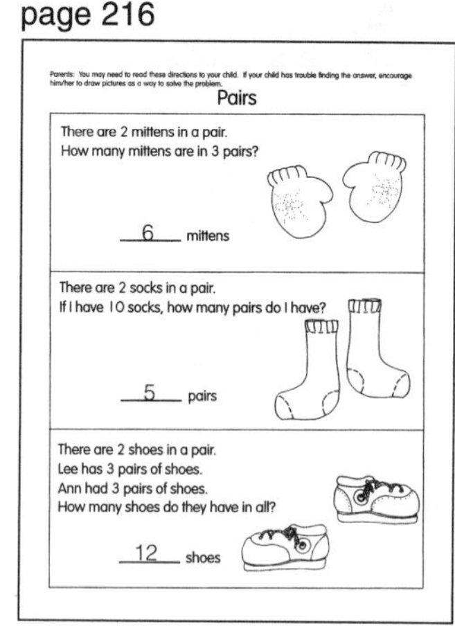

page 217

page 218

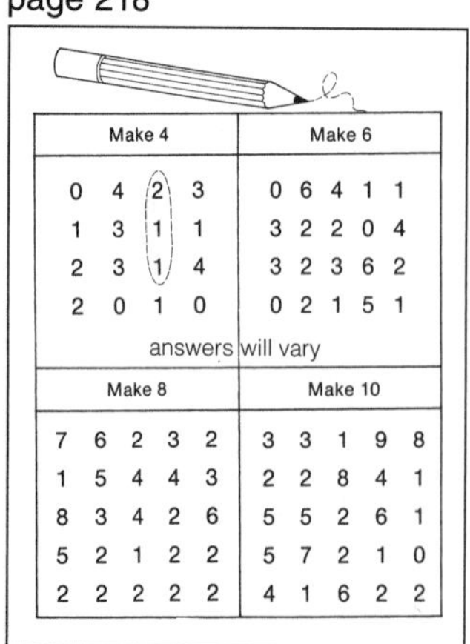

page 219

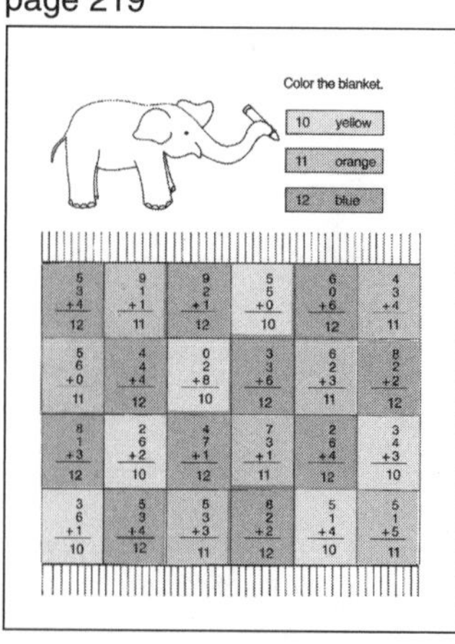

page 220

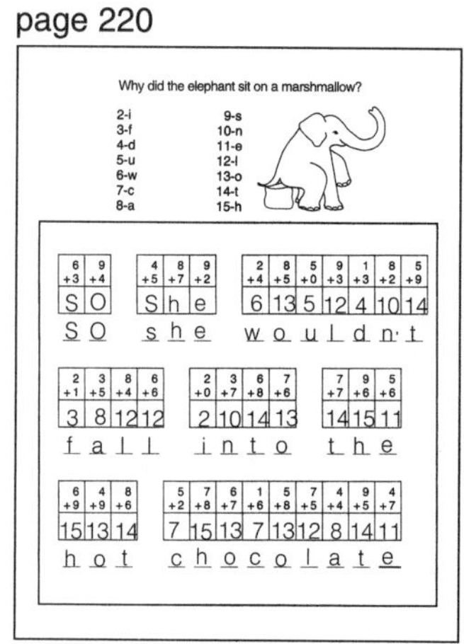

page 221

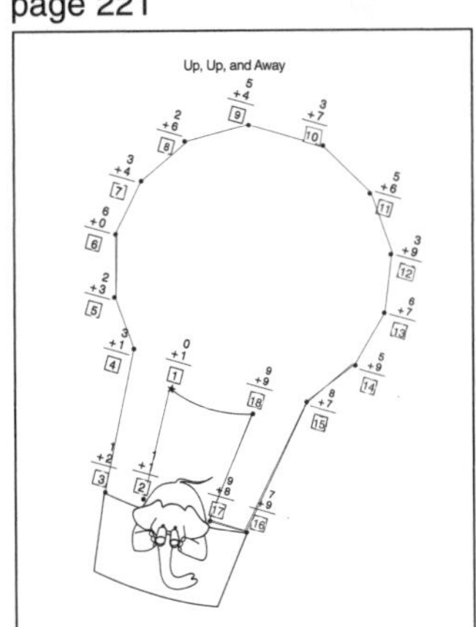
Up, Up, and Away

page 222

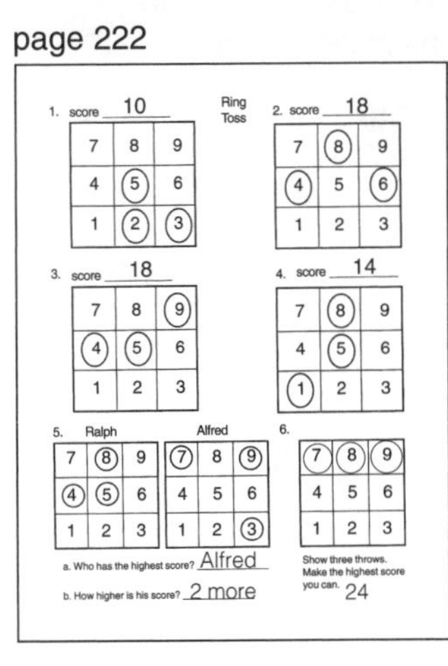
Ring Toss

1. score 10
2. score 18
3. score 18
4. score 14
5. Ralph Alfred
6.

a. Who has the highest score? Alfred

b. How higher is his score? 2 more

Show three throws. Make the highest score you can. 24

page 223

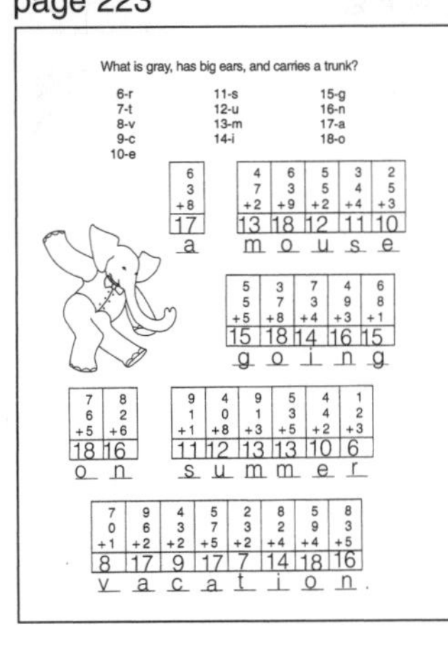
What is gray, has big ears, and carries a trunk?

6-r, 7-t, 8-v, 9-c, 10-e, 11-s, 12-u, 13-m, 14-i, 15-g, 16-n, 17-a, 18-o

a mouse going on summer vacation

page 224

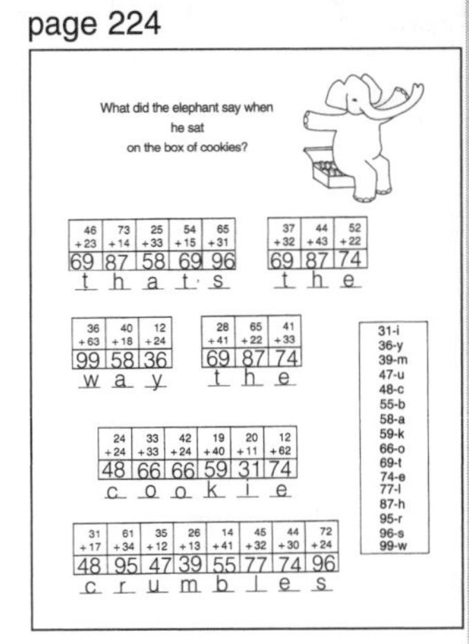
What did the elephant say when he sat on the box of cookies?

that's the way the cookie crumbles

31-i, 36-y, 39-m, 47-u, 48-c, 55-b, 58-a, 59-k, 66-o, 69-t, 74-e, 77-l, 87-h, 95-r, 96-s, 99-w

page 225

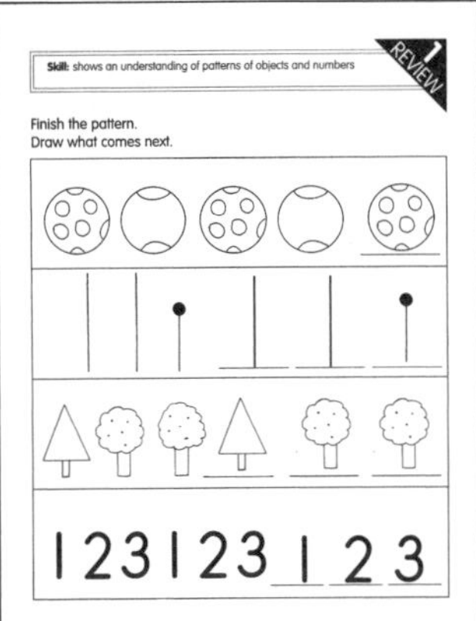
Skill: shows an understanding of patterns of objects and numbers

Finish the pattern.
Draw what comes next.

1 2 3 1 2 3 1 2 3

page 226

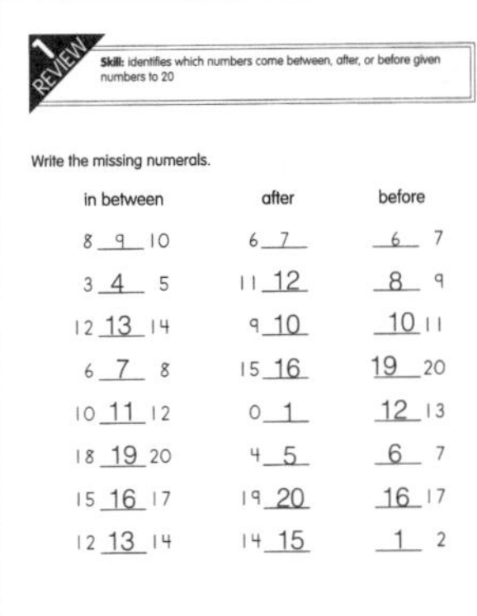
Skill: identifies which numbers come between, after, or before given numbers to 20

Write the missing numerals.

in between	after	before
8 9 10	6 7	6 7
3 4 5	11 12	8 9
12 13 14	9 10	10 11
6 7 8	15 16	19 20
10 11 12	0 1	12 13
18 19 20	4 5	6 7
15 16 17	19 20	16 17
12 13 14	14 15	1 2

page 228

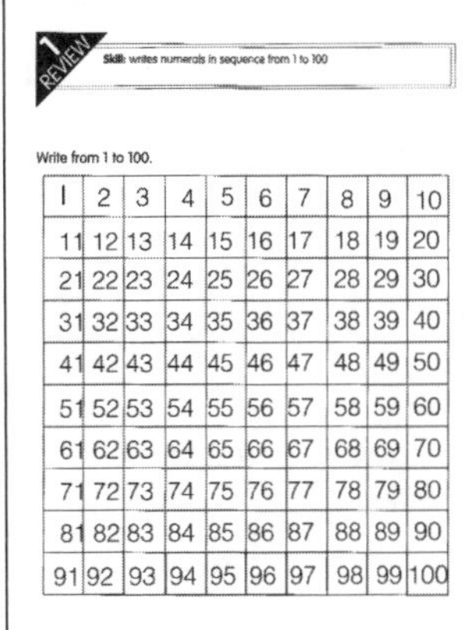
Skill: writes numerals in sequence from 1 to 100

Write from 1 to 100.

1	2	3	4	5	6	7	8	9	10
11	12	13	14	15	16	17	18	19	20
21	22	23	24	25	26	27	28	29	30
31	32	33	34	35	36	37	38	39	40
41	42	43	44	45	46	47	48	49	50
51	52	53	54	55	56	57	58	59	60
61	62	63	64	65	66	67	68	69	70
71	72	73	74	75	76	77	78	79	80
81	82	83	84	85	86	87	88	89	90
91	92	93	94	95	96	97	98	99	100

page 229

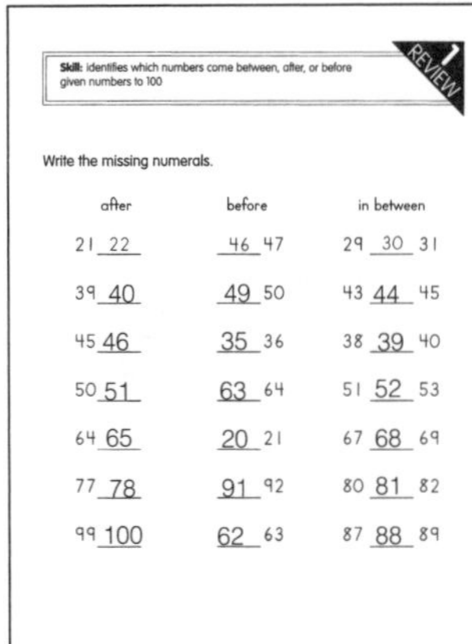
Skill: identifies which numbers come between, after, or before given numbers to 100

Write the missing numerals.

after	before	in between
21 22	46 47	29 30 31
39 40	49 50	43 44 45
45 46	35 36	38 39 40
50 51	63 64	51 52 53
64 65	20 21	67 68 69
77 78	91 92	80 81 82
99 100	62 63	87 88 89

page 230

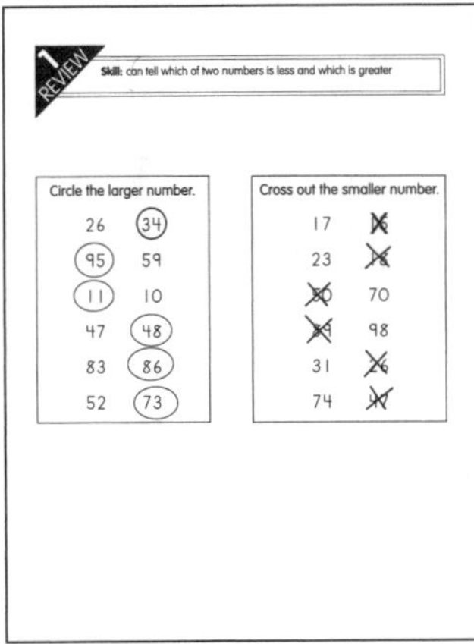
Skill: can tell which of two numbers is less and which is greater

Circle the larger number.	
26	(34)
(95)	59
(11)	10
47	(48)
83	(86)
52	(73)

Cross out the smaller number.	
17	~~16~~
23	~~14~~
~~60~~	70
~~84~~	98
31	~~26~~
74	~~47~~

page 231

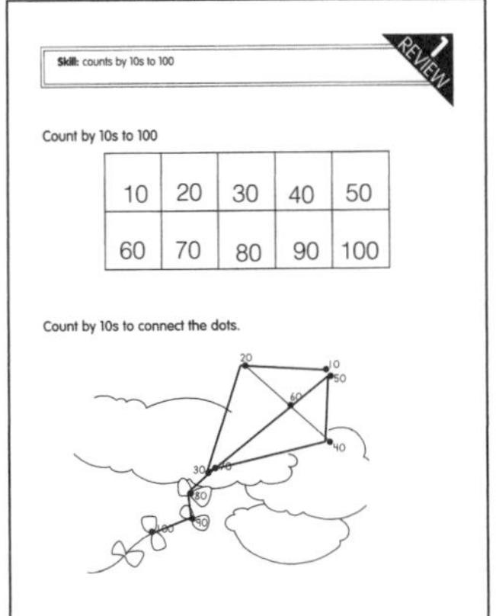
Skill: counts by 10s to 100

Count by 10s to 100

10	20	30	40	50
60	70	80	90	100

Count by 10s to connect the dots.

page 232

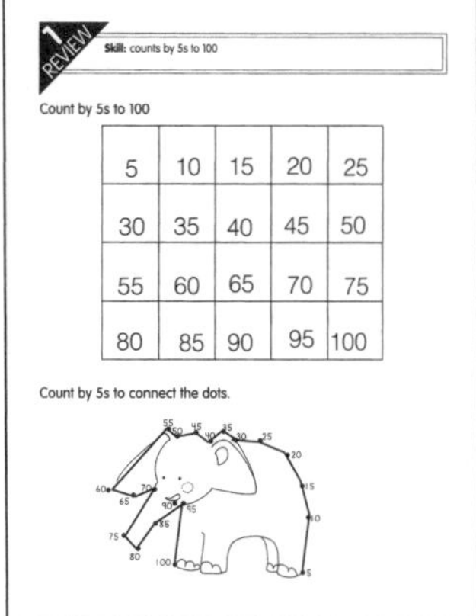
Skill: counts by 5s to 100

Count by 5s to 100

5	10	15	20	25
30	35	40	45	50
55	60	65	70	75
80	85	90	95	100

Count by 5s to connect the dots.

page 233

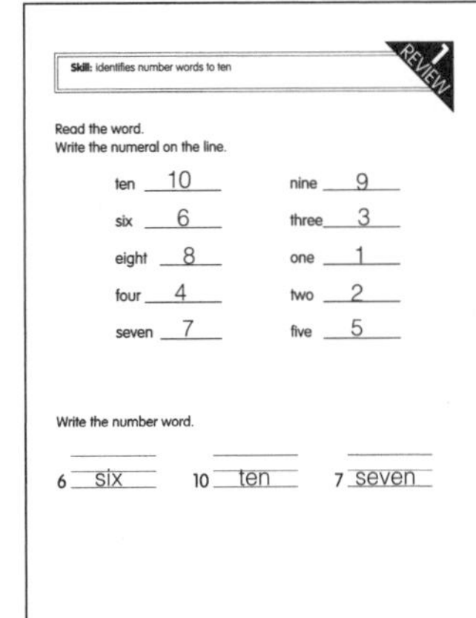
Skill: identifies number words to ten

Read the word.
Write the numeral on the line.

ten	10	nine	9
six	6	three	3
eight	8	one	1
four	4	two	2
seven	7	five	5

Write the number word.

6 six 10 ten 7 seven

page 234

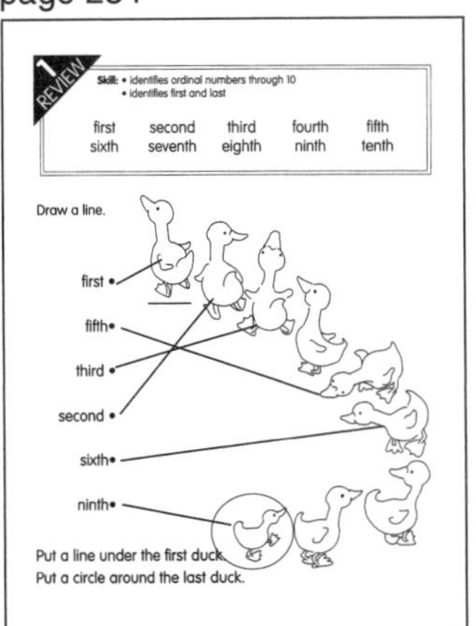
Skill: • identifies ordinal numbers through 10 • identifies first and last

first second third fourth fifth
sixth seventh eighth ninth tenth

Draw a line.

first, fifth, third, second, sixth, ninth

Put a line under the first duck.
Put a circle around the last duck.

page 235

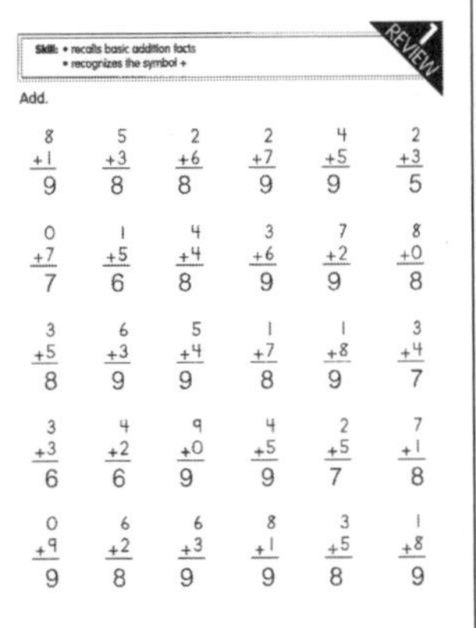
Skill: • recalls basic addition facts • recognizes the symbol +

Add.

8+1=9, 5+3=8, 2+6=8, 2+7=9, 4+5=9, 2+3=5
0+7=7, 1+5=6, 4+4=8, 3+6=9, 7+2=9, 8+0=8
3+5=8, 6+3=9, 5+4=9, 1+7=8, 1+8=9, 3+4=7
3+3=6, 4+2=6, 9+0=9, 4+5=9, 2+5=7, 7+1=8
0+9=9, 6+2=8, 6+3=9, 8+1=9, 3+5=8, 1+8=9

page 236

Skill: • recalls basic subtraction facts

Subtract.

7−2=5, 8−2=6, 6−2=4, 7−5=2, 8−4=4, 3−0=3
5−1=4, 10−5=5, 9−7=2, 8−7=1, 7−3=4, 6−3=3
9−2=7, 5−2=3, 6−1=5, 9−6=3, 9−4=5, 5−3=2
9−3=6, 7−7=0, 7−4=3, 9−1=8, 5−4=1, 8−3=5
8−6=2, 9−5=4, 7−6=1, 8−8=0, 9−8=1, 8−5=3

page 237

Skill: adds numbers in a series to sums of 10 or less

Add.

2+3+4=9, 3+5+1=9, 6+1+2=9, 4+3+1=8, 8+0+2=10, 1+7+1=9
1+6+3=10, 2+5+2=9, 3+4+3=10, 4+3+2=9, 5+2+3=10, 6+1+2=9
3+4+2=9, 5+2+1=8, 7+0+2=9, 2+6+1=9, 9+1+0=10, 6+3+0=9

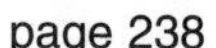

page 238

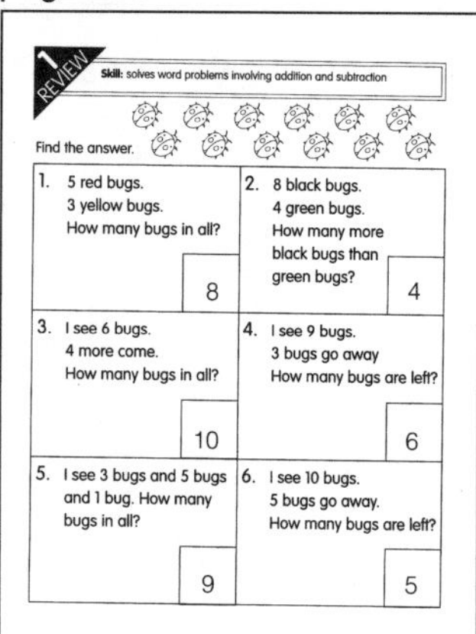

REVIEW 1

Skill: solves word problems involving addition and subtraction

Find the answer.

1. 5 red bugs. 3 yellow bugs. How many bugs in all? 8
2. 8 black bugs. 4 green bugs. How many more black bugs than green bugs? 4
3. I see 6 bugs. 4 more come. How many bugs in all? 10
4. I see 9 bugs. 3 bugs go away. How many bugs are left? 6
5. I see 3 bugs and 5 bugs and 1 bug. How many bugs in all? 9
6. I see 10 bugs. 5 bugs go away. How many bugs are left? 5

page 239

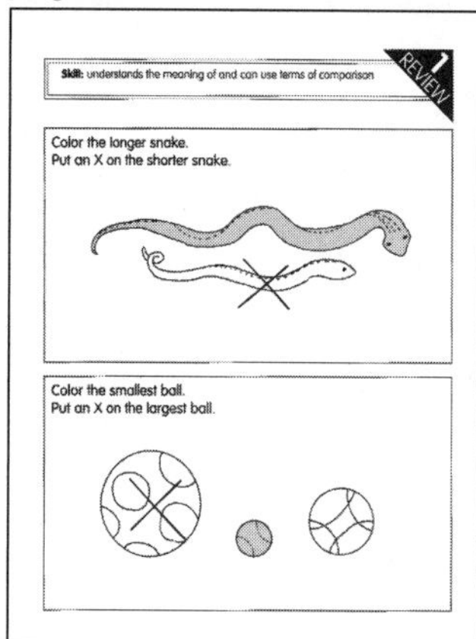

REVIEW 1

Skill: understands the meaning of and can use terms of comparison

Color the longer snake. Put an X on the shorter snake.

Color the smallest ball. Put an X on the largest ball.

page 240

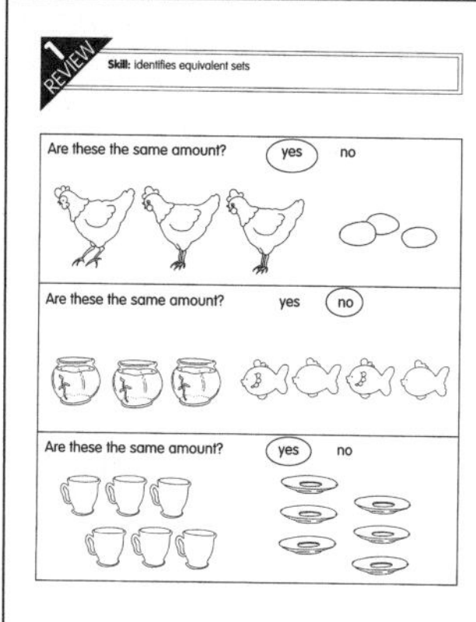

REVIEW 1

Skill: identifies equivalent sets

Are these the same amount? yes no

Are these the same amount? yes no

Are these the same amount? yes no

page 241

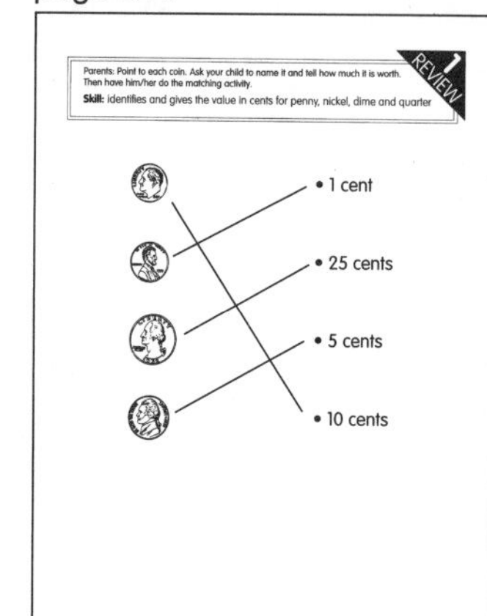

REVIEW 1

Parents: Point to each coin. Ask your child to name it and tell how much it is worth. Then have him/her do the matching activity.

Skill: identifies and gives the value in cents for penny, nickel, dime and quarter

• 1 cent

• 25 cents

• 5 cents

• 10 cents

page 242

REVIEW 1

Skill: gives the value for groups of coins

Count the money. How much is it?

4 ¢ 13 ¢ 14 ¢ 25 ¢ 15 ¢ 14 ¢

page 243

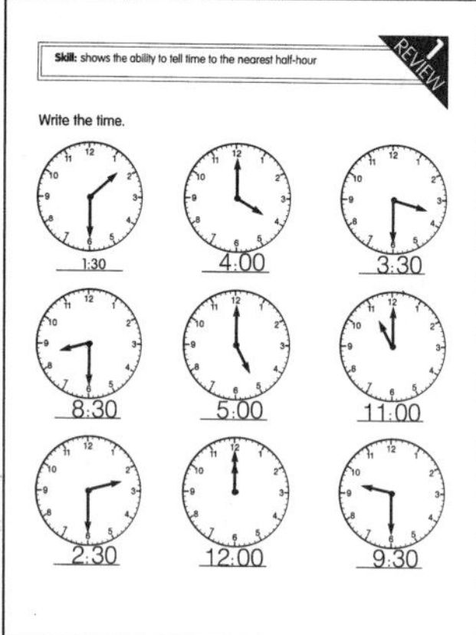

REVIEW 1

Skill: shows the ability to tell time to the nearest half-hour

Write the time.

1:30 4:00 3:30

8:30 5:00 11:00

2:30 12:00 9:30

page 244

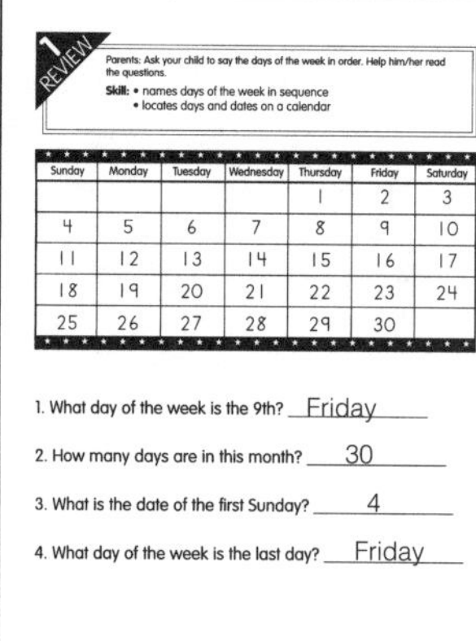

REVIEW 1

Parents: Ask your child to say the days of the week in order. Help him/her read the questions.

Skill: • names days of the week in sequence • locates days and dates on a calendar

Sunday	Monday	Tuesday	Wednesday	Thursday	Friday	Saturday
				1	2	3
4	5	6	7	8	9	10
11	12	13	14	15	16	17
18	19	20	21	22	23	24
25	26	27	28	29	30	

1. What day of the week is the 9th? Friday
2. How many days are in this month? 30
3. What is the date of the first Sunday? 4
4. What day of the week is the last day? Friday

page 245

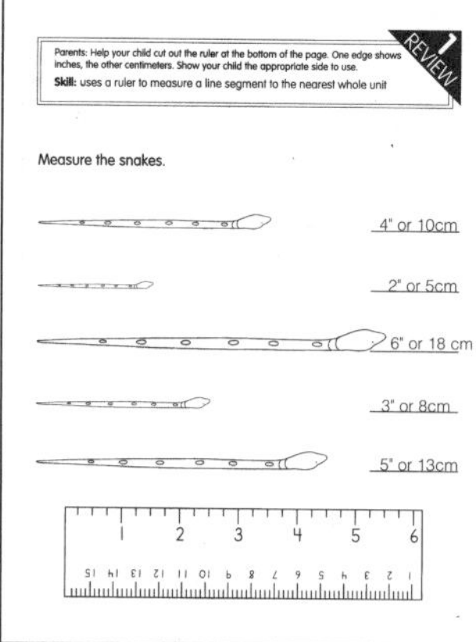

REVIEW 1

Parents: Help your child cut out the ruler at the bottom of the page. One edge shows inches, the other centimeters. Show your child the appropriate side to use.

Skill: uses a ruler to measure a line segment to the nearest whole unit

Measure the snakes.

4" or 10cm

2" or 5cm

6" or 18 cm

3" or 8cm

5" or 13cm

page 246

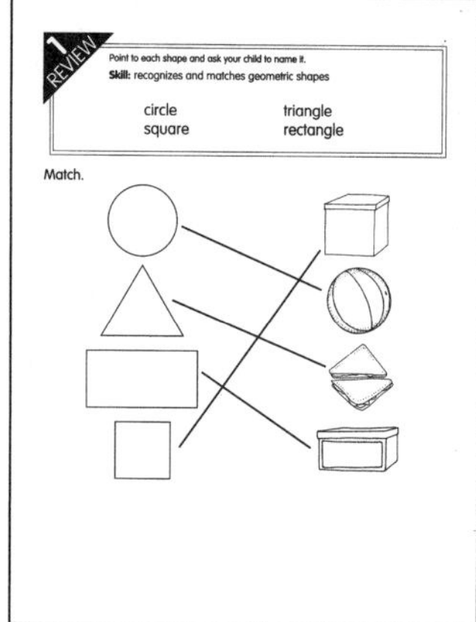

REVIEW 1

Point to each shape and ask your child to name it.

Skill: recognizes and matches geometric shapes

circle triangle square rectangle

Match.

page 247

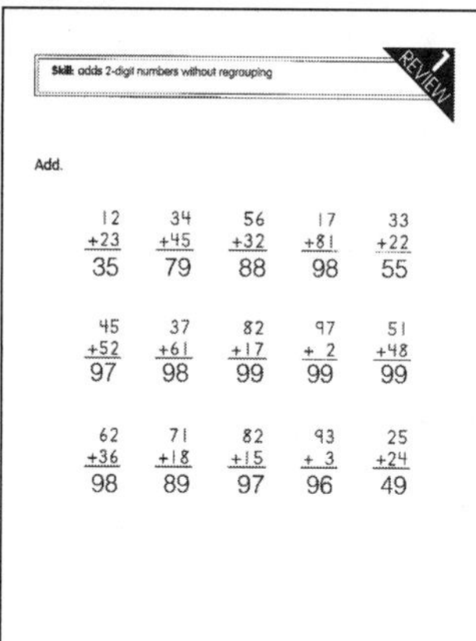

REVIEW 1

Skill: adds 2-digit numbers without regrouping

Add.

12 + 23 = 35; 34 + 45 = 79; 56 + 32 = 88; 17 + 81 = 98; 33 + 22 = 55

45 + 52 = 97; 37 + 61 = 98; 82 + 17 = 99; 97 + 2 = 99; 51 + 48 = 99

62 + 36 = 98; 71 + 18 = 89; 82 + 15 = 97; 93 + 3 = 96; 25 + 24 = 49

page 248

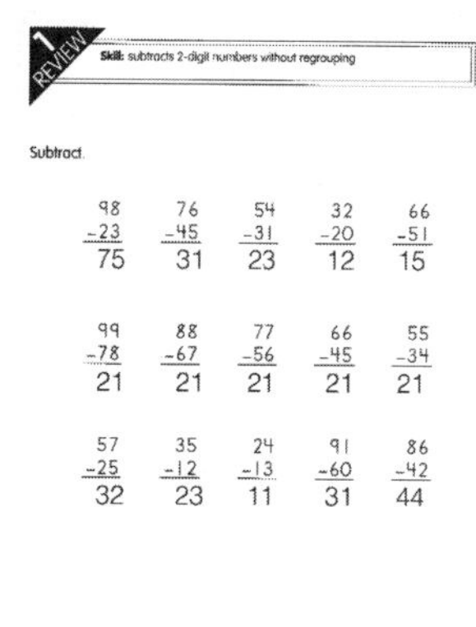

REVIEW 1

Skill: subtracts 2-digit numbers without regrouping

Subtract.

98 − 23 = 75; 76 − 45 = 31; 54 − 31 = 23; 32 − 20 = 12; 66 − 51 = 15

99 − 78 = 21; 88 − 67 = 21; 77 − 56 = 21; 66 − 45 = 21; 55 − 34 = 21

57 − 25 = 32; 35 − 12 = 23; 24 − 13 = 11; 91 − 60 = 31; 86 − 42 = 44

page 249

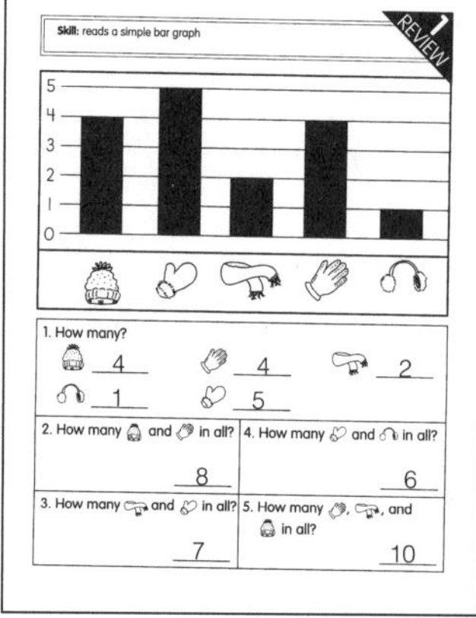

REVIEW 1

Skill: reads a simple bar graph

1. How many? 4 4 2 1 5

2. How many and in all? 8

3. How many and in all? 7

4. How many and in all? 6

5. How many, , and in all? 10

page 250

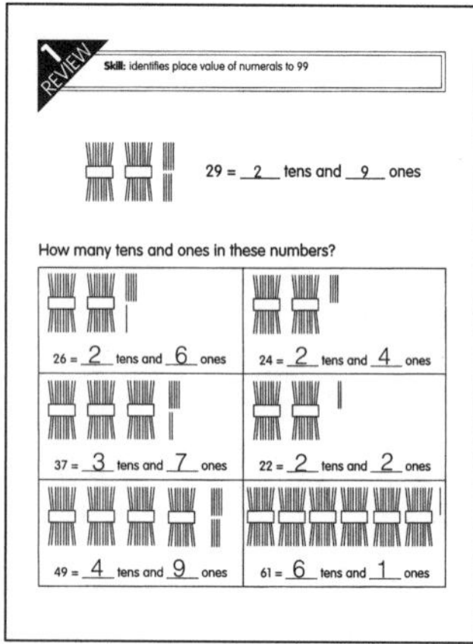

REVIEW 1

Skill: identifies place value of numerals to 99

29 = 2 tens and 9 ones

How many tens and ones in these numbers?

26 = 2 tens and 6 ones

24 = 2 tens and 4 ones

37 = 3 tens and 7 ones

22 = 2 tens and 2 ones

49 = 4 tens and 9 ones

61 = 6 tens and 1 ones

page 251

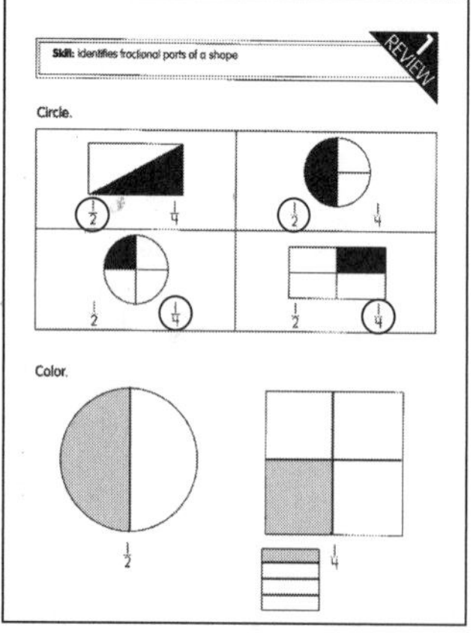

REVIEW 1

Skill: identifies fractional parts of a shape

Circle.

1/2 1/4

1/2 1/4

1/2 1/4

1/2 1/4

Color.

1/2 1/4

page 252

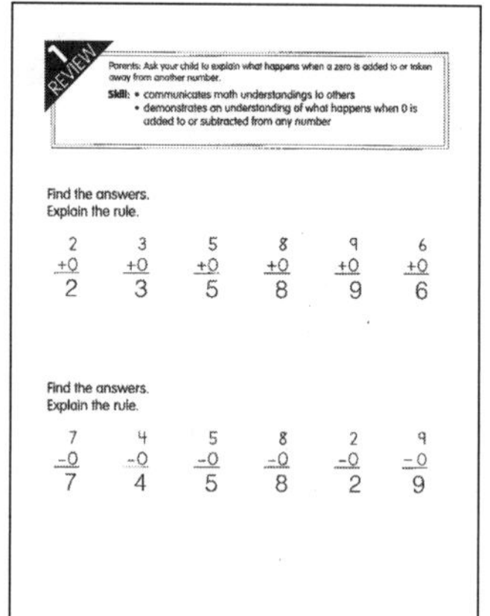

REVIEW 1

Parents: Ask your child to explain what happens when a zero is added to or taken away from another number.

Skill: • communicates math understandings to others • demonstrates an understanding of what happens when 0 is added to or subtracted from any number

Find the answers. Explain the rule.

2 + 0 = 2; 3 + 0 = 3; 5 + 0 = 5; 8 + 0 = 8; 9 + 0 = 9; 6 + 0 = 6

Find the answers. Explain the rule.

7 − 0 = 7; 4 − 0 = 4; 5 − 0 = 5; 8 − 0 = 8; 2 − 0 = 2; 9 − 0 = 9

Why did the bunny paint her toenails red?

0-u	4-y	9-t
1-l	5-s	10-r
2-o	6-c	11-h
3-d	7-i	12-e
	8-n	

3 + 2	1 + 1
5	2
s	o

4 + 1	5 + 6	9 + 3
5	11	12
s	h	e

3 + 3	2 + 0	0 + 0	1 + 0	2 + 1
6	2	0	1	3
c	o	u	l	d

9 + 2	5 + 2	3 + 0	6 + 6
11	7	3	12
h	i	d	e

4 + 3	4 + 4
7	8
i	n

5 + 4	7 + 4	4 + 8
9	11	12
t	h	e

4 + 2	3 + 8	3 + 9	6 + 4	5 + 5	2 + 2
6	11	12	10	10	4
c	h	e	r	r	y

6 + 3	7 + 3	7 + 5	12 + 0
9	10	12	12
t	r	e	e

Second Grade Math

Start at 1.
Connect the dots.

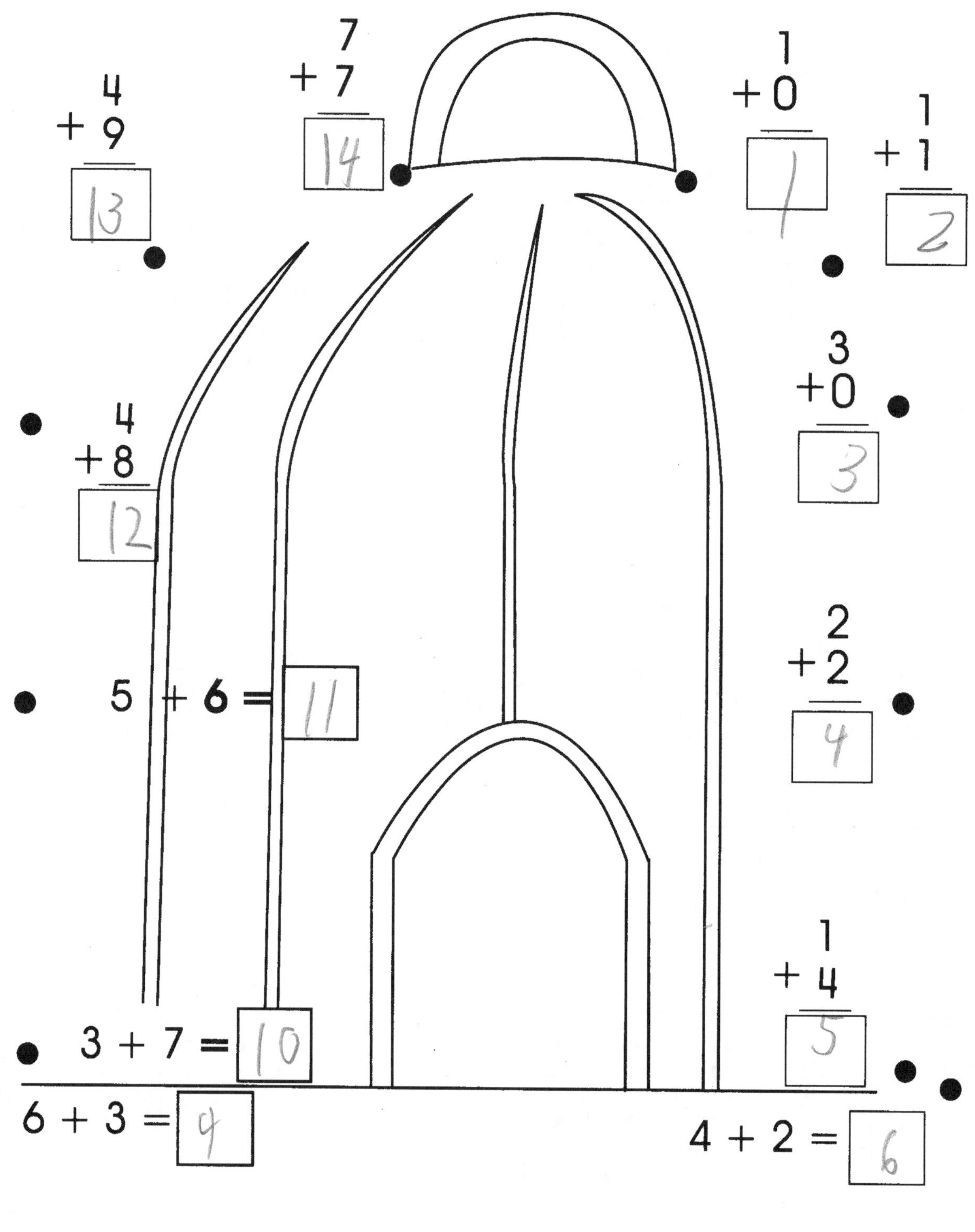

Seeing Double

1 + 1 = 2　　5 + 5 = 10

4 + 4 = 8　　0 + 0 = 0

7 + 7 = 14　　8 + 8 = 16

9 + 9 = 18　　2 + 2 = 4

3 + 3 = 6　　6 + 6 = 12

Second Grade Math

Adding Ten

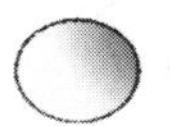

Add ten to the numbers below.
Look for a pattern.

5 + 10 = 15 8 + 10 = 18

2 + 10 = 12 3 + 10 = 13

6 + 10 = 16 7 + 10 = 17

4 + 10 = 14 9 + 10 = 19

1 + 10 = 11

Do you see a pattern?

Write your rule. "When you add ten to a number...

____

____

____

Count the bananas.

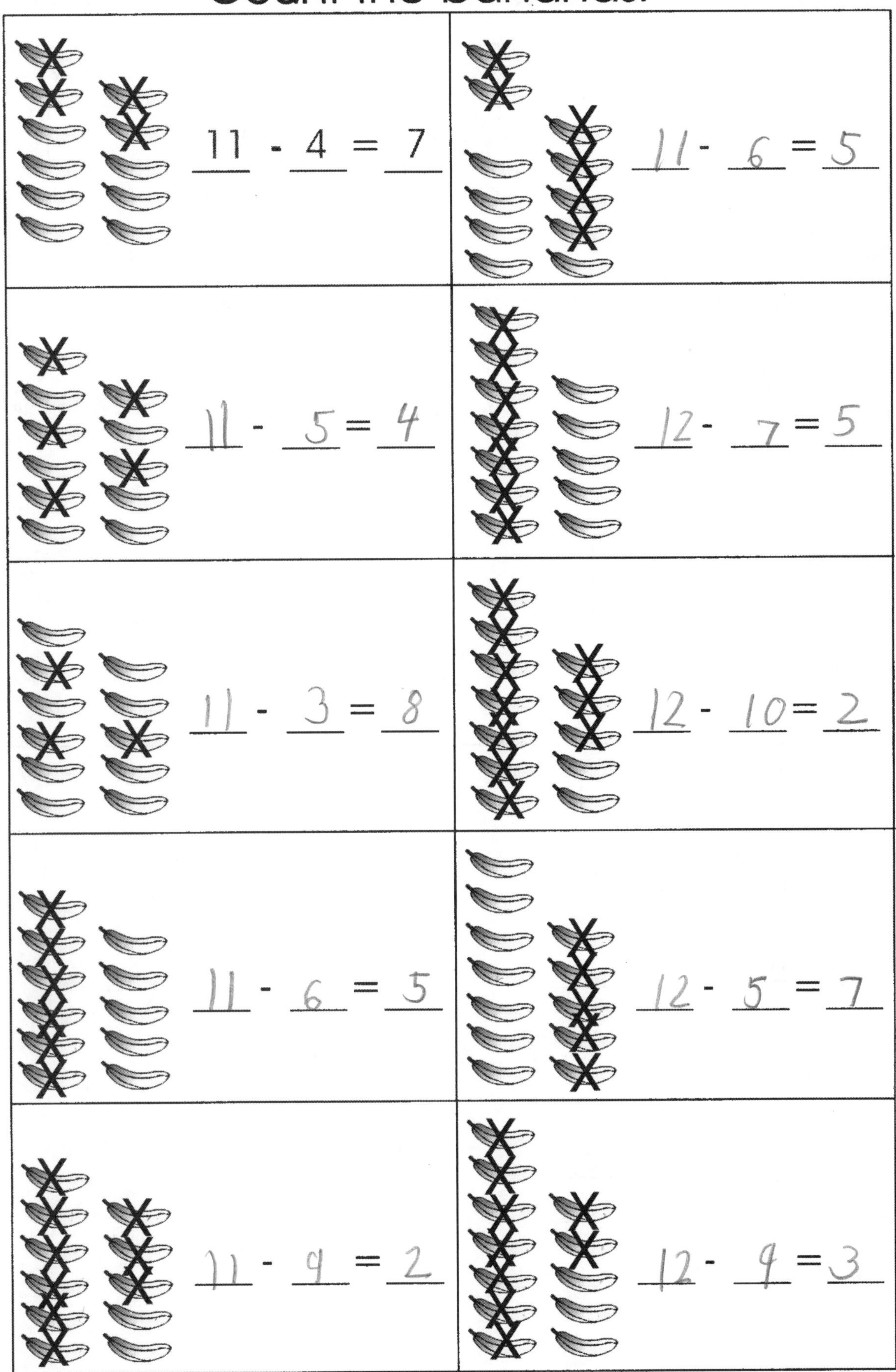

Cover up the monkeys to help you find the answers.

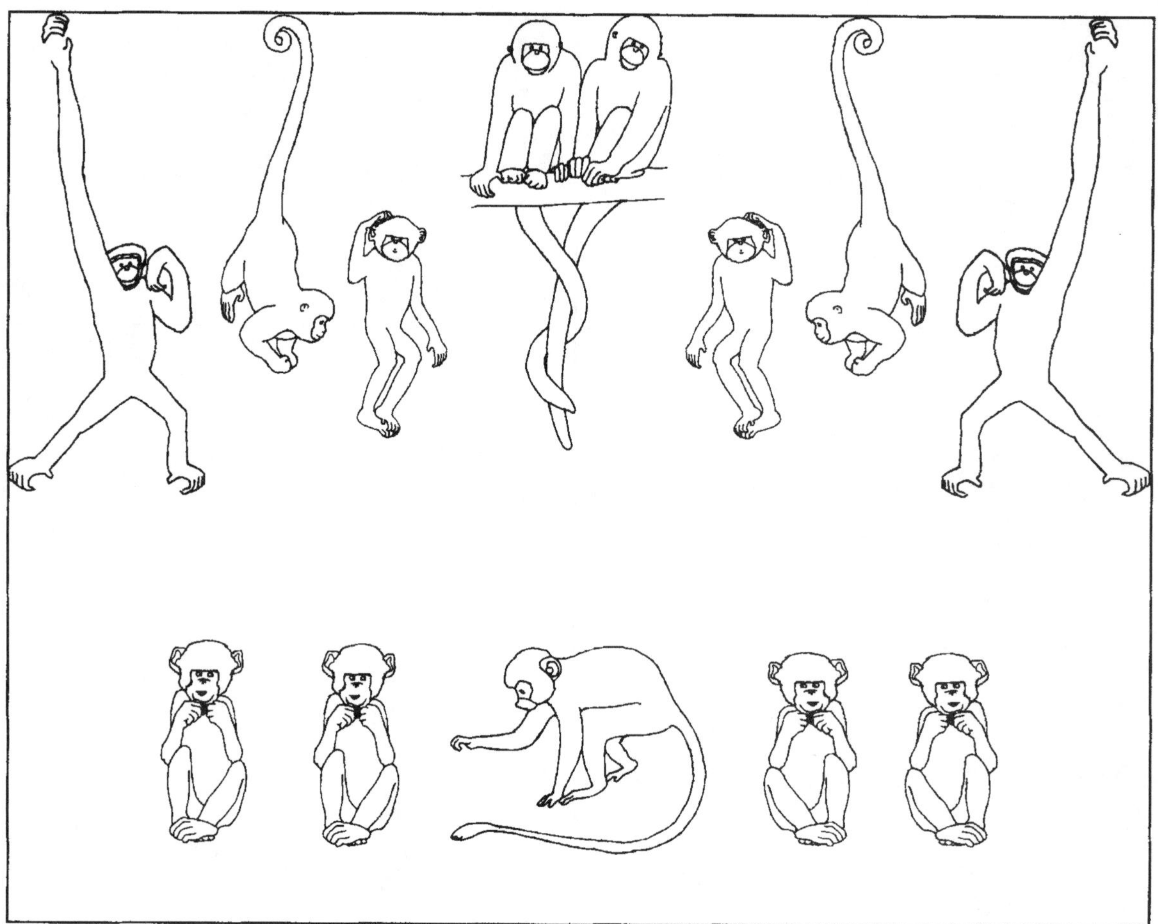

13 - 6 = 7

13 - 8 = 5

13 - 4 = 9

13 - 3 = 10

13 - 9 = 4

13 - 7 = 6

13 - 5 = 8

13 - 10 = 3

13 - 2 = 11

13 - 1 = 12

Keep subtracting to help us climb down the banana trees.

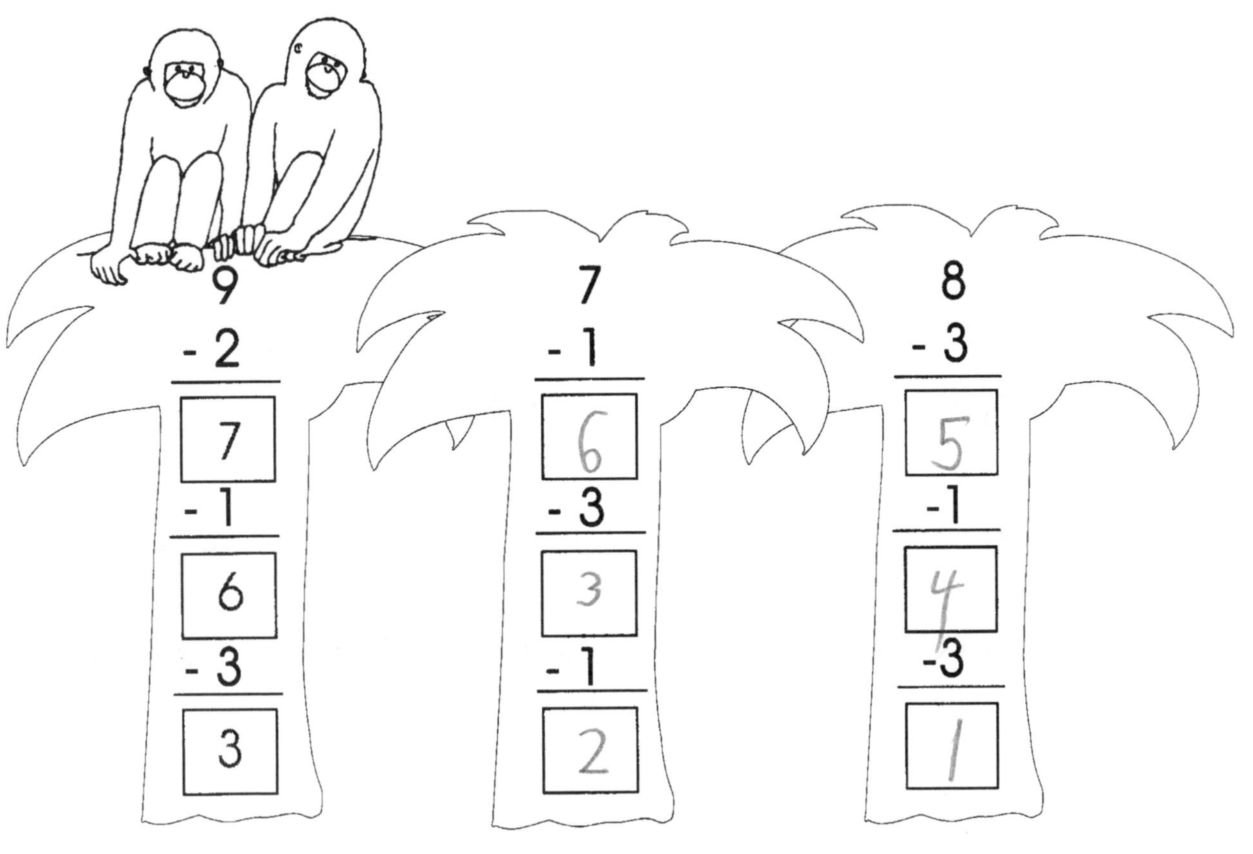

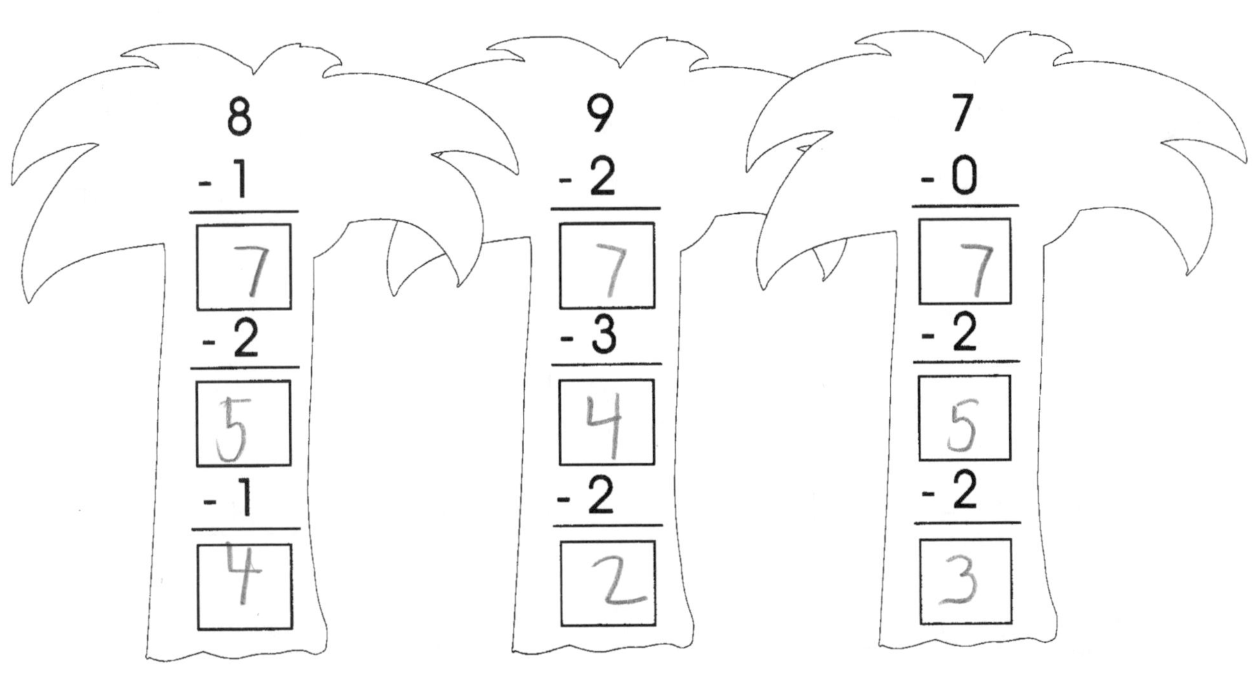

Second Grade Math

Use the chimps to help you find the answers.

15 - 7 = 8   15 - 9 = 6

15 - 5 = 10   15 - 8 = 7

15 - 6 = 7   15 - 4 = 11

Use the orangutans to help you find the answers.

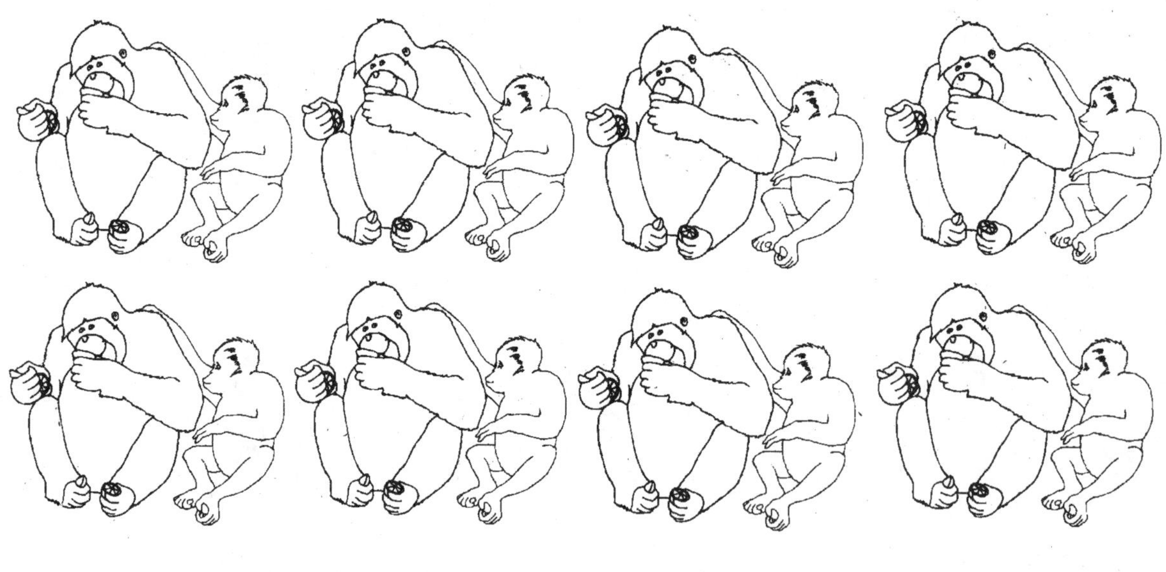

16 - 9 = 7   16 - 10 = 6

16 - 7 = 9   16 - 5 = 11

16 - 6 = 10   16 - 8 = 8

Check subtraction by adding.

9 -8 1	1 +8 9

11 − 9 = 2 ; [2] + 9 = 11	12 − 5 = ___ ; [ ] + 5 = ___	11 − 7 = ___ ; [ ] + 7 = ___
13 − 6 = ___ ; [ ] + 6 = ___	14 − 3 = ___ ; [ ] + 3 = ___	15 − 6 = ___ ; [ ] + 6 = ___
12 − 9 = ___ ; [ ] + 9 = ___	11 − 5 = ___ ; [ ] + 5 = ___	14 − 9 = ___ ; [ ] + 9 = ___
16 − 4 = ___ ; [ ] + 4 = ___	15 − 1 = ___ ; [ ] + 1 = ___	19 − 2 = ___ ; [ ] + 2 = ___

Match the types of graphs.

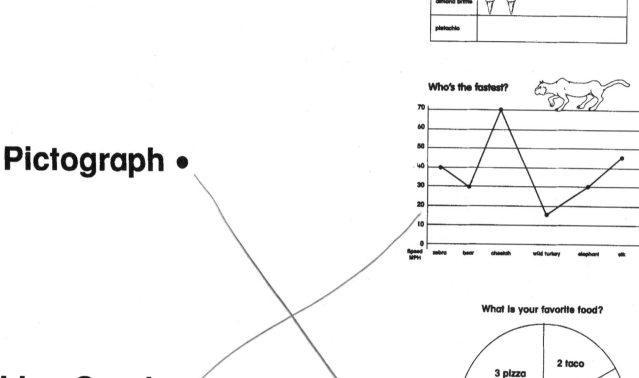

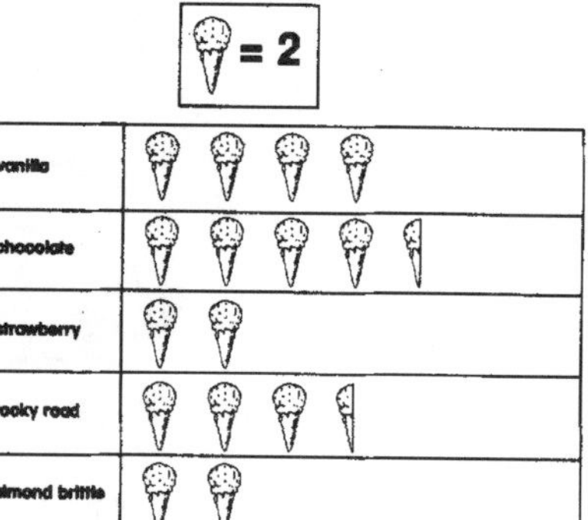

Bar Graph •

Pictograph •

Line Graph •

Circle Graph •

What is your favorite kind of ice cream?
= 2
vanilla
chocolate
strawberry
rocky road
almond brittle
pistachio

Who's the fastest?
70
60
50
40
30
20
10
0
Speed MPH
zebra
bear
cheetah
wild turkey
elephant
elk

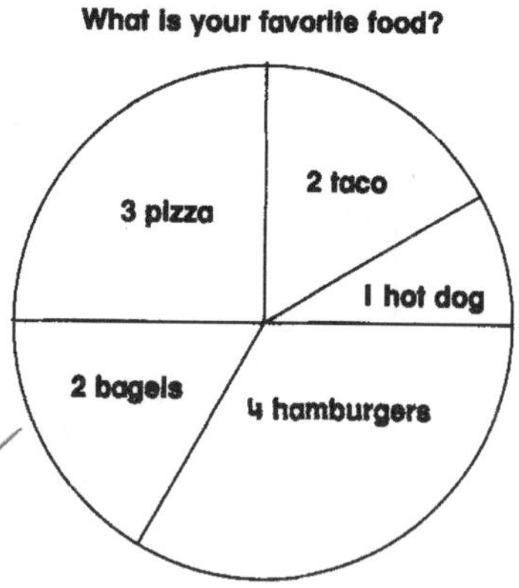

What is your favorite food?
3 pizza
2 taco
1 hot dog
2 bagels
4 hamburgers

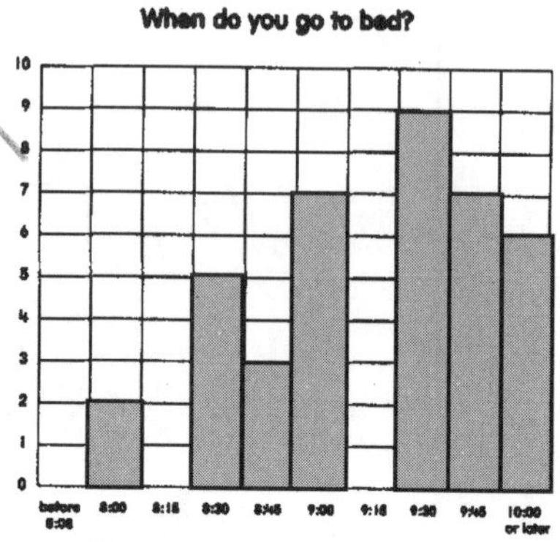

When do you go to bed?
10
9
8
7
6
5
4
3
2
1
0
before 8:00
8:00
8:15
8:30
8:45
9:00
9:15
9:30
9:45
10:00 or later

Dinner Time

Read this graph to answer the questions.

8
7
6
5
4
3
2
1
0

5:00 5:30 6:00 6:30 7:00

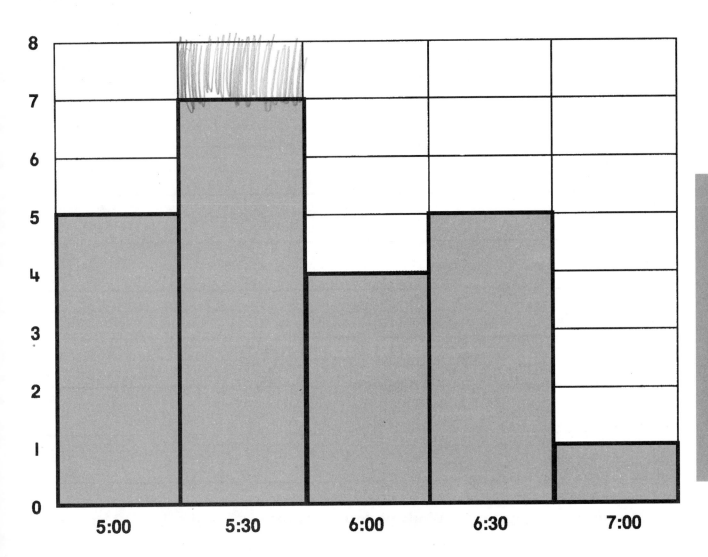

1. How many people ate at 7:00? 1
2. How many ate at 5:30? 7
3. How many ate at 6:00? 4
4. How many more ate at 6:00 than at 7:00? 3
5. What time do you eat dinner? 5:30

   Color a square on the graph to show this time. ____________

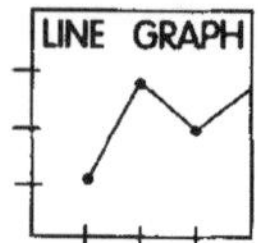

Going Fishing

Read the graph to answer the questions.

How many fish did you catch?

8
7
6
5
4
3
2
1
0

Monday **Tuesday** **Wednesday** **Thursday** **Friday** **Saturday**

1. How many fish were caught on Monday?

    Tuesday 4

    Thursday 3

    Saturday 7

2. Were more fish caught on Monday or Friday? Monday

3. Were more fish caught on Tuesday or Saturday? Saturday

4. On which two days were the same amount of fish caught? Mon, Thurs

Bonus

5. How many fish were caught in all? 19

What is your favorite fast food?

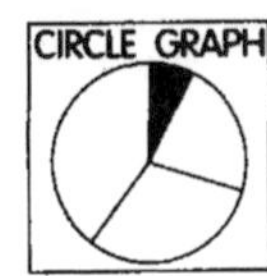

Read the graph to answer these questions.

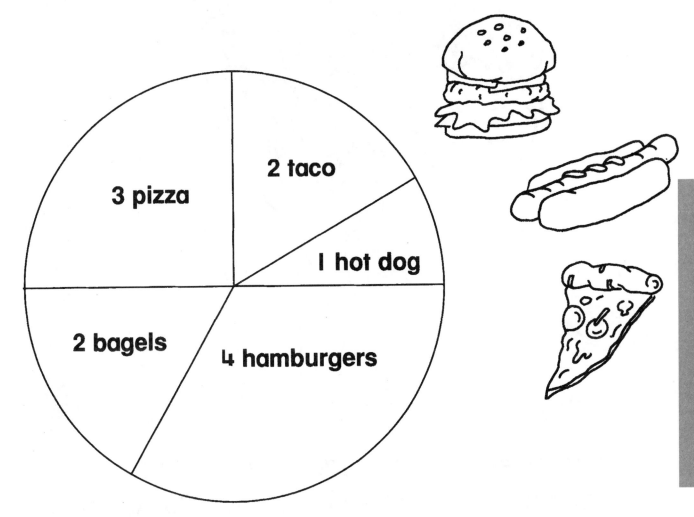

3 pizza

2 taco

1 hot dog

2 bagels

4 hamburgers

1. How many students were asked the question? 12
2. How many different fast foods were named? 5
3. How many said "taco"? 2
4. Which fast food did the most people like? Hamburgers

Bonus:

5. What fraction said "pizza" 3 ?

I have been watching squirrels in the park for three days. Altogether I have seen 25 squirrels. I saw 9 squirrels the first day and 3 squirrels the second day.

How many did I see the third day?

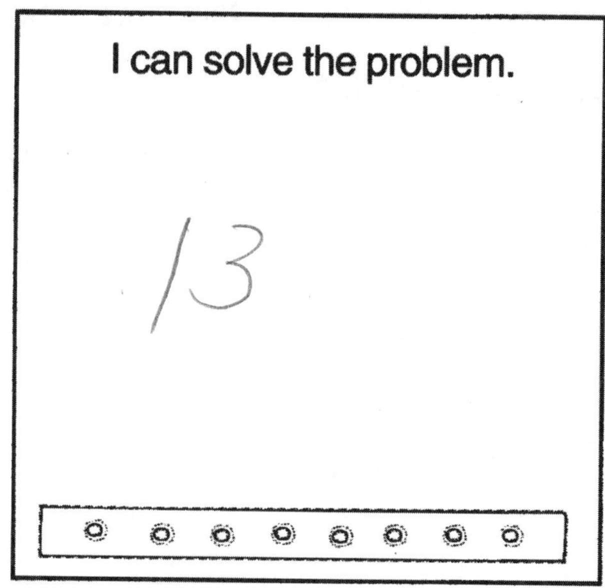
I can solve the problem.

6 9 12 16

18 21 24

- Which number in this pattern is wrong?
- What should the number be?

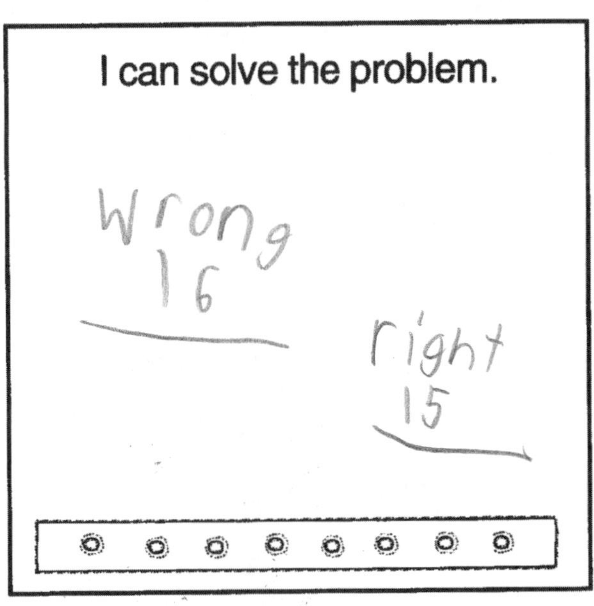

I can solve the problem.
Wrong
16
right
15

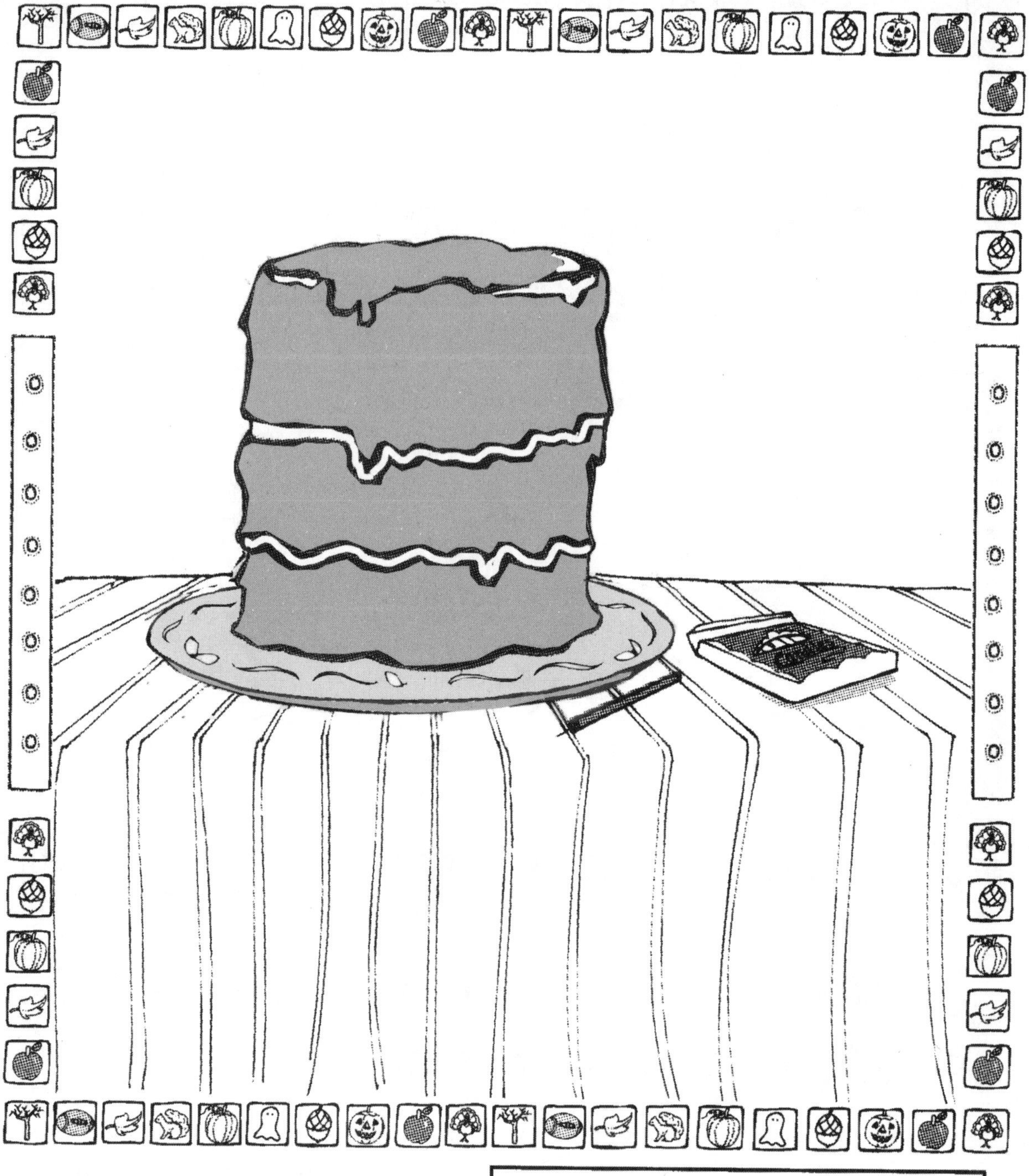

How many candles will be on my birthday cake if I am 3 1/2 years older than my 5 1/2 year old friend?

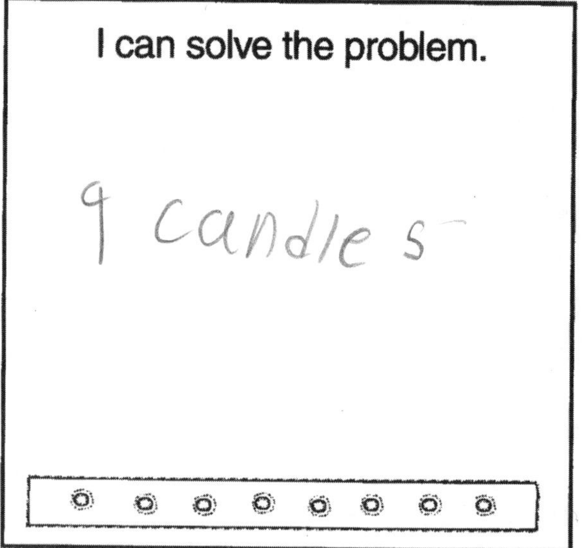
I can solve the problem.
9 candles

Inch - 1/2 inch

Use an inch ruler.
Measure the pictures to the nearest 1/2 inch.

1 1/2 inches

2

6 1/2 inches

5 1/2 inches

4 1/2 inches

3 1/2 inches

1 1/2 inches

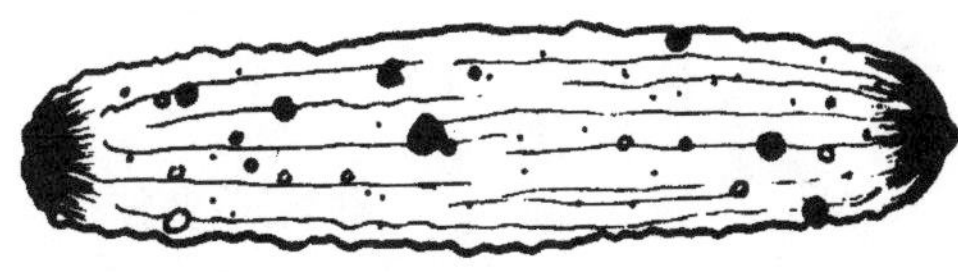

2 1/2 inches

How Long Is It?

Cut out the ruler at the bottom of this page.
Measure the pictures in inches.

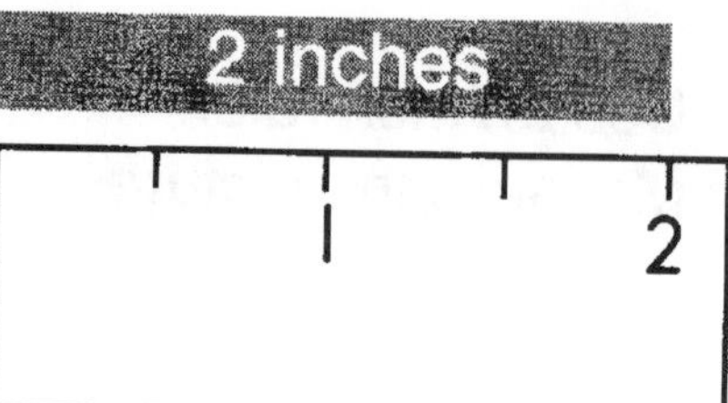

NO. 2 ___6___ inches

BALLPOINT PEN ___5___ inches

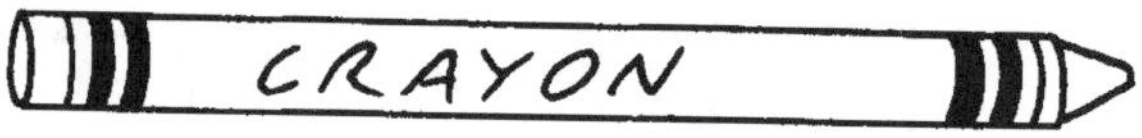

CRAYON ___3___ inches

NO. 2 ___4___ inches

CRAYON ___2___ inches

MARKER ___4___ inches

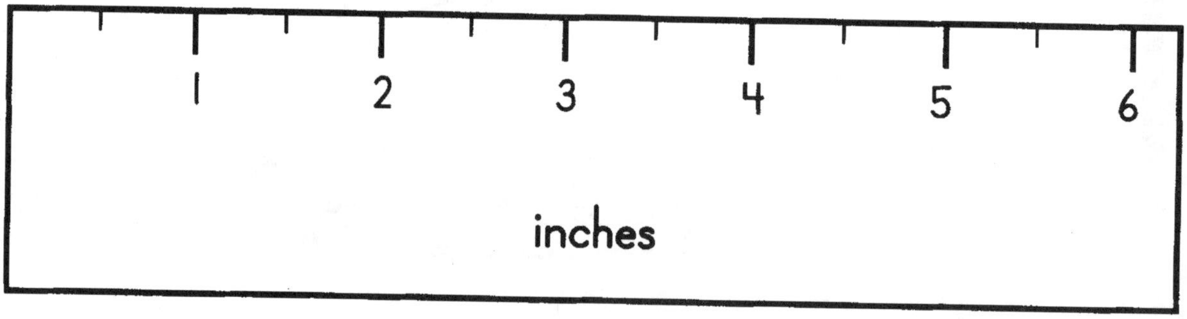

1 2 3 4 5 6

inches

How Many Centimeters?

Cut out the ruler at the bottom of this page.
Measure the pictures.

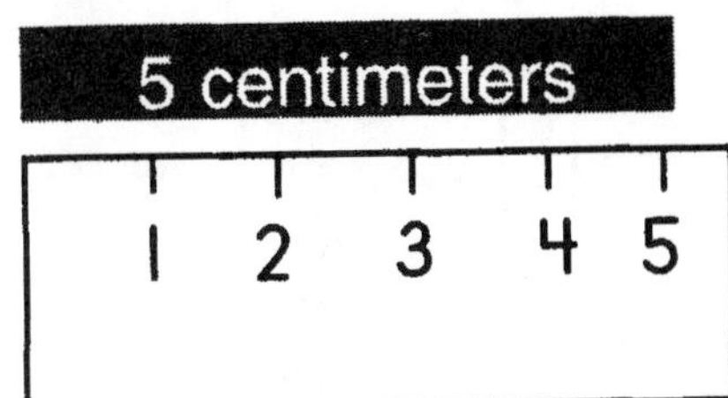

15 cm

8 cm

6 cm

10 cm

12 cm

7 cm

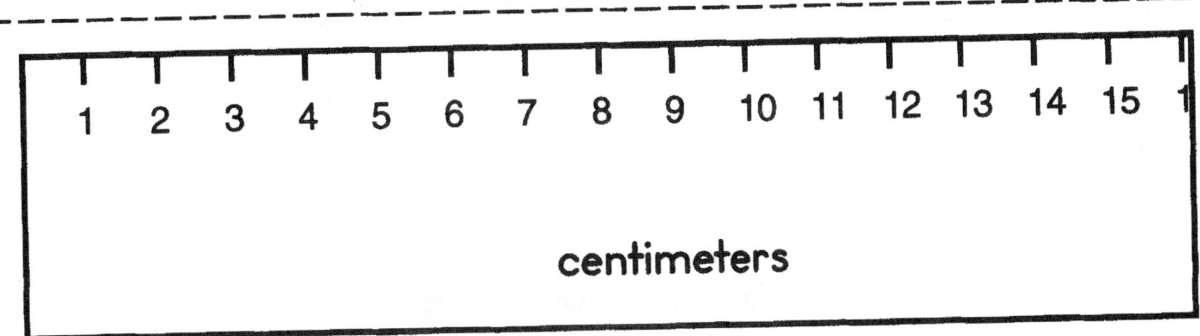

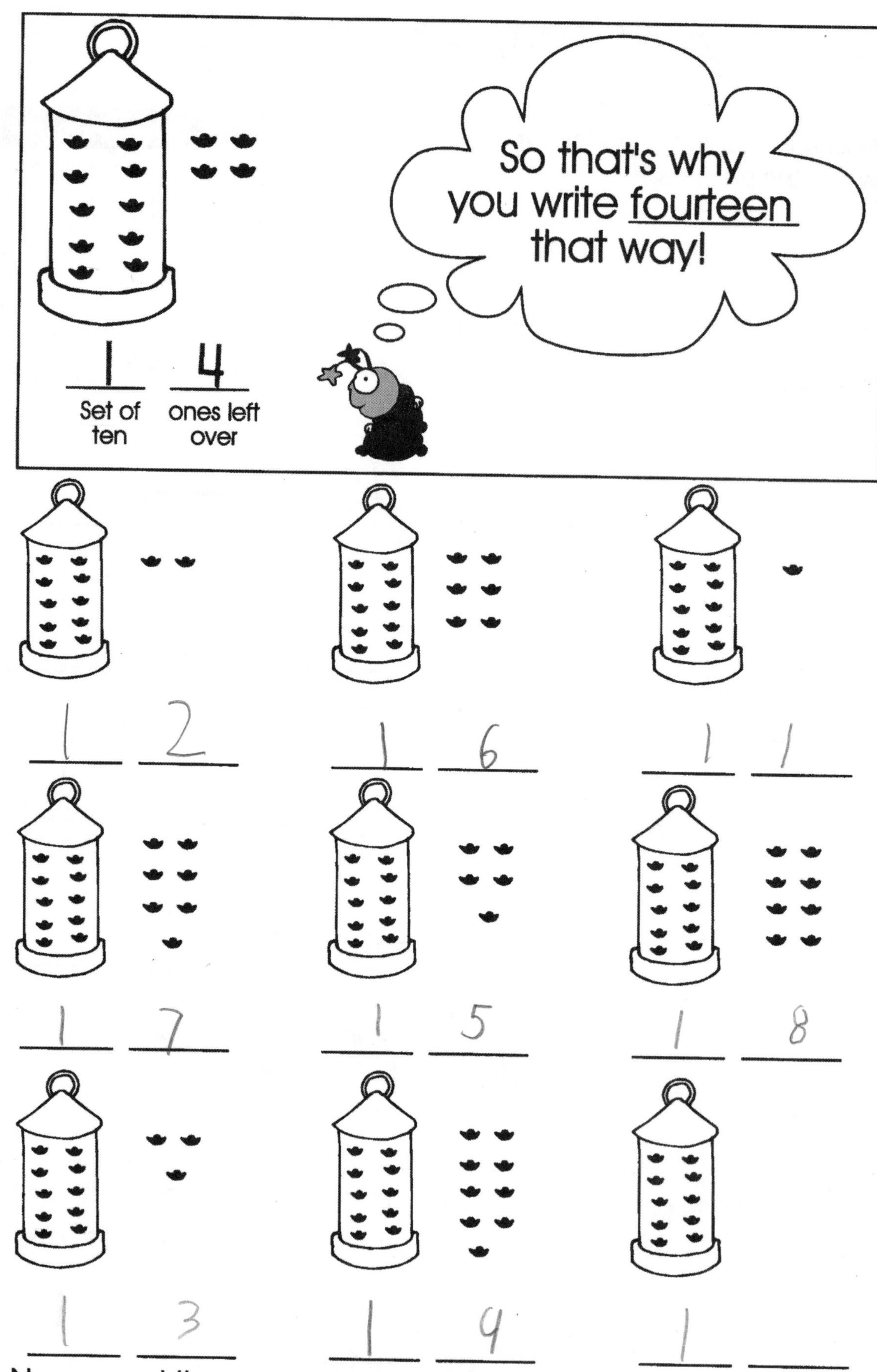

Now, read these numbers to someone.

Write the number.

 = 13 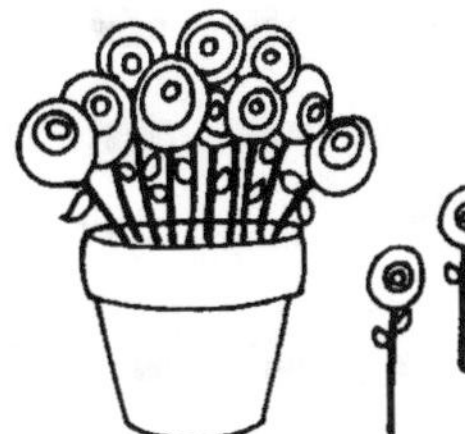 = 15

 = 18  = 12

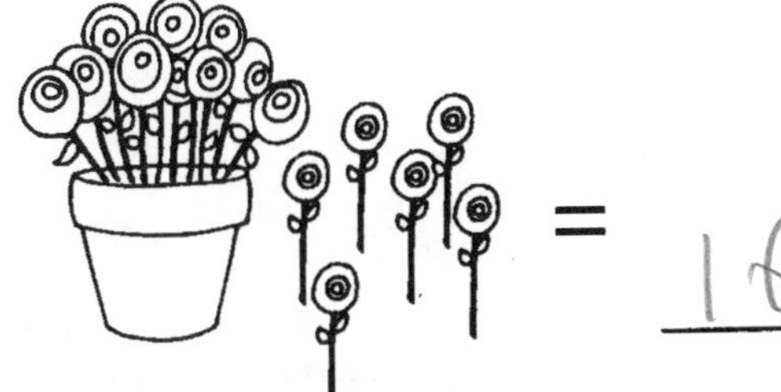 = 16 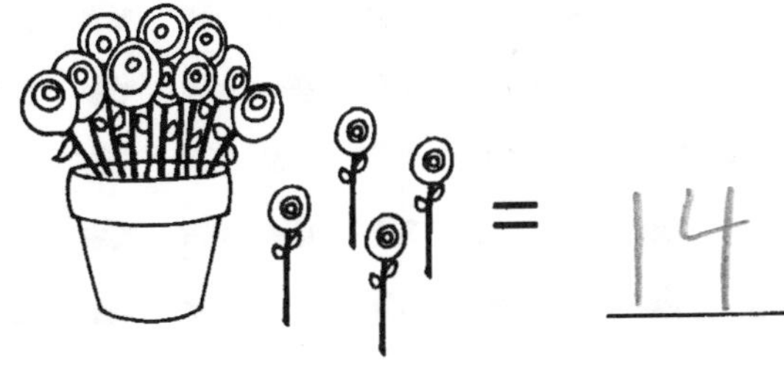 = 14

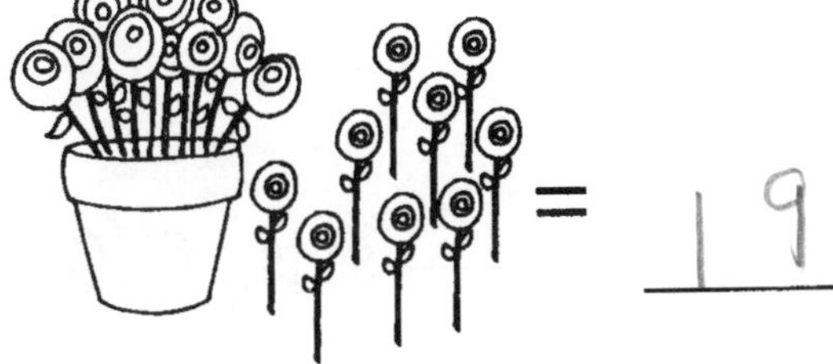 = 19 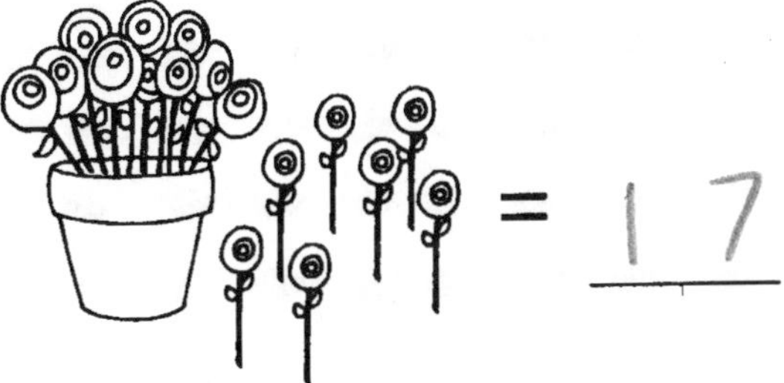 = 17

Fill in the missing numbers.

1	2	3	4	5	6	7	8	9	10
11	12	13	14	15	16	17	18	19	20

Circle sets of 10

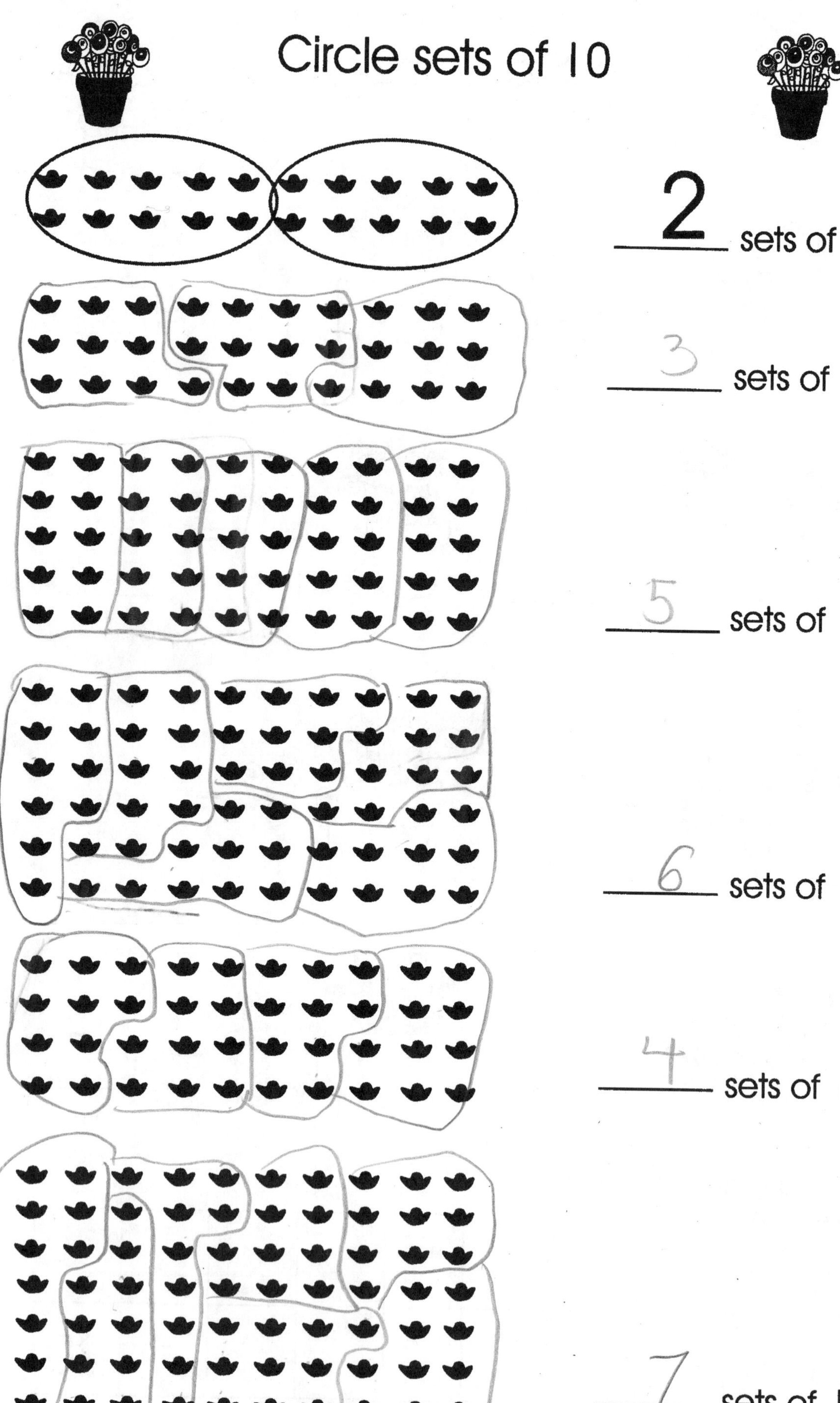

__2__ sets of 10

__3__ sets of 10

__5__ sets of 10

__6__ sets of 10

__4__ sets of 10

__7__ sets of 10

Match each set to its number.

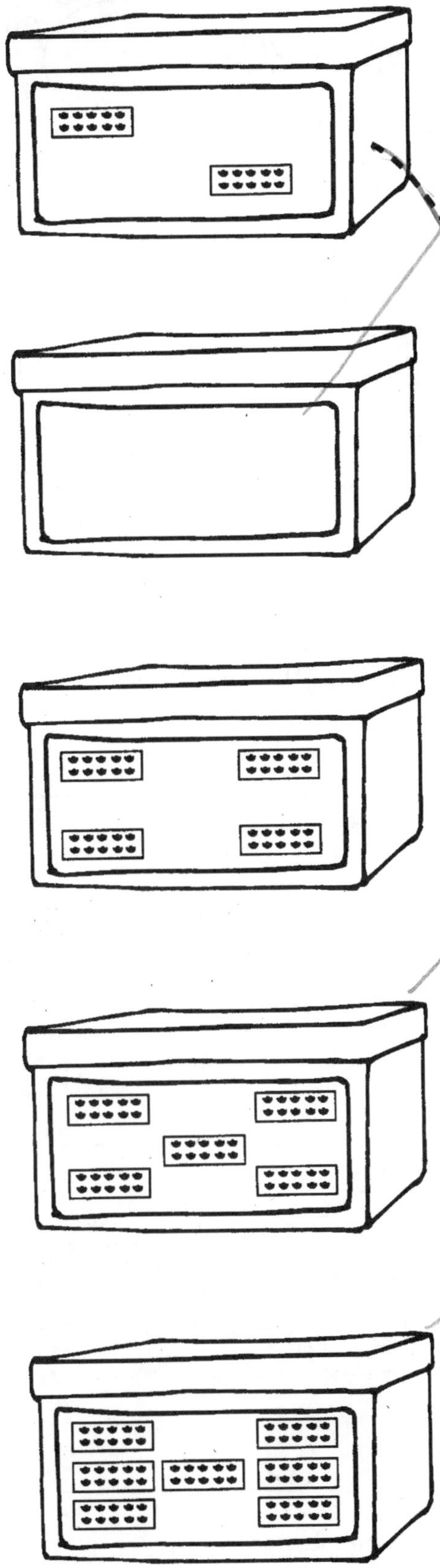

0

10

20

30

40

50

60

70

80

90

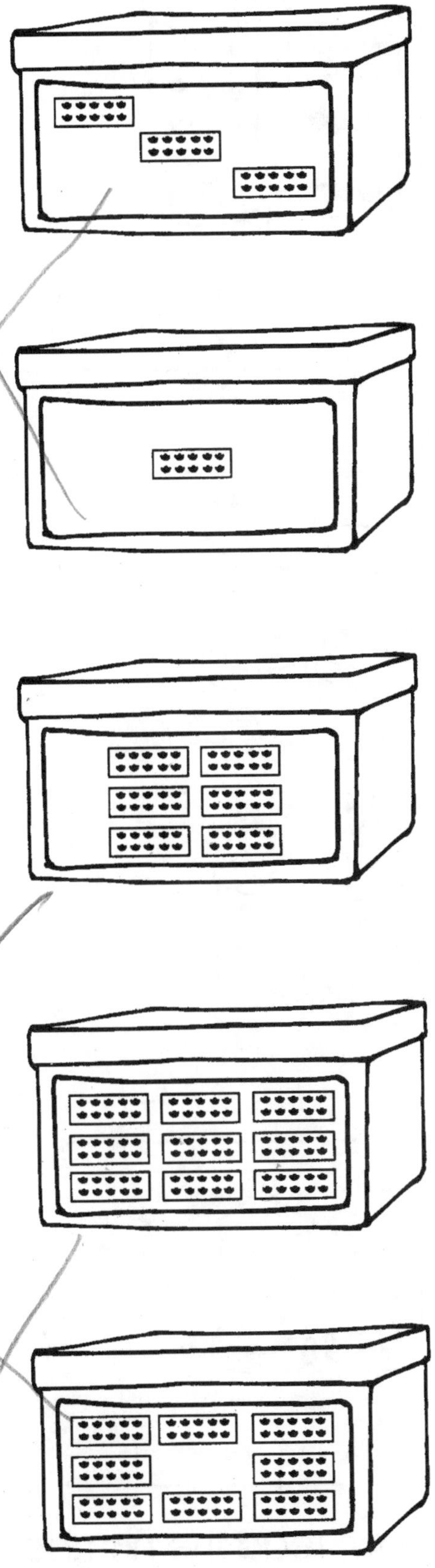

Second Grade Math

Now, read the numbers you wrote to someone.

So that's why you write 43 that way.
4
sets of ten
3
ones left over

Fill in the missing numbers.

40	41	42	43	44
45	46	47	48	49

Write the numbers.

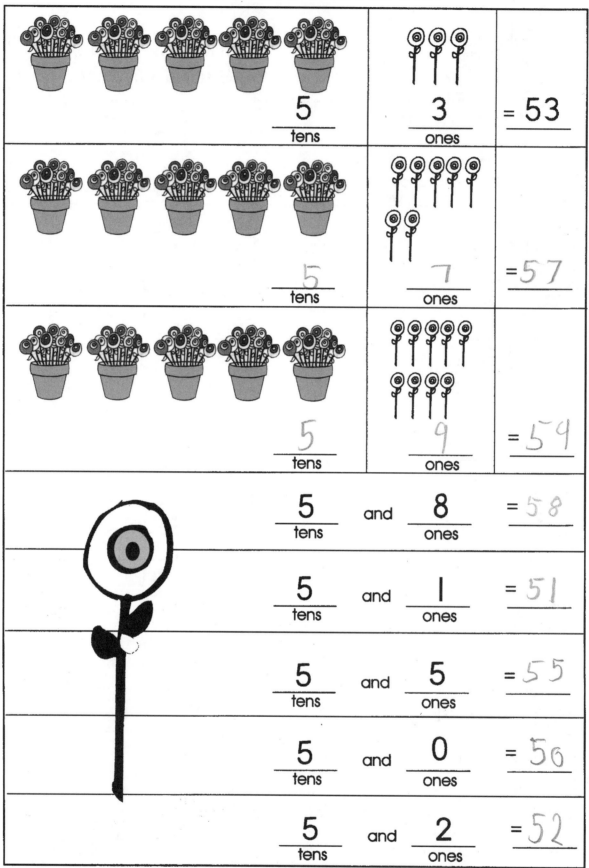

5 tens	3 ones	= 53
5 tens	7 ones	= 57
5 tens	9 ones	= 59
5 tens and	8 ones	= 58
5 tens and	1 ones	= 51
5 tens and	5 ones	= 55
5 tens and	0 ones	= 50
5 tens and	2 ones	= 52

Now, read the numbers you wrote to someone.

So that's
why you write 76
that way.

7 tens 6 ones = 76

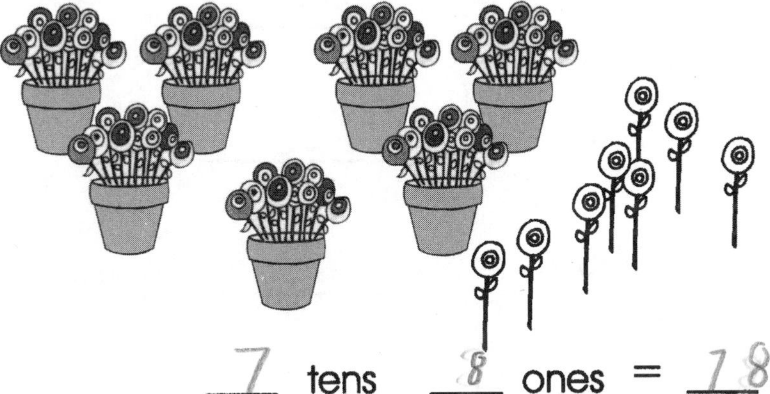

7 tens 8 ones = 78

7 tens 3 ones = 73	7 tens 4 ones = 74
7 tens 5 ones = 75	7 tens 2 ones = 72
0 tens 9 ones = 9	7 tens 0 ones = 70

Count:

61	62	63	64	65	66	67	68	69	70
71	72	73	74	75	76	77	78	79	80

Think about what you know about tens and ones. Write the number

8 tens and 2 ones = 82

8 tens and 6 ones = 86

8 tens and 3 ones = 83

8 tens and 9 ones = 89

8 tens and 0 ones = 80

8 tens and 7 ones = 87

8 tens and 4 ones = 84

8 tens and 1 ones = 81

8 tens and 8 ones = 88

8 tens and 5 ones = 85

Count the 10s.

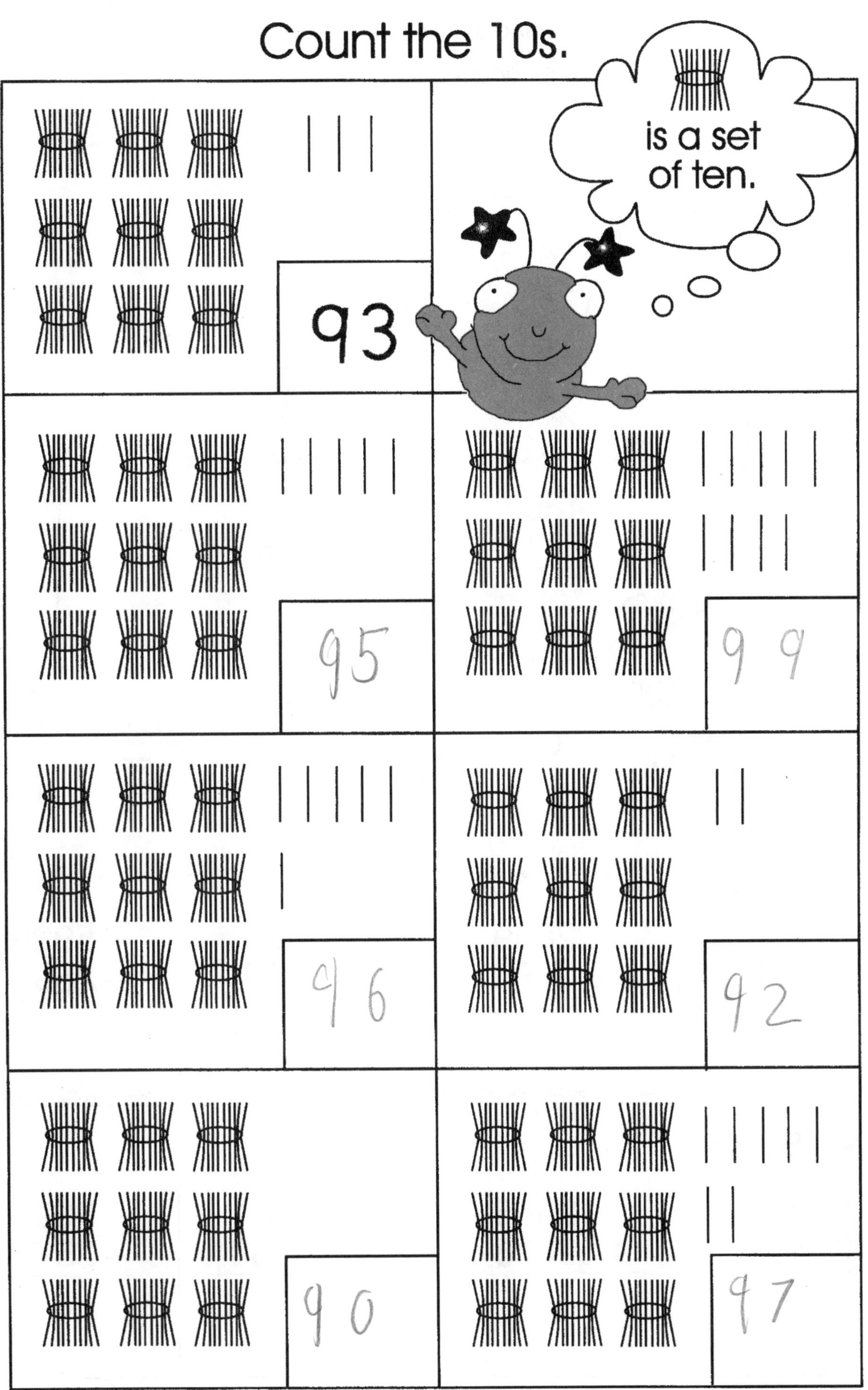

Second Grade Math

Can you find the answers before this hungry elephant eats all of the hay?

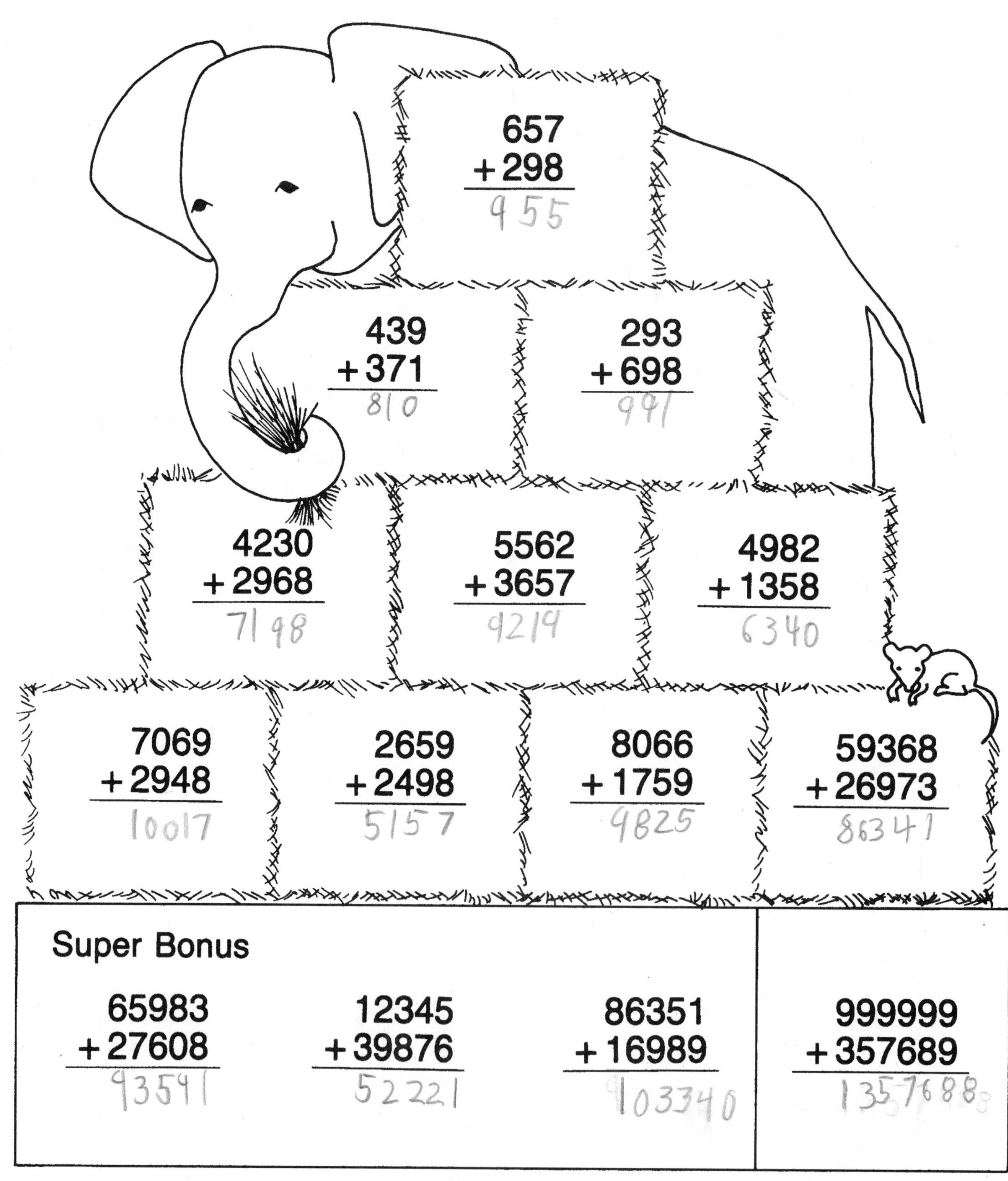

Match the families.

Second Grade Math

How does an elephant get up in a tree?

111	s	425	i
130	t	482	e
175	h	536	n
212	o	555	d
297	f	600	g
303	r	674	a
321	c	747	w

586 − 411	589 − 107
175	482
h	e

437 − 326	935 − 510	353 − 223	624 − 513
111	425	130	111
s	i	t	s

496 − 284	767 − 231
212	536

977 − 303	999 − 463

786 − 112	477 − 156	868 − 656	943 − 640	688 − 152

796 − 122	676 − 140	777 − 222

998 − 251	889 − 215	589 − 164	781 − 651	581 − 470

798 − 501	539 − 327	528 − 225

657 − 232	476 − 346

592 − 462	925 − 713

773 − 173	795 − 492	794 − 582	869 − 122

____ ____ ____ ____ ____ ____ .

Skill: reads and understands the value of number names

Read the word. Write the numeral.

six ______

four ______

one ______

ten ______

seven ______

two ______

nine ______

three ______

eight ______

five ______

twelve ______

fifteen ______

seventeen ______

eleven ______

twenty ______

thirteen ______

eighteen ______

fourteen ______

nineteen ______

sixteen ______

Skill: • count by 10s to 100
• count by 5s to 100

Count by 10s.

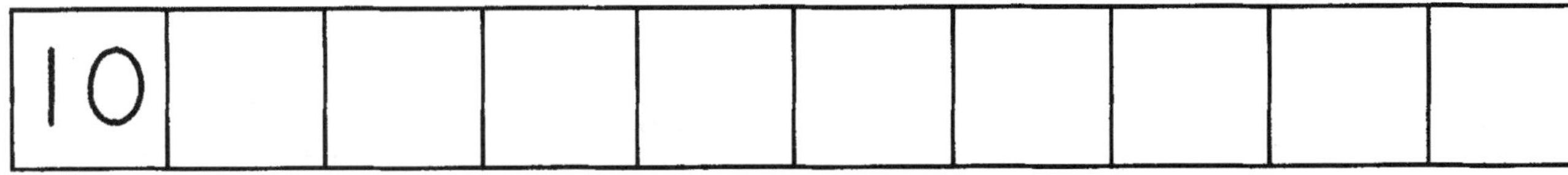

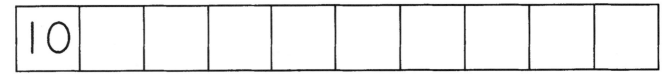

Count by 10s to connect the dots.

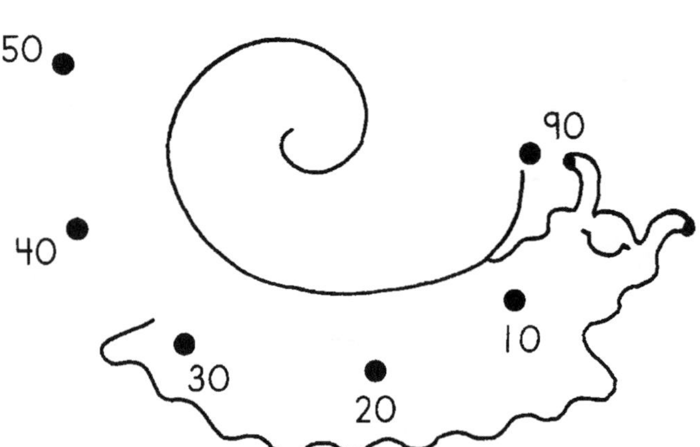

Count by 5s to 100.

5									

Count by 5s to connect the dots.

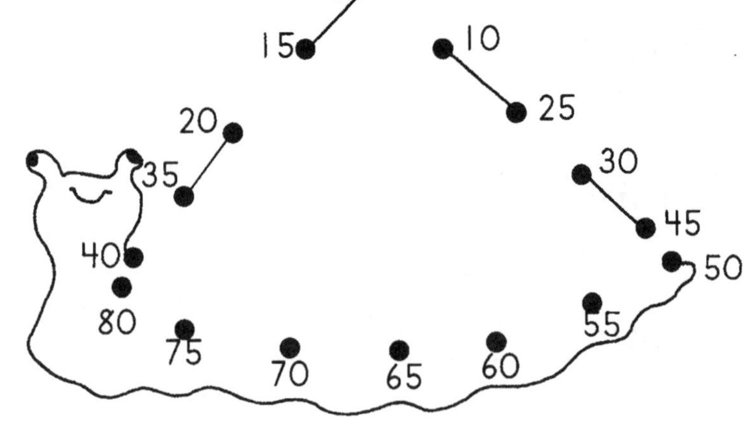

Skill: count by 2s to 100

Count by 2s

2	4								

Count by 2s to connect the dots.

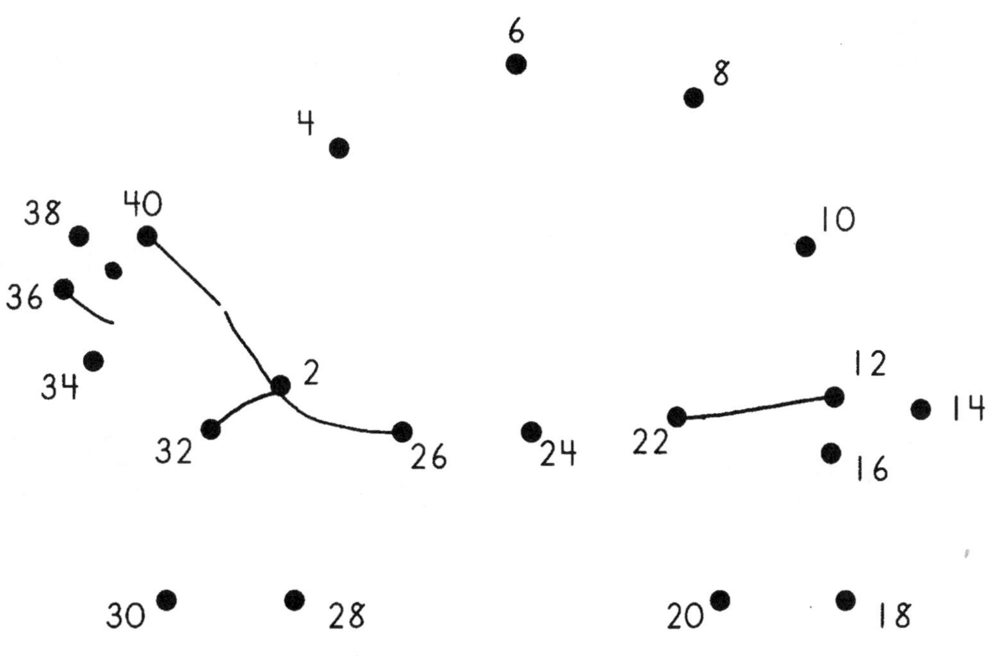

Skill: counts to 1000 by 100s.

Count to 1000 by 100s.

100 ____ ____ ____ ____

____ ____ ____ ____ ____

What comes 100 before and 100 after?

500 600 700 ____ 200 ____

____ 800 ____ ____ 400 ____

____ 300 ____ ____ 900 ____

____ 700 ____ ____ 500 ____

Skill: identifies what comes before and after to 999

REVIEW 2

What comes before and after?

28	29	30	___	60	___
___	88	___	___	176	___
___	243	___	___	329	___
___	460	___	___	519	___
___	622	___	___	781	___
___	806	___	___	987	___

2 REVIEW

Skill: determines the correct sign to be used in a number sentence

$2 \boxed{+} 2 = 4$ $2 \boxed{-} 2 = 0$

Fill in the missing signs.

$4 \square 3 = 7$ $4 \square 3 = 1$ $9 \square 1 = 8$

$6 \square 2 = 4$ $4 \square 4 = 8$ $7 \square 5 = 2$

$1 \square 8 = 9$ $5 \square 5 = 0$ $9 \square 3 = 6$

$12 \square 4 = 8$ $6 \square 6 = 12$ $18 \square 9 = 9$

$7 \square 5 = 12$ $9 \square 4 = 13$ $15 \square 6 = 9$

Skill: reads and understands ordinal numbers

Match:

- first
- second
- third
- fifth
- sixth
- seventh
- tenth

2 REVIEW

Skill: • understands greater than, less than, and equal
• can use the correct symbol < > =

8 > 2　　2 < 6

Fill in the circle.

9 ○ 5	7 ○ 9	3 ○ 5
11 ○ 21	23 ○ 32	64 ○ 48
59 ○ 54	27 ○ 27	63 ○ 10
87 ○ 88	47 ○ 74	55 ○ 51

Fill in the blanks.

______ < ______　　　______ > ______

Skill: recalls basic addition and subtraction facts to 18

REVIEW 2

Find the answer.

$$\begin{array}{r} 9 \\ +9 \\ \hline \end{array} \qquad \begin{array}{r} 5 \\ +8 \\ \hline \end{array} \qquad \begin{array}{r} 13 \\ -4 \\ \hline \end{array} \qquad \begin{array}{r} 8 \\ +4 \\ \hline \end{array} \qquad \begin{array}{r} 14 \\ -5 \\ \hline \end{array}$$

$$\begin{array}{r} 18 \\ -9 \\ \hline \end{array} \qquad \begin{array}{r} 16 \\ -8 \\ \hline \end{array} \qquad \begin{array}{r} 8 \\ +7 \\ \hline \end{array} \qquad \begin{array}{r} 14 \\ -6 \\ \hline \end{array} \qquad \begin{array}{r} 7 \\ +6 \\ \hline \end{array}$$

$$\begin{array}{r} 9 \\ +6 \\ \hline \end{array} \qquad \begin{array}{r} 15 \\ -9 \\ \hline \end{array} \qquad \begin{array}{r} 13 \\ -6 \\ \hline \end{array} \qquad \begin{array}{r} 12 \\ -3 \\ \hline \end{array} \qquad \begin{array}{r} 9 \\ +4 \\ \hline \end{array}$$

$$\begin{array}{r} 7 \\ +9 \\ \hline \end{array} \qquad \begin{array}{r} 9 \\ +5 \\ \hline \end{array} \qquad \begin{array}{r} 15 \\ -6 \\ \hline \end{array} \qquad \begin{array}{r} 16 \\ -7 \\ \hline \end{array} \qquad \begin{array}{r} 13 \\ -5 \\ \hline \end{array}$$

$$\begin{array}{r} 17 \\ -8 \\ \hline \end{array} \qquad \begin{array}{r} 8 \\ -8 \\ \hline \end{array} \qquad \begin{array}{r} 4 \\ +9 \\ \hline \end{array} \qquad \begin{array}{r} 12 \\ -8 \\ \hline \end{array} \qquad \begin{array}{r} 17 \\ -7 \\ \hline \end{array}$$

Skill: adds three 1-digit numbers to sums of 18

Add.

3	6	4	8	2
1	7	2	4	1
+8	+2	+4	+1	+7

5	5	4	8	9
6	4	3	5	6
+4	+6	+6	+4	+3

9	8	7	9	8
4	0	7	5	4
+4	+9	+4	+1	+2

Skill: adds two-digit numbers with or without regrouping

Add.

$18 + 51$ $63 + 28$ $45 + 32$ $37 + 59$ $46 + 29$

$19 + 40$ $63 + 35$ $52 + 17$ $23 + 68$ $25 + 65$

$13 + 67$ $45 + 23$ $27 + 64$ $59 + 39$ $55 + 28$

$52 + 29$ $24 + 45$ $90 + 30$ $28 + 61$ $35 + 45$

Skill: adds three 2-digit numbers without regrouping

Add.

25	64	17	33	51
41	25	60	33	24
+ 32	+ 10	+ 22	+ 33	+ 14

12	34	28	22	28
42	43	51	33	60
+ 45	+ 12	+ 20	+ 44	+ 11

40	25	16	18	63
20	31	33	50	16
+ 30	+ 22	+ 50	+ 11	+ 20

Skill: subtracts 2-digit numbers with or without regrouping

Subtract.

87 − 23	96 − 55	69 − 36	86 − 39
93 − 67	79 − 15	39 − 14	91 − 46
68 − 55	22 − 17	87 − 54	74 − 14
82 − 27	90 − 36	68 − 27	99 − 86

2 REVIEW

Skill: adds and subtracts 3-digit numbers without regrouping

Subtract.

689 − 465	655 − 324	735 − 123	488 − 408
684 − 203	569 − 150	968 − 851	367 − 212
448 − 442	357 − 341	699 − 290	652 − 120

Skill: • recalls multiplication facts with products less than 25
• recognizes x as a symbol for multiply

REVIEW 2

Multiply.

3 x 4 = ______ 2 x 2 = ______ 3 x 2 = ______

5 x 2 = ______ 1 x 3 = ______ 4 x 3 = ______

6 x 3 = ______ 2 x 4 = ______ 5 x 4 = ______

$\begin{array}{r} 8 \\ \times 2 \\ \hline \end{array}$ $\begin{array}{r} 4 \\ \times 4 \\ \hline \end{array}$ $\begin{array}{r} 9 \\ \times 2 \\ \hline \end{array}$ $\begin{array}{r} 7 \\ \times 3 \\ \hline \end{array}$ $\begin{array}{r} 3 \\ \times 5 \\ \hline \end{array}$

$\begin{array}{r} 6 \\ \times 4 \\ \hline \end{array}$ $\begin{array}{r} 1 \\ \times 5 \\ \hline \end{array}$ $\begin{array}{r} 3 \\ \times 3 \\ \hline \end{array}$ $\begin{array}{r} 4 \\ \times 2 \\ \hline \end{array}$ $\begin{array}{r} 8 \\ \times 3 \\ \hline \end{array}$

Skill: • recalls division facts with dividends less than 25
• recognizes ÷ and $\overline{)\ }$ as symbols for divide

$6 \div 2 =$ $4 \div 2 =$ $10 \div 5 =$

$8 \div 4 =$ $9 \div 3 =$ $2 \div 1 =$

$2\overline{)14}$ $3\overline{)21}$ $4\overline{)8}$

$5\overline{)5}$ $3\overline{)18}$ $2\overline{)10}$

$5\overline{)15}$ $3\overline{)12}$ $2\overline{)16}$

Skill: identifies these basic geometric shapes

circle square
rectangle triangle

Match:

• circle

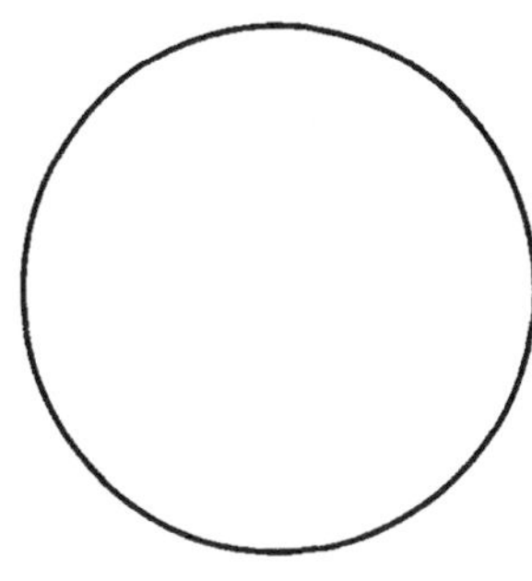

• triangle

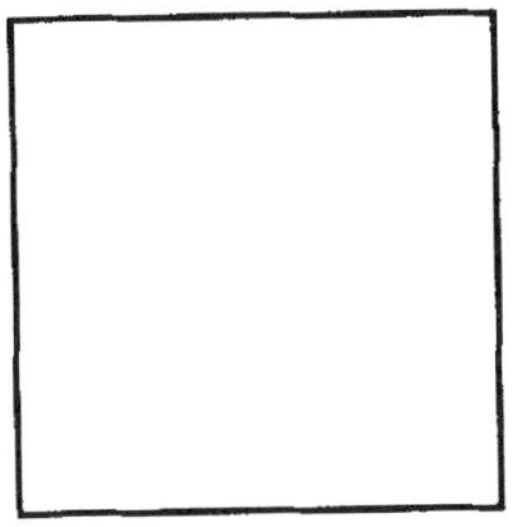

• rectangle

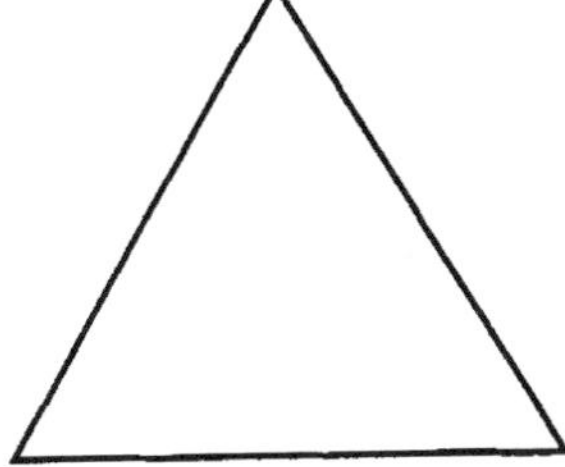

• square

2 REVIEW

Skill: figures the perimeter of a rectangle when given the length of all sides

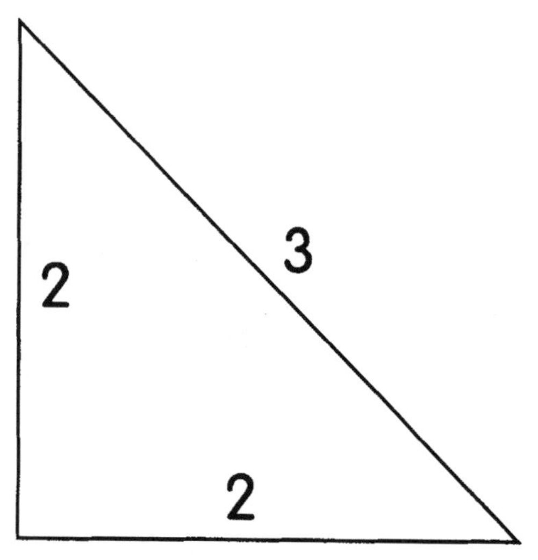

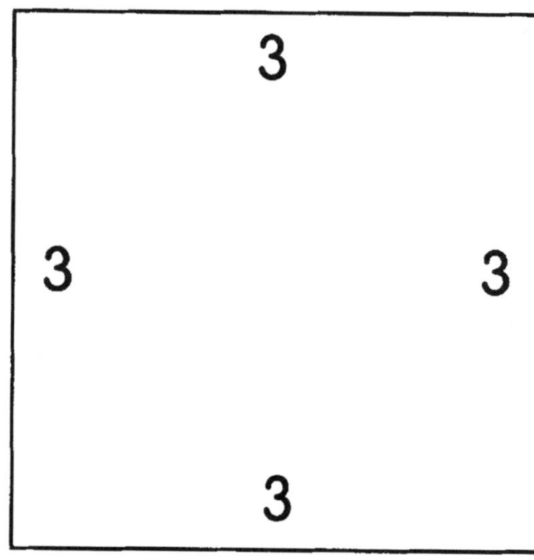

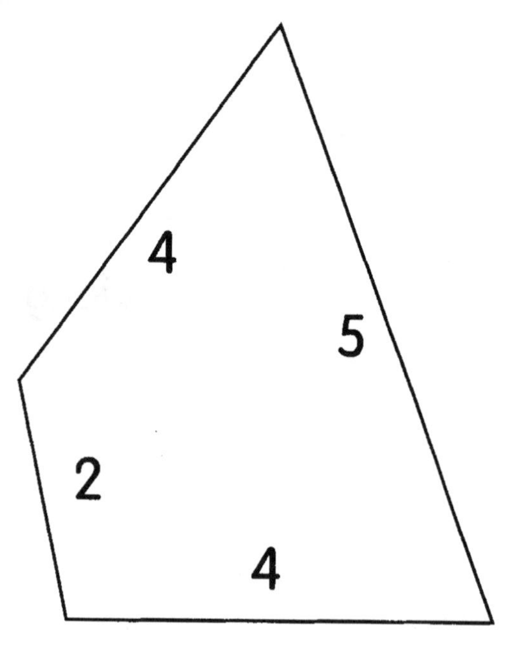

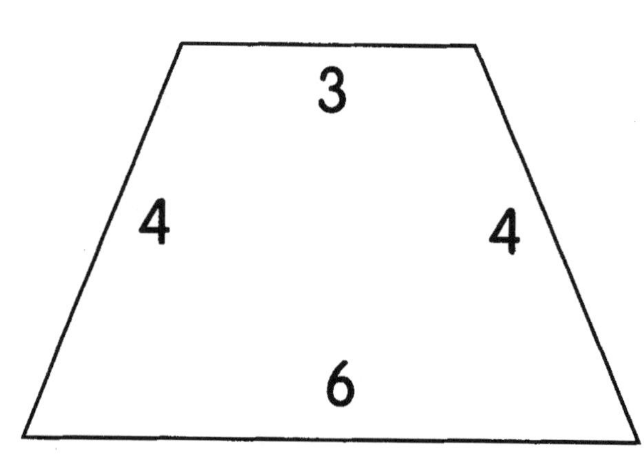

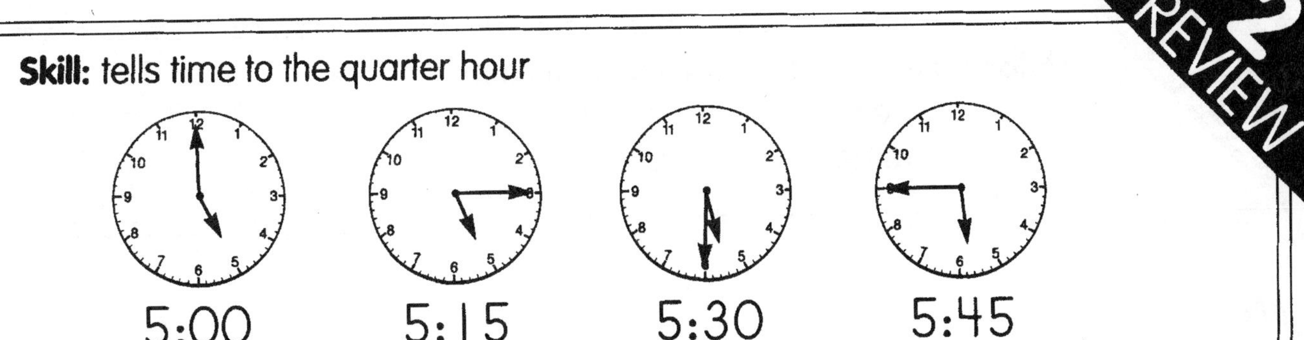

Write the time.

4:00

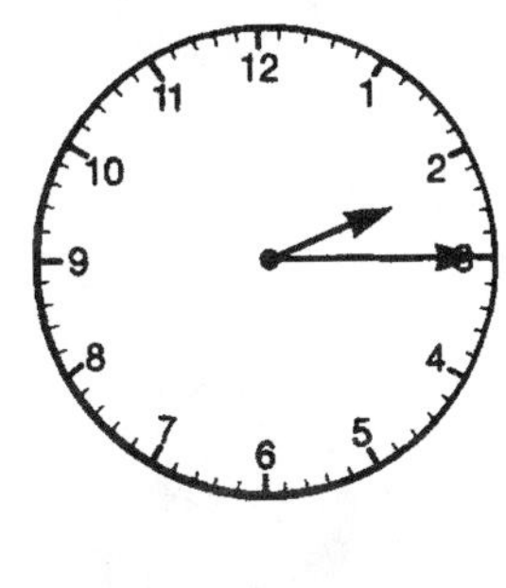

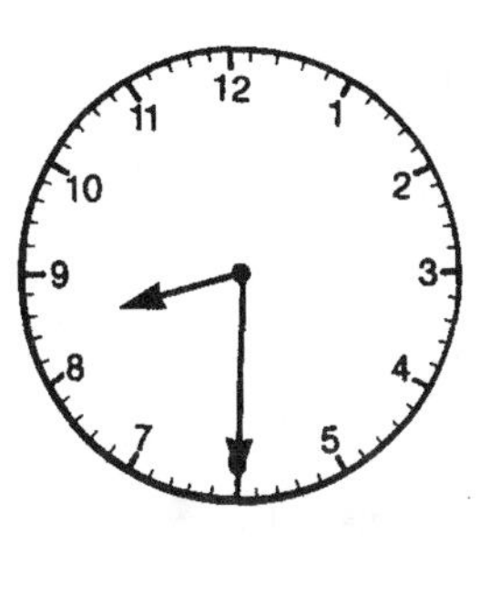

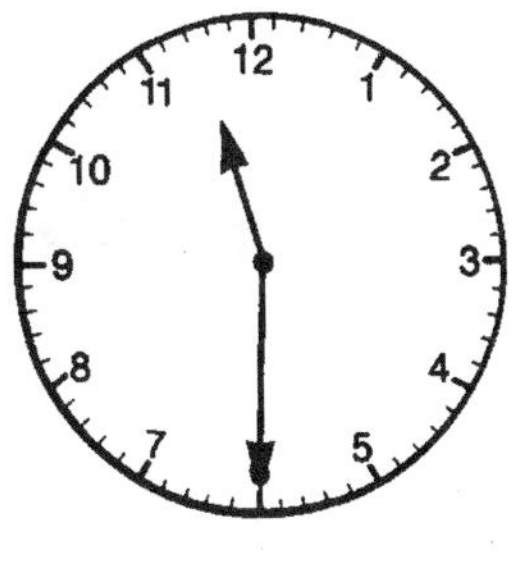

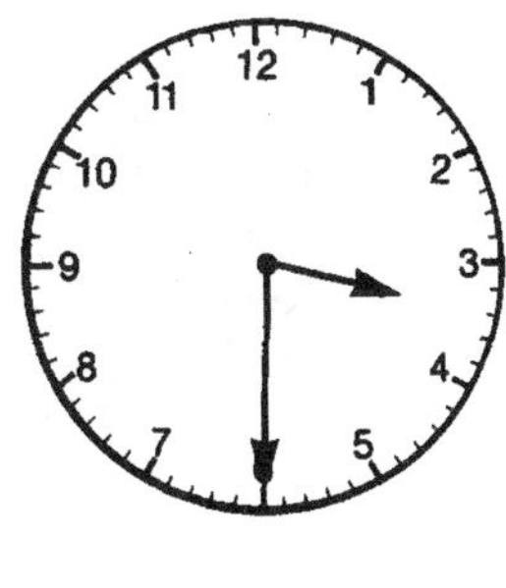

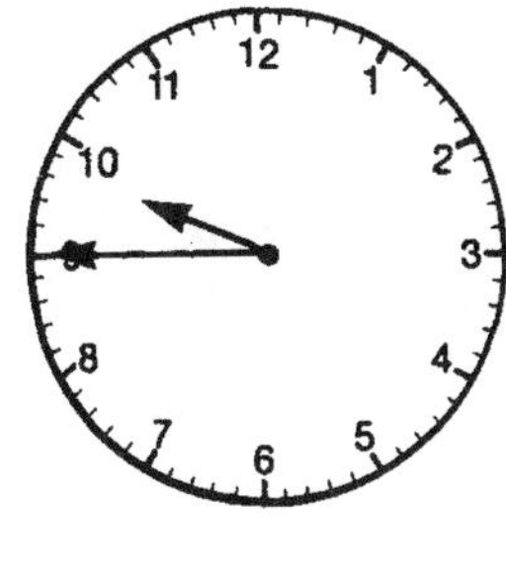

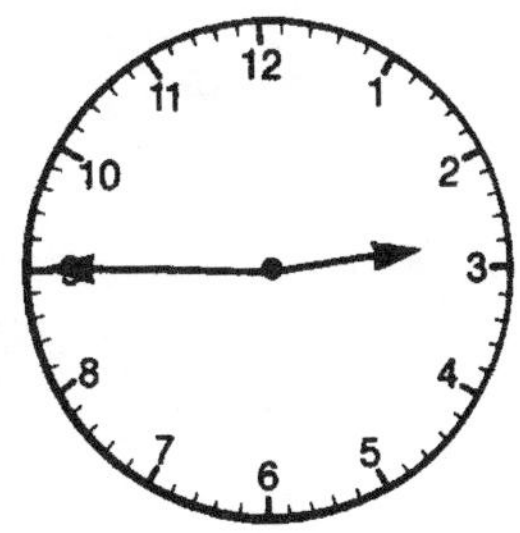

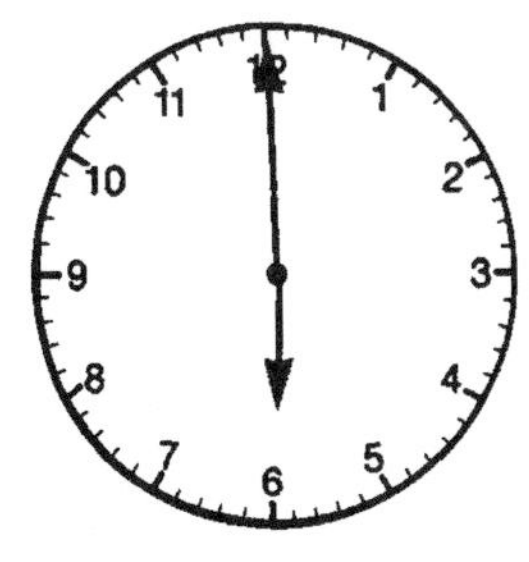

Skill: names and gives the value of coins

penny	nickel
dime	quarter

Match:

dime •		• 5 cents
penny •		• 1 cent
quarter •		• 25 cents
nickel •		• 10 cents

Skill: determines the value for a collection of coins

How much money is in the box?

______ ¢	______ ¢
______ ¢	______ ¢
______ ¢	______ ¢

Second Grade Math

2 REVIEW

Skill: identifies the day of the month and the day of the week on a calendar

S	M	T	W	T	F	S
				1	2	3
4	5	6	7	8	9	10
11	12	13	14	15	16	17
18	19	20	21	22	23	24
25	26	27	28	29	30	

1. What day of the month is circled? ____________________

2. What day of the week has an X on it? ____________________

3. What is the number of the last day of the month?

____

4. What day of the week is the 18th? ____________________

5. What is the number of the first Sunday of the month?

____

Parents: Have your child cut out the ruler at the bottom of this page. One side shows inches. Use it with this page. The other side has centimeters to use with page 26.

Skill: measure lengths to the nearest 1/2 inch

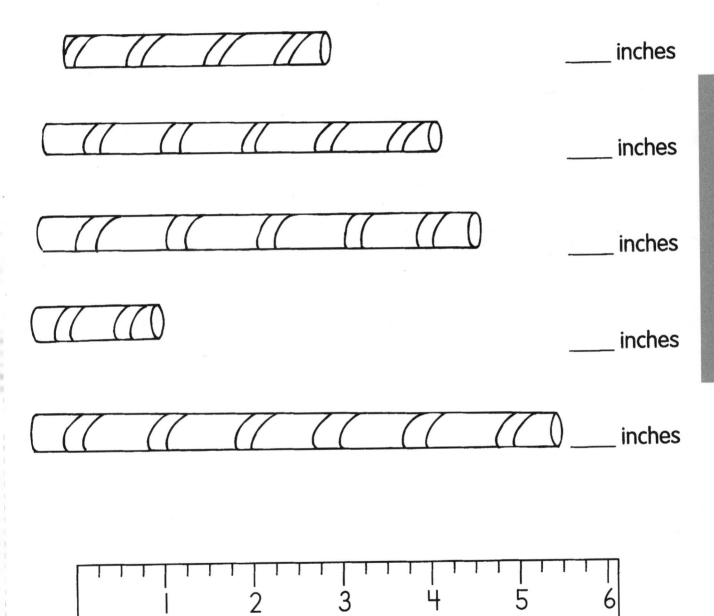

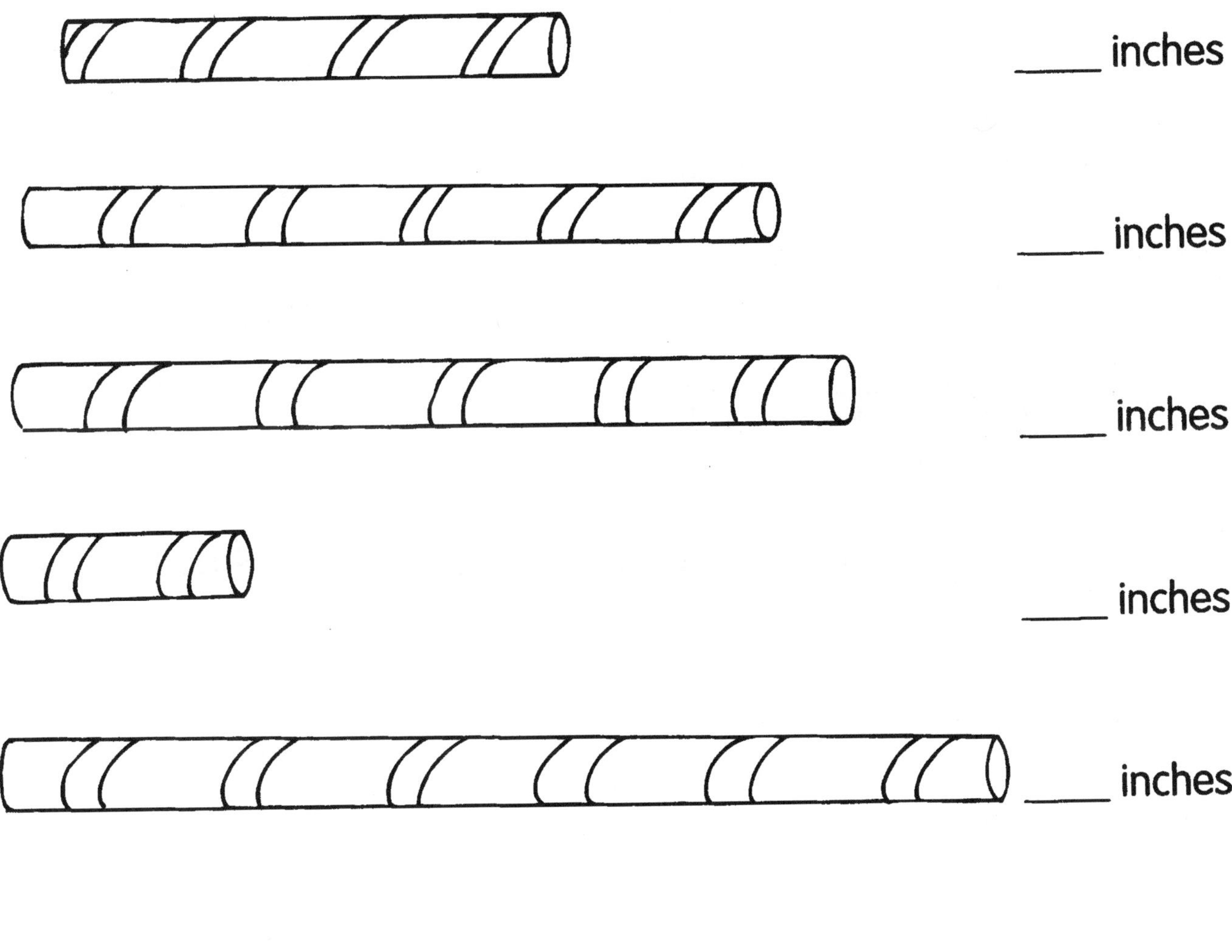

1 2 3 4 5 6

inches

Parents: Have your child cut out the ruler at the bottom of this page.
Use the centimeter side with this page.

Skill: measure lengths to nearst centimeter

____ centimeters

____ centimeters

____ centimeters

____ centimeters

____ centimeters

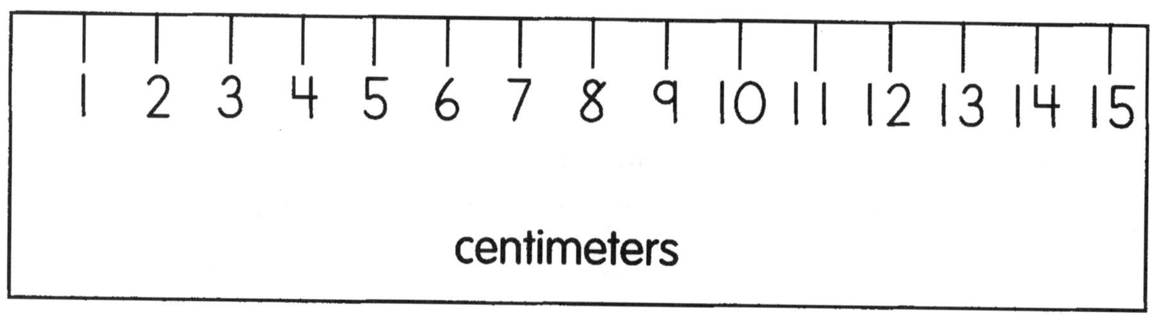

Skill: identifies and names fractional parts of a region

$\frac{1}{2}$ $\frac{1}{4}$ $\frac{1}{3}$

Circle the fraction.

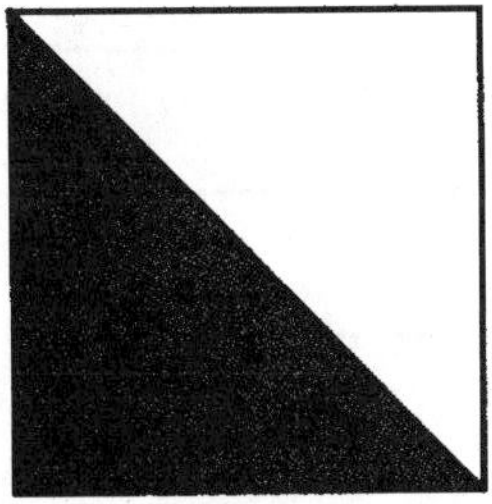

$\frac{1}{2}$ $\frac{1}{4}$ $\frac{1}{3}$

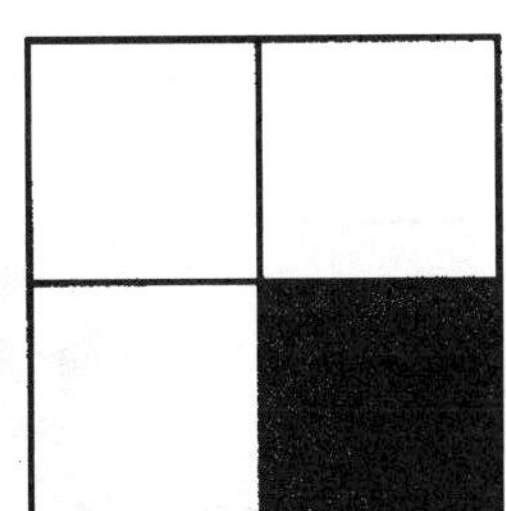

$\frac{1}{2}$ $\frac{1}{4}$ $\frac{1}{3}$

$\frac{1}{2}$ $\frac{1}{4}$ $\frac{1}{3}$

Color the fraction.

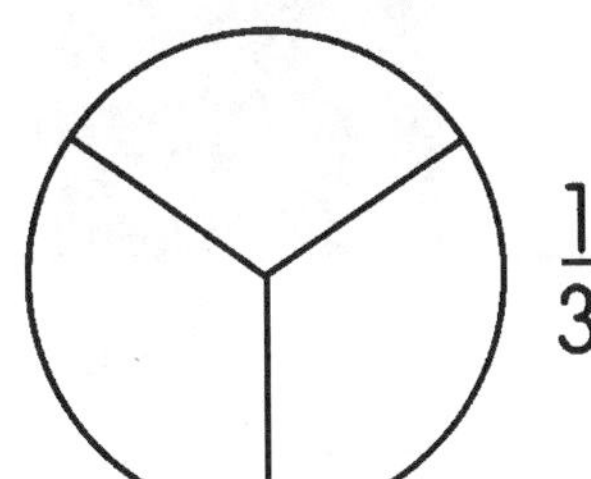

$\frac{1}{3}$

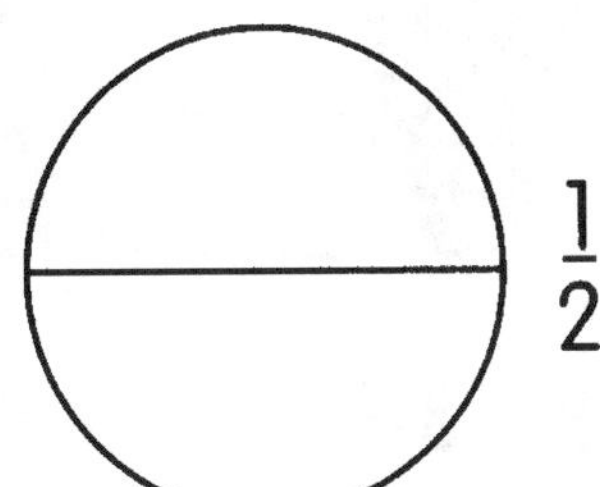

$\frac{1}{2}$

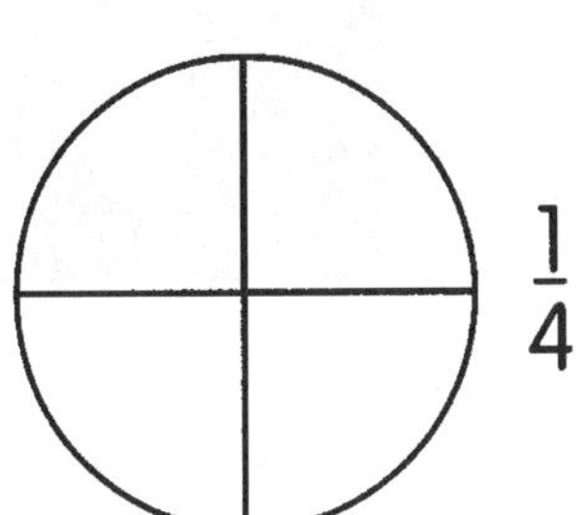

$\frac{1}{4}$

Match the fraction to its name.

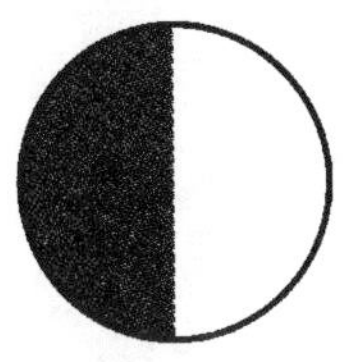

• $\frac{1}{4}$

• $\frac{1}{3}$

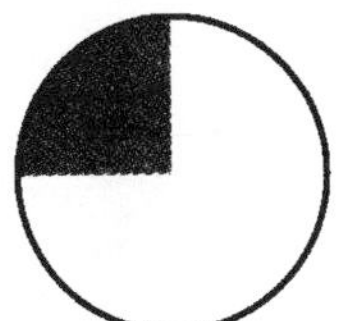

• $\frac{1}{2}$

Skill: interprets information on a bar graph to solve problems

Favorite Colors

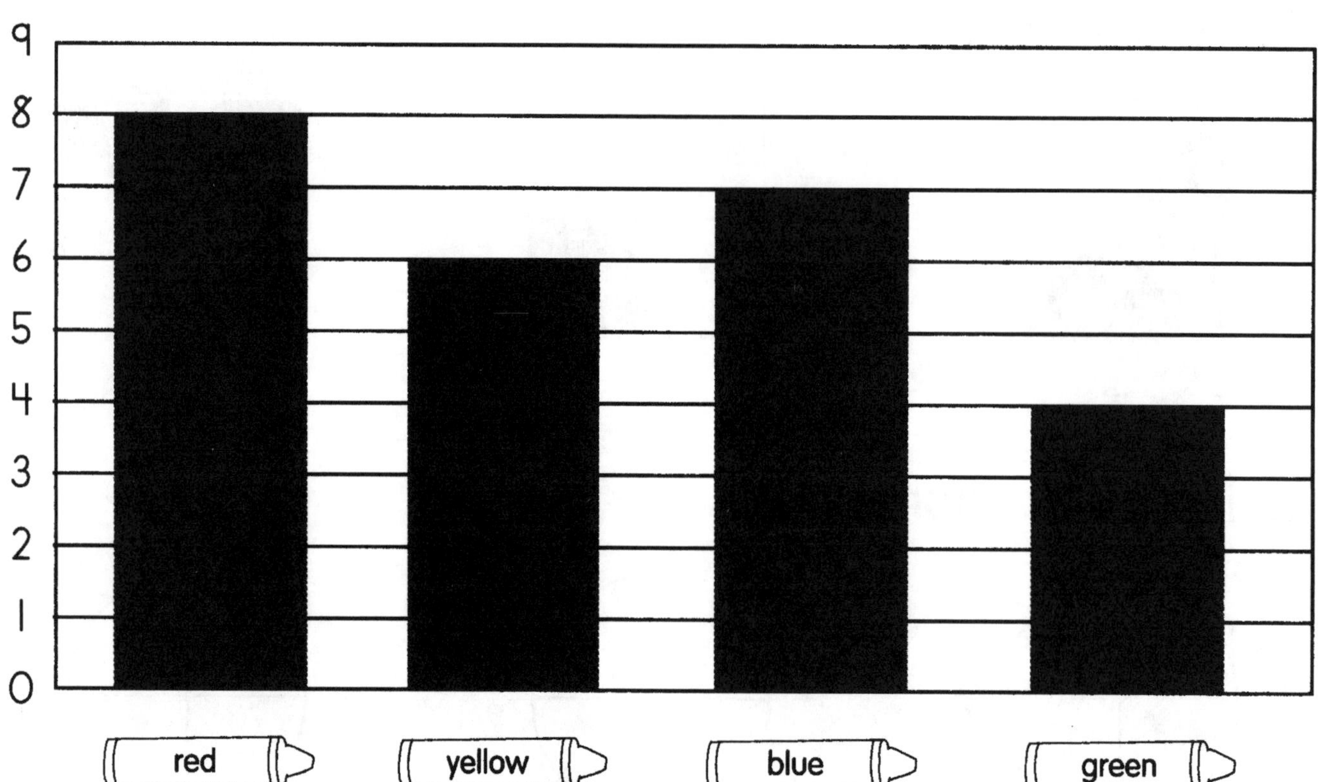

1. How many picked:

red?____ yellow?____ green?____ blue?____

2. What color was picked most? ____________________

3. How many picked green and red together? ____________________

4. How many more picked red than green? ____________________

Skill: solves word problems involving addition, subtraction, and money

Find the answer.
Draw a picture if you need help.

1. 9 friends ate cake. 6 friends ate cookies. How many more ate cake than cookies?	2. 8 girls and 5 boys went on a hike. How many went on the hike?
3. Eric put 4 pennies, 1 nickel, and 1 dime in his bank. How much money did he save?	4. One red balloon costs 10 cents. How much will 5 cost?
5. Tom collects rocks. He has 15 small rocks and 6 big rocks. How many more small rocks does he have?	6. Mark has 7 marbles, Ann has 6 marbles, and Sam has 5 marbles. How many marbles are there in all?

2 REVIEW

Skill: demonstrates an understanding of place value

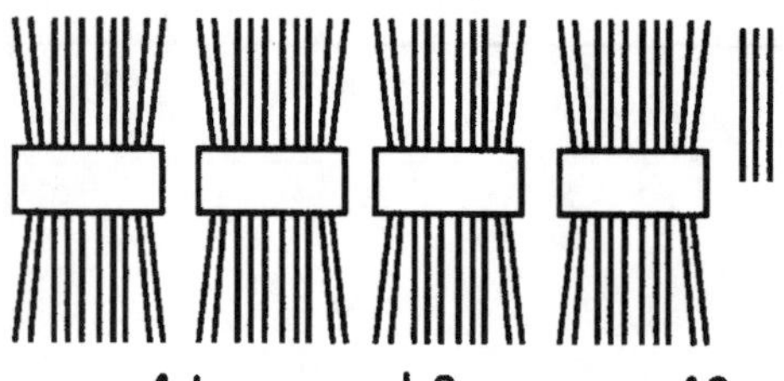

4 tens and 3 ones = 43

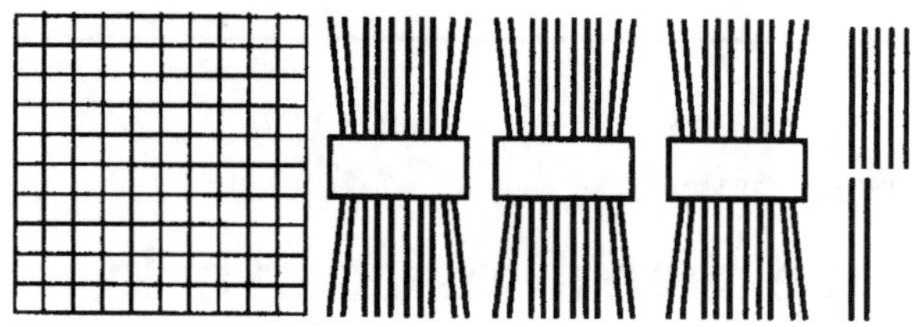

1 hundred, 3 tens and 7 ones = 137

Write the numeral on the line.

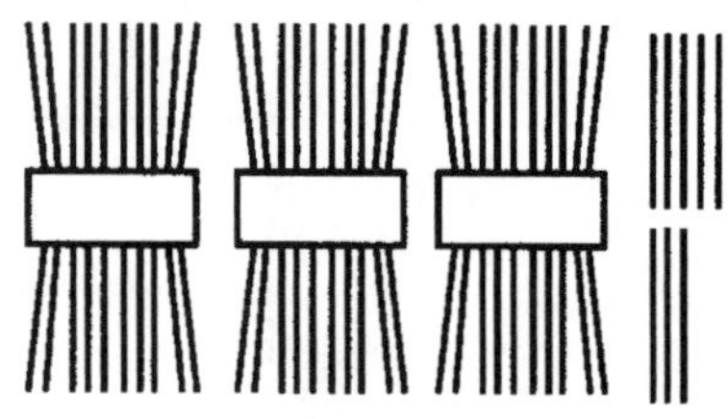

_____ tens and _____ ones = _____

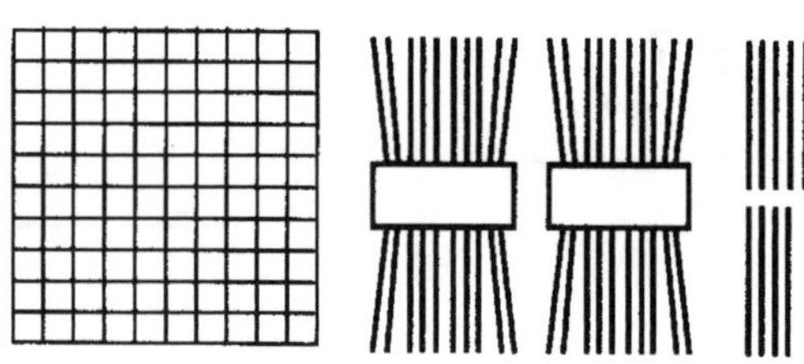

_____ hundreds, _____ tens and _____ ones = _____

6 tens and 7 ones = _____

1 ten and 9 ones = _____

8 ten and 0 ones = _____

2 hundreds, 5 tens and 3 ones = _____

4 hundreds, 6 tens and 6 ones = _____

1 hundred, 1 ten and 8 ones = _____

Answer Key

Please take time to go over the work your child has completed. Ask your child to explain what he/she has done. Praise both success and effort. If mistakes have been made, explain what the answer should have been and how to find it. Let your child know that mistakes are a part of learning. The time you spend with your child helps let him/her know you feel learning is important.

page 257

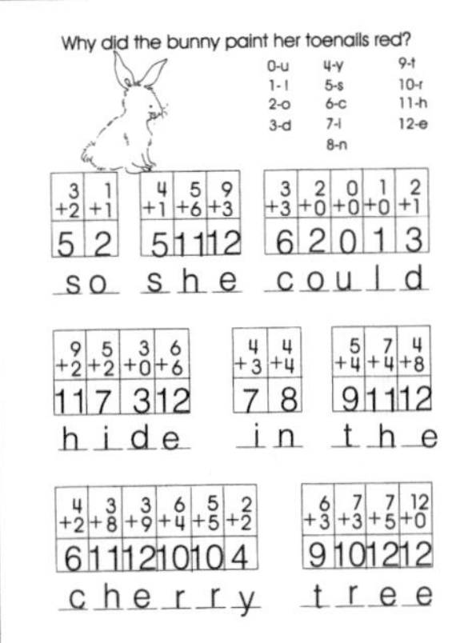
Why did the bunny paint her toenails red?

0-u 4-y 9-t
1-l 5-s 10-r
2-o 6-c 11-h
3-d 7-l 12-e
8-n

so she could hide in the cherry tree

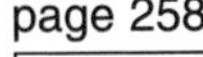
page 258

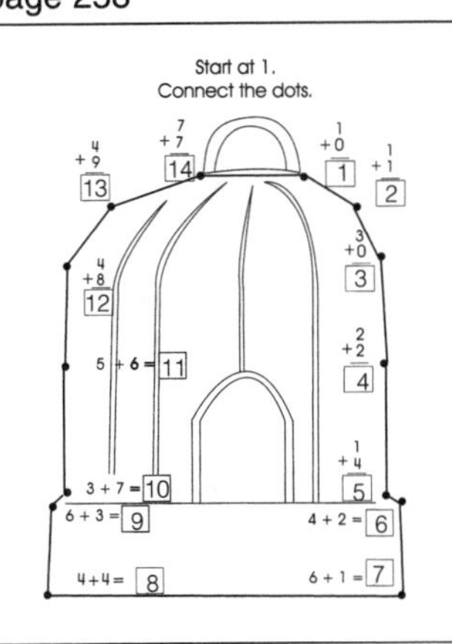
Start at 1.
Connect the dots.

page 259

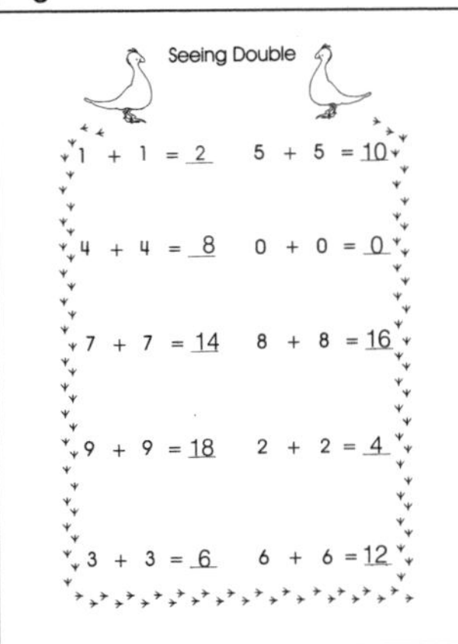
Seeing Double

1 + 1 = 2 5 + 5 = 10
4 + 4 = 8 0 + 0 = 0
7 + 7 = 14 8 + 8 = 16
9 + 9 = 18 2 + 2 = 4
3 + 3 = 6 6 + 6 = 12

page 260

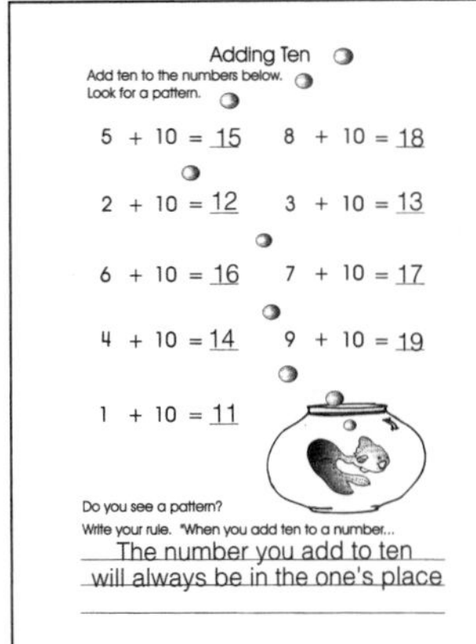
Adding Ten

Add ten to the numbers below.
Look for a pattern.

5 + 10 = 15 8 + 10 = 18
2 + 10 = 12 3 + 10 = 13
6 + 10 = 16 7 + 10 = 17
4 + 10 = 14 9 + 10 = 19
1 + 10 = 11

Do you see a pattern?
Write your rule. "When you add ten to a number...
The number you add to ten will always be in the one's place

page 261

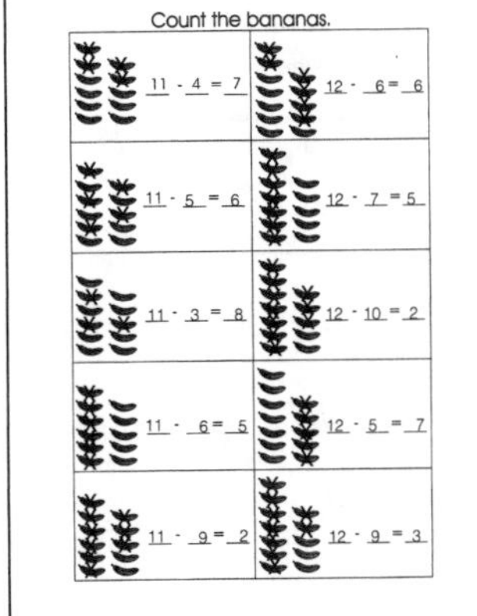
Count the bananas.

11 - 4 = 7 12 - 6 = 6
11 - 5 = 6 12 - 7 = 5
11 - 3 = 8 12 - 10 = 2
11 - 6 = 5 12 - 5 = 7
11 - 9 = 2 12 - 9 = 3

page 262

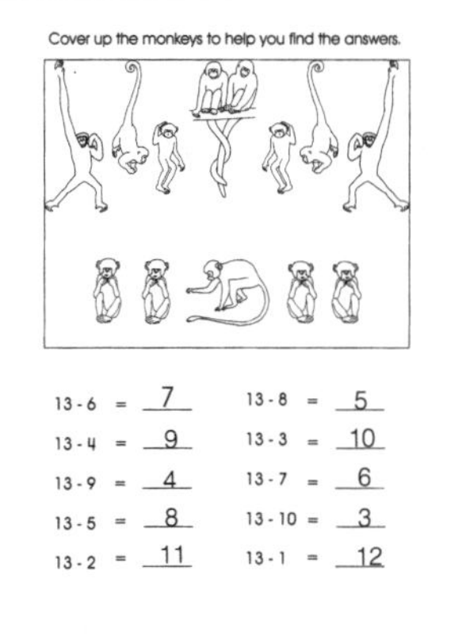
Cover up the monkeys to help you find the answers.

13 - 6 = 7 13 - 8 = 5
13 - 4 = 9 13 - 3 = 10
13 - 9 = 4 13 - 7 = 6
13 - 5 = 8 13 - 10 = 3
13 - 2 = 11 13 - 1 = 12

page 263

Keep subtracting to help us climb down the banana trees.

page 264

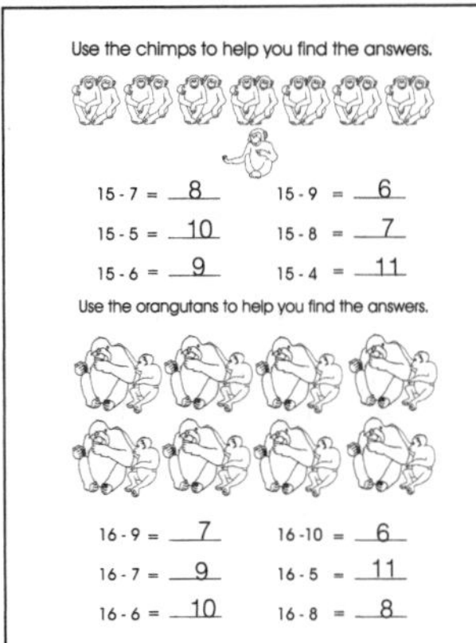
Use the chimps to help you find the answers.

15 - 7 = 8 15 - 9 = 6
15 - 5 = 10 15 - 8 = 7
15 - 6 = 9 15 - 4 = 11

Use the orangutans to help you find the answers.

16 - 9 = 7 16 - 10 = 6
16 - 7 = 9 16 - 5 = 11
16 - 6 = 10 16 - 8 = 8

page 265

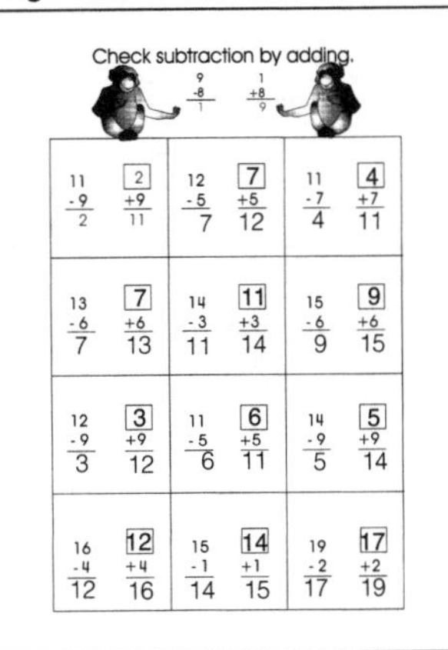
Check subtraction by adding.

page 266

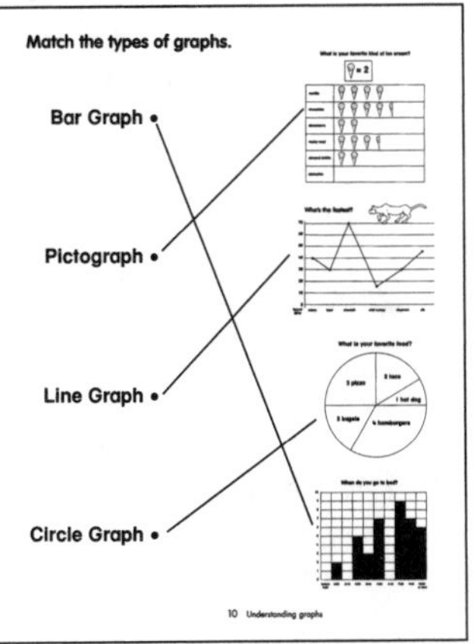
Match the types of graphs.

Bar Graph
Pictograph
Line Graph
Circle Graph

page 267

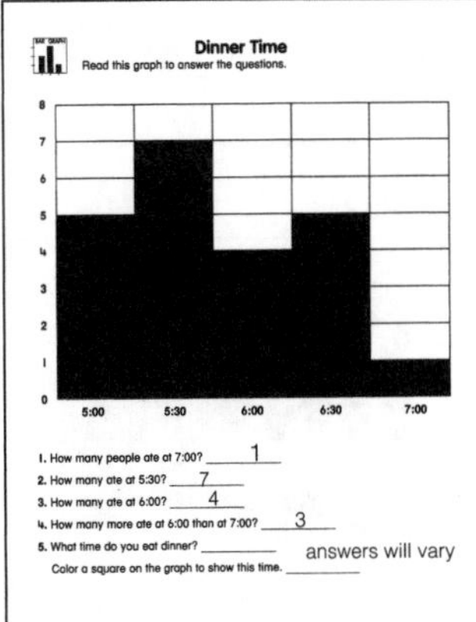
Dinner Time

Read this graph to answer the questions.

1. How many people ate at 7:00? 1
2. How many ate at 5:30? 7
3. How many ate at 6:00? 4
4. How many more ate at 6:00 than at 7:00? 3
5. What time do you eat dinner? answers will vary

Color a square on the graph to show this time.

page 268

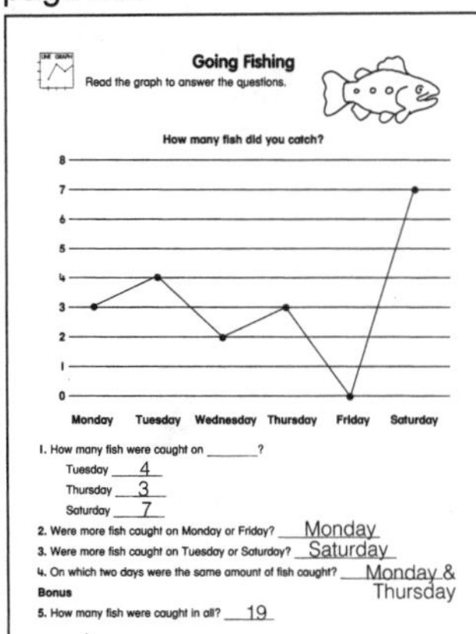
Going Fishing

Read the graph to answer the questions.

How many fish did you catch?

1. How many fish were caught on ___?
   Tuesday 4
   Thursday 3
   Saturday 7
2. Were more fish caught on Monday or Friday? Monday
3. Were more fish caught on Tuesday or Saturday? Saturday
4. On which two days were the same amount of fish caught? Monday & Thursday

Bonus

5. How many fish were caught in all? 19

page 269

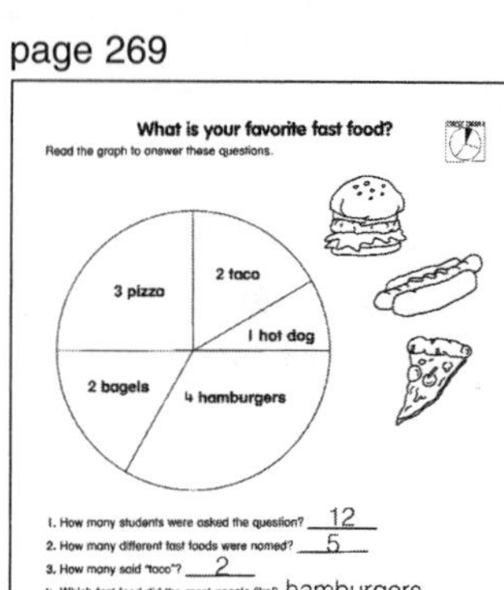

What is your favorite fast food?

Read the graph to answer these questions.

3 pizza, 2 taco, 1 hot dog, 2 bagels, 4 hamburgers

1. How many students were asked the question? 12
2. How many different fast foods were named? 5
3. How many sold "taco"? 2
4. Which fast food did the most people like? hamburgers

Bonus:
5. What fraction sold "pizza" $\frac{3}{12}$ or $\frac{1}{4}$?

page 270

I have been watching squirrels in the park for three days. Altogether I have seen 25 squirrels. I saw 9 squirrels the first day and 3 squirrels the second day.

How many did I see the third day?

I can solve the problem.

13 Squirrels

page 271

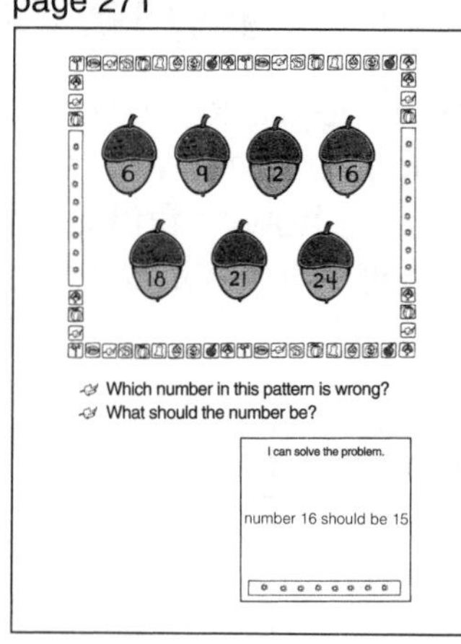

Which number in this pattern is wrong?
What should the number be?

I can solve the problem.

number 16 should be 15

page 272

How many candles will be on my birthday cake if I am 3 1/2 years older than my 5 1/2 year old friend?

I can solve the problem.

9 candles

page 273

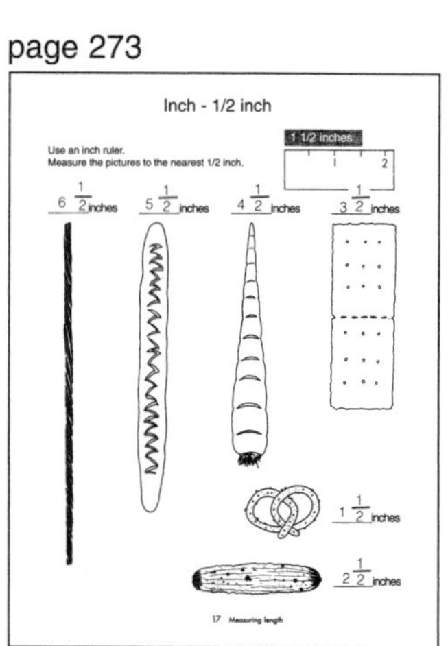

Inch - 1/2 inch

Use an inch ruler.
Measure the pictures to the nearest 1/2 inch.

$6\frac{1}{2}$ inches, $5\frac{1}{2}$ inches, $4\frac{1}{2}$ inches, $3\frac{1}{2}$ inches, $1\frac{1}{2}$ inches, $2\frac{1}{2}$ inches

page 274

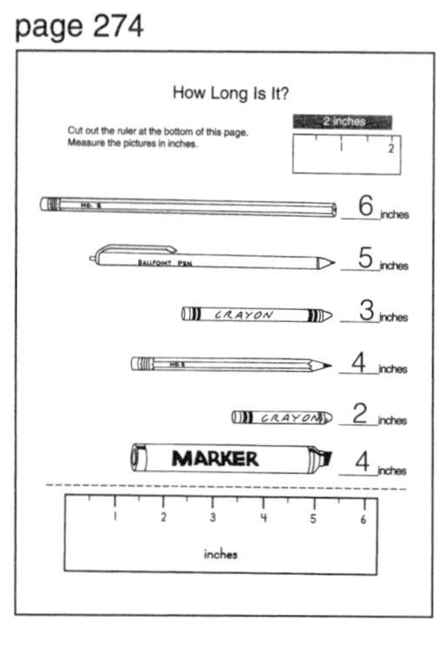

How Long Is It?

Cut out the ruler at the bottom of this page.
Measure the pictures in inches.

6 inches, 5 inches, 3 inches, 4 inches, 2 inches, 4 inches

page 275

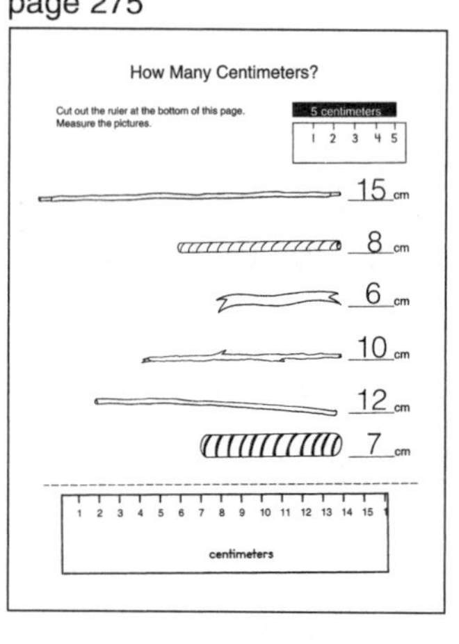

How Many Centimeters?

Cut out the ruler at the bottom of this page.
Measure the pictures.

15 cm, 8 cm, 6 cm, 10 cm, 12 cm, 7 cm

page 276

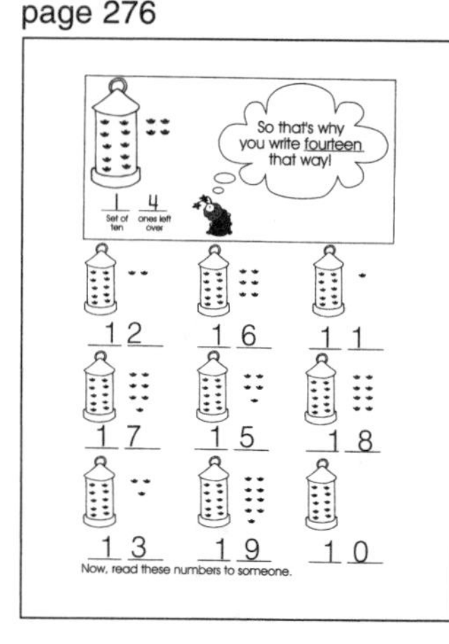

So that's why you write fourteen that way!

1 set of ten, 4 ones left over

12, 16, 11, 17, 15, 18, 13, 19, 10

Now, read these numbers to someone.

page 277

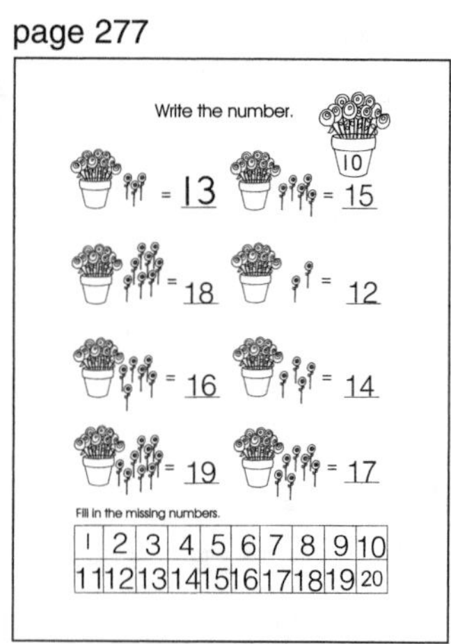

Write the number.

= 13, = 15, = 18, = 12, = 16, = 14, = 19, = 17

Fill in the missing numbers.

1	2	3	4	5	6	7	8	9	10
11	12	13	14	15	16	17	18	19	20

page 278

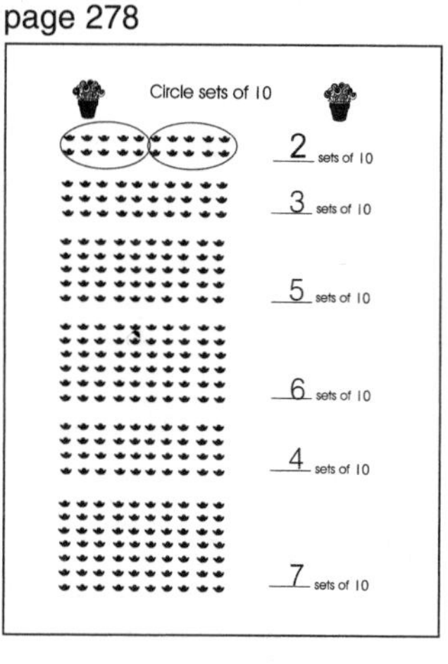

Circle sets of 10

2 sets of 10
3 sets of 10
5 sets of 10
6 sets of 10
4 sets of 10
7 sets of 10

page 279

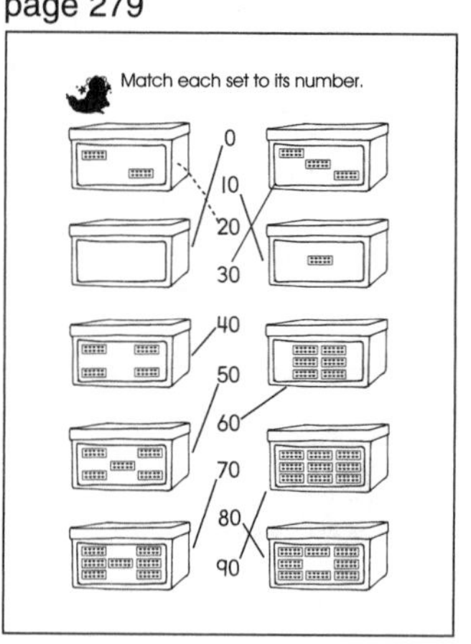

Match each set to its number.

0, 10, 20, 30, 40, 50, 60, 70, 80, 90

page 280

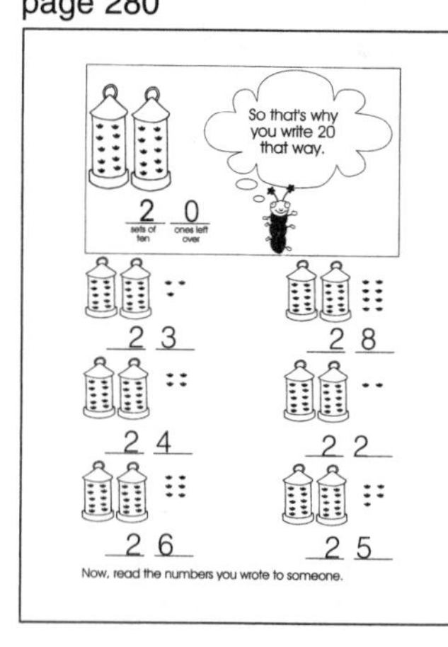

So that's why you write 20 that way.

2 sets of ten, 0 ones left over

23, 28, 24, 22, 26, 25

Now, read the numbers you wrote to someone.

page 281

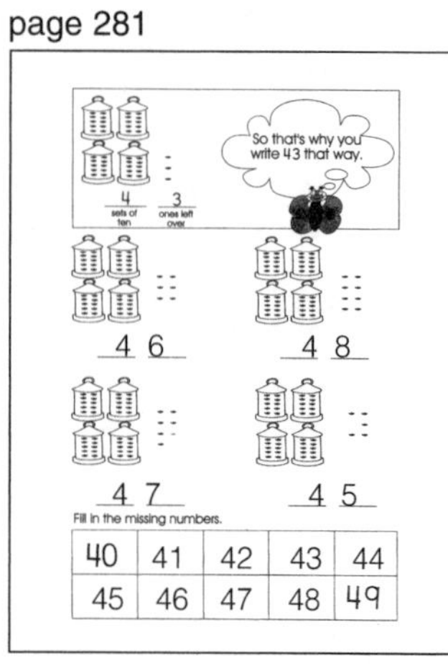

So that's why you write 43 that way.

4 sets of ten, 3 ones left over

46, 48, 47, 45

Fill in the missing numbers.

40	41	42	43	44
45	46	47	48	49

page 282

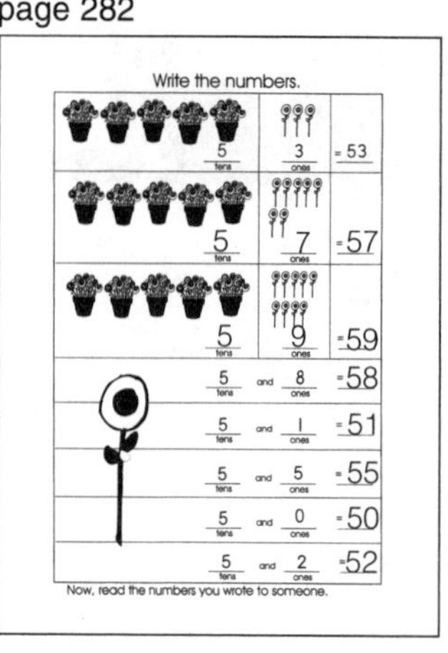

Write the numbers.

5 tens 3 ones = 53
5 tens 7 ones = 57
5 tens 9 ones = 59
5 tens and 8 ones = 58
5 tens and 1 ones = 51
5 tens and 5 ones = 55
5 tens and 0 ones = 50
5 tens and 2 ones = 52

Now, read the numbers you wrote to someone.

page 283

So that's why you write 76 that way.

7 tens 6 ones = 76
7 tens 8 ones = 78
7 tens 3 ones = 73
7 tens 4 ones = 74
7 tens 5 ones = 75
7 tens 2 ones = 72
0 tens 9 ones = 9
7 tens 0 ones = 70

Count:

61	62	63	64	65	66	67	68	69	70
71	72	73	74	75	76	77	78	79	80

page 284

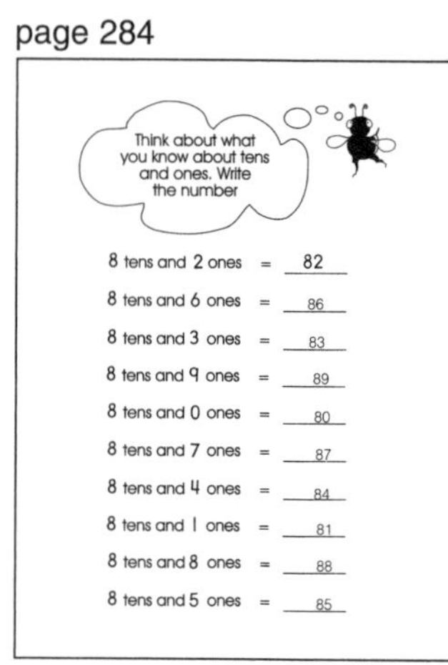

Think about what you know about tens and ones. Write the number

8 tens and 2 ones = 82
8 tens and 6 ones = 86
8 tens and 3 ones = 83
8 tens and 9 ones = 89
8 tens and 0 ones = 80
8 tens and 7 ones = 87
8 tens and 4 ones = 84
8 tens and 1 ones = 81
8 tens and 8 ones = 88
8 tens and 5 ones = 85

page 285

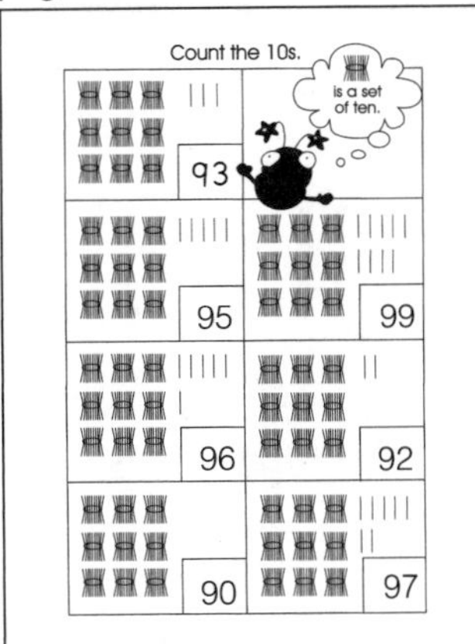

page 286

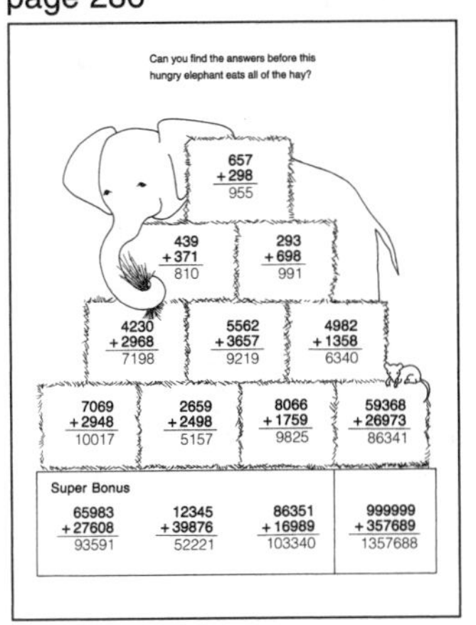

page 287

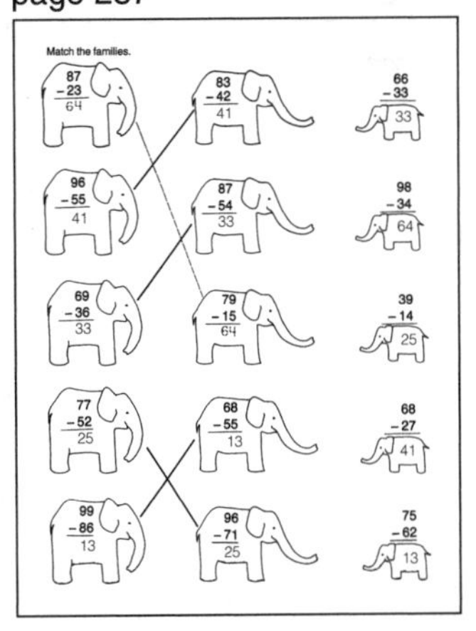

page 288

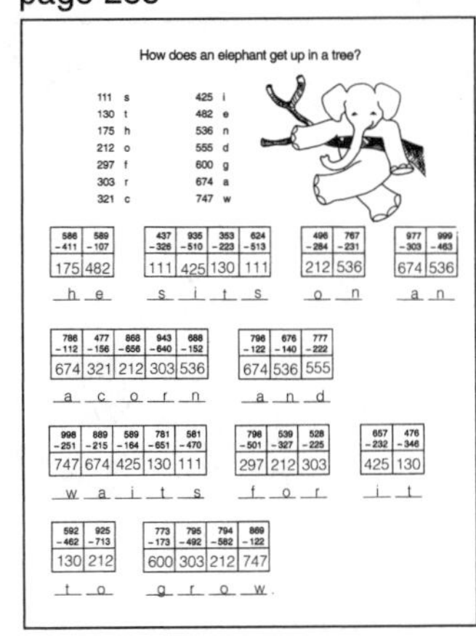

page 289

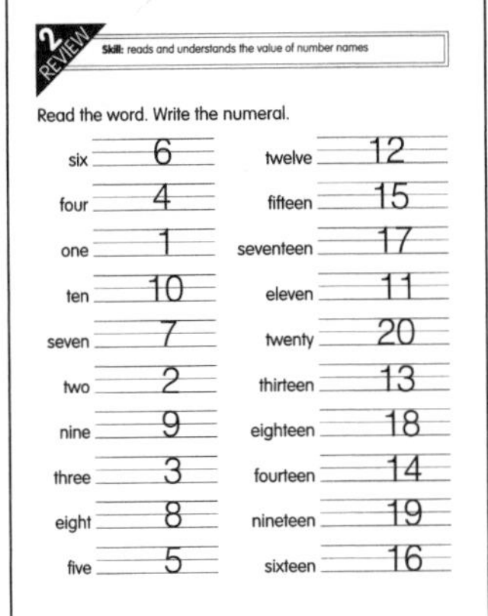

page 290

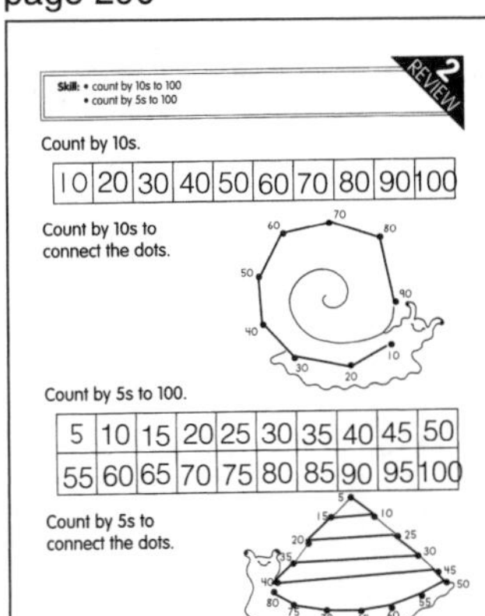

page 291

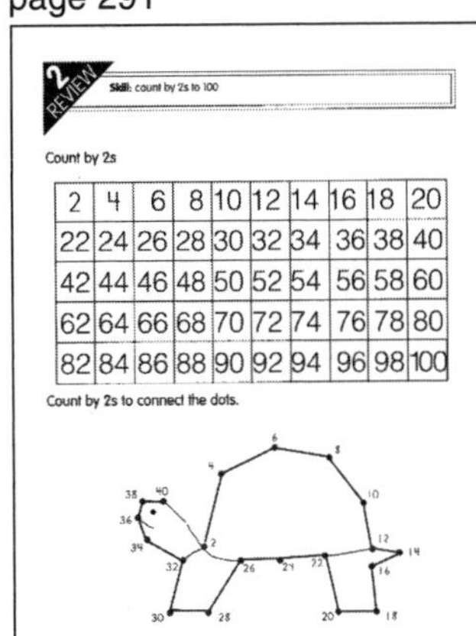

page 292

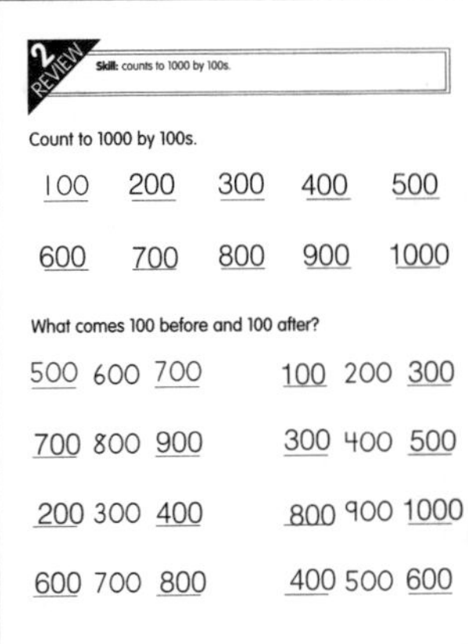

page 293

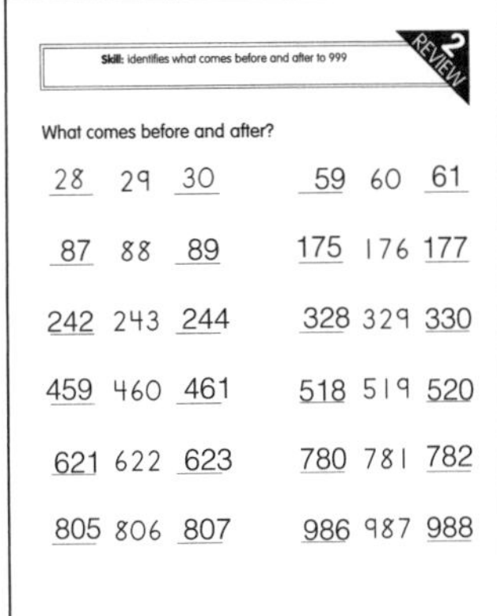

page 294

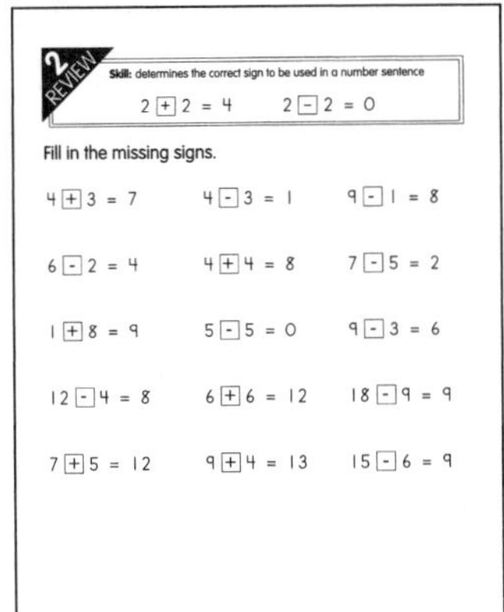

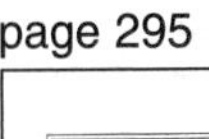

page 295

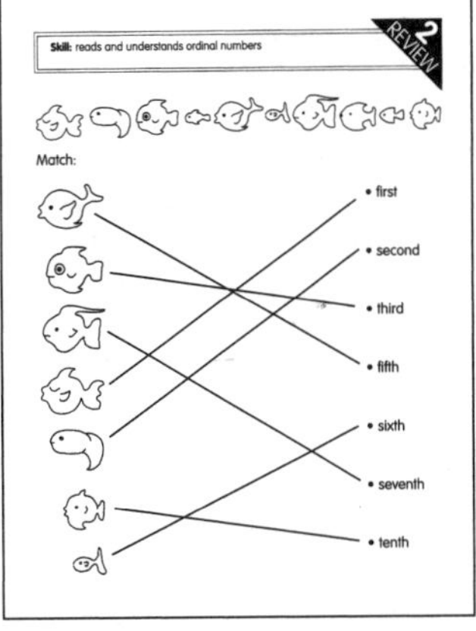

page 296

Skill: • understands greater than, less than, and equal • can use the correct symbol $<$ $>$ $=$

$8 > 2$ $2 < 6$

Fill in the circle.

$9 > 5$	$7 < 9$	$3 < 5$
$11 < 21$	$23 < 32$	$64 > 48$
$59 > 54$	$27 = 27$	$63 > 10$
$87 < 88$	$47 < 74$	$55 > 51$

Fill in the blanks.

answers will vary

___ $<$ ___ ___ $>$ ___

page 297

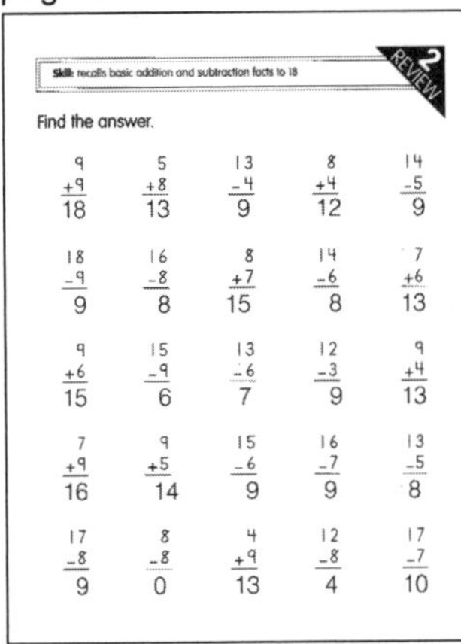

page 298

Skill: adds three 1-digit numbers to sums of 18

Add.

3 + 1 + 8 = 12	6 + 7 + 2 = 15	4 + 2 + 4 = 10	8 + 4 + 1 = 13	2 + 1 + 7 = 10
5 + 6 + 4 = 15	5 + 4 + 6 = 15	4 + 3 + 6 = 13	8 + 5 + 4 = 17	9 + 6 + 3 = 18
9 + 4 + 4 = 17	8 + 0 + 9 = 17	7 + 7 + 4 = 18	9 + 5 + 1 = 15	8 + 4 + 2 = 14

page 299

Skill: adds two-digit numbers with or without regrouping

Add.

18 + 51 = 69	63 + 28 = 91	45 + 32 = 77	37 + 59 = 96	46 + 29 = 75
19 + 40 = 59	63 + 35 = 98	52 + 17 = 69	23 + 68 = 91	25 + 65 = 90
13 + 67 = 80	45 + 23 = 68	27 + 64 = 91	59 + 39 = 98	55 + 28 = 83
52 + 29 = 81	24 + 45 = 69	90 + 30 = 120	28 + 61 = 89	35 + 45 = 80

page 300

Skill: adds three 2-digit numbers without regrouping

Add.

25 + 41 + 32 = 98	64 + 25 + 10 = 99	17 + 60 + 22 = 99	33 + 33 + 33 = 99	51 + 24 + 14 = 89
12 + 42 + 45 = 99	34 + 43 + 12 = 89	28 + 51 + 20 = 99	22 + 33 + 44 = 99	28 + 60 + 11 = 99
40 + 20 + 30 = 90	25 + 31 + 22 = 78	16 + 33 + 50 = 99	18 + 50 + 11 = 79	63 + 16 + 20 = 99

page 301

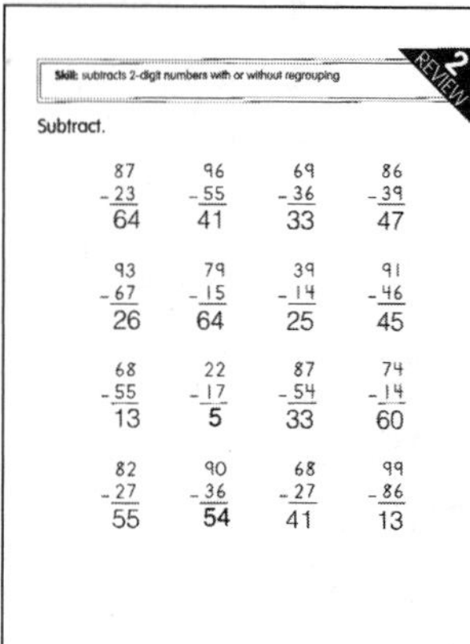

Skill: subtracts 2-digit numbers with or without regrouping

Subtract.

87 − 23 = 64	96 − 55 = 41	69 − 36 = 33	86 − 39 = 47
93 − 67 = 26	79 − 15 = 64	39 − 14 = 25	91 − 46 = 45
68 − 55 = 13	22 − 17 = 5	87 − 54 = 33	74 − 14 = 60
82 − 27 = 55	90 − 36 = 54	68 − 27 = 41	99 − 86 = 13

page 302

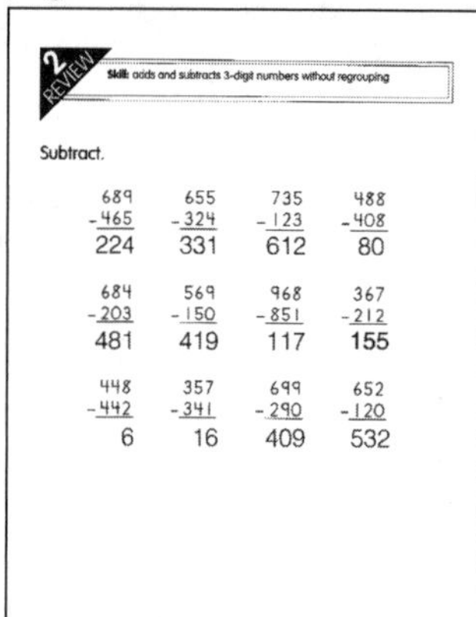

Skill: adds and subtracts 3-digit numbers without regrouping

Subtract.

689 − 465 = 224	655 − 324 = 331	735 − 123 = 612	488 − 408 = 80
684 − 203 = 481	569 − 150 = 419	968 − 851 = 117	367 − 212 = 155
448 − 442 = 6	357 − 341 = 16	699 − 290 = 409	652 − 120 = 532

page 303

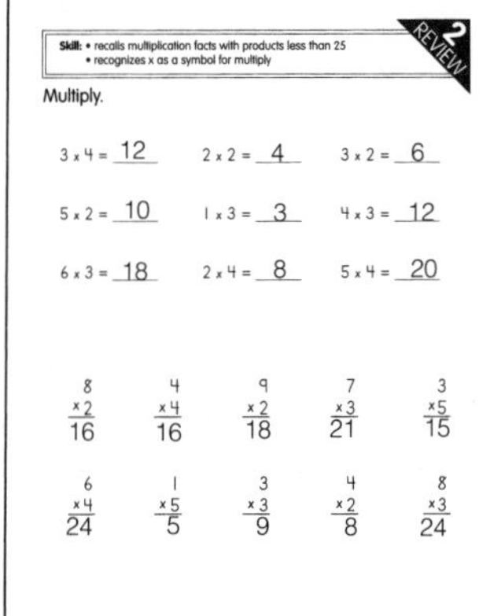

Skill: • recalls multiplication facts with products less than 25
• recognizes x as a symbol for multiply

Multiply.

3 x 4 = 12 2 x 2 = 4 3 x 2 = 6
5 x 2 = 10 1 x 3 = 3 4 x 3 = 12
6 x 3 = 18 2 x 4 = 8 5 x 4 = 20

8 x 2 = 16	4 x 4 = 16	9 x 2 = 18	7 x 3 = 21	3 x 5 = 15
6 x 4 = 24	1 x 5 = 5	3 x 3 = 9	4 x 2 = 8	8 x 3 = 24

page 304

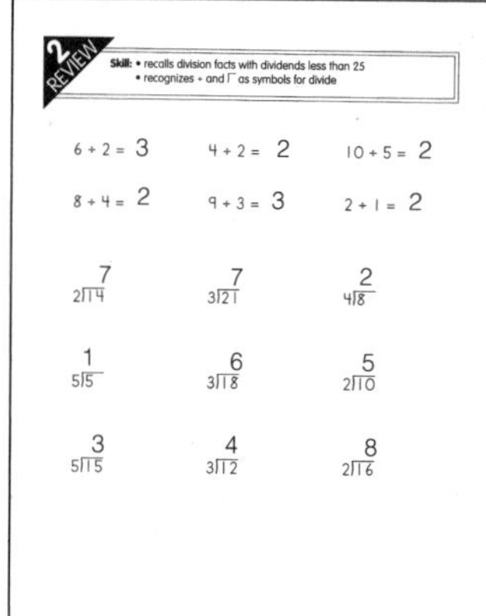

Skill: • recalls division facts with dividends less than 25
• recognizes ÷ and ⟌ as symbols for divide

6 ÷ 2 = 3 4 ÷ 2 = 2 10 ÷ 5 = 2
8 ÷ 4 = 2 9 ÷ 3 = 3 2 ÷ 1 = 2

$2\overline{)14}$ = 7	$3\overline{)21}$ = 7	$4\overline{)8}$ = 2
$5\overline{)5}$ = 1	$3\overline{)18}$ = 6	$2\overline{)10}$ = 5
$5\overline{)15}$ = 3	$3\overline{)12}$ = 4	$2\overline{)16}$ = 8

page 305

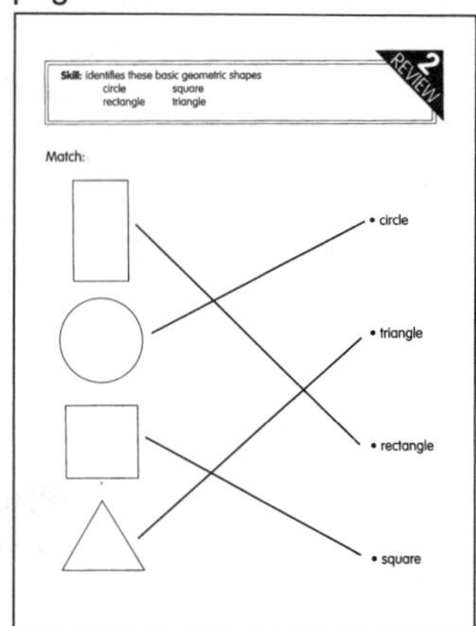

Skill: identifies these basic geometric shapes
circle square
rectangle triangle

Match:

• circle
• triangle
• rectangle
• square

page 306

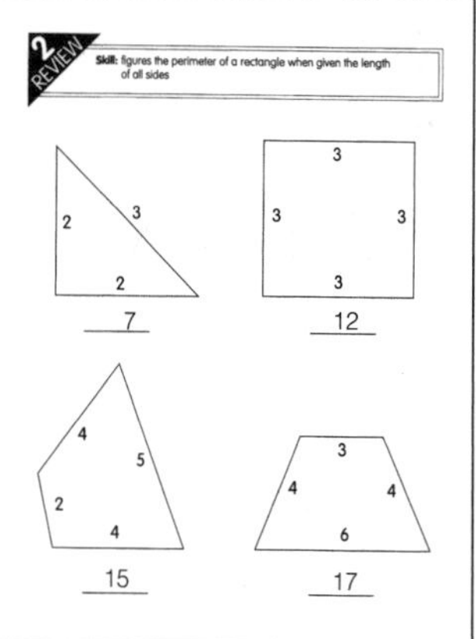

Skill: figures the perimeter of a rectangle when given the length of all sides

7 12
15 17

page 307

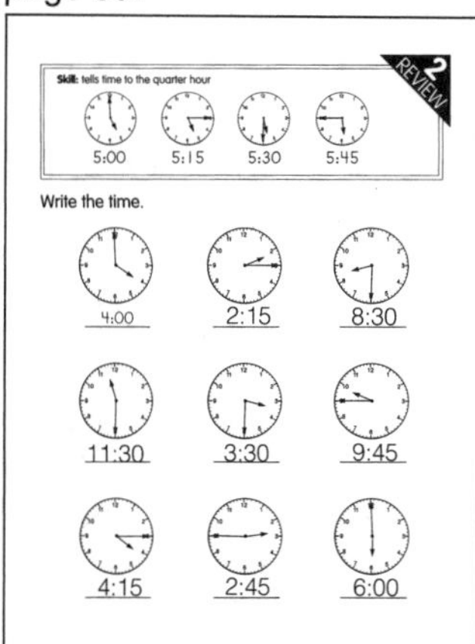

Skill: tells time to the quarter hour

5:00 5:15 5:30 5:45

Write the time.

4:00 2:15 8:30
11:30 3:30 9:45
4:15 2:45 6:00

page 308

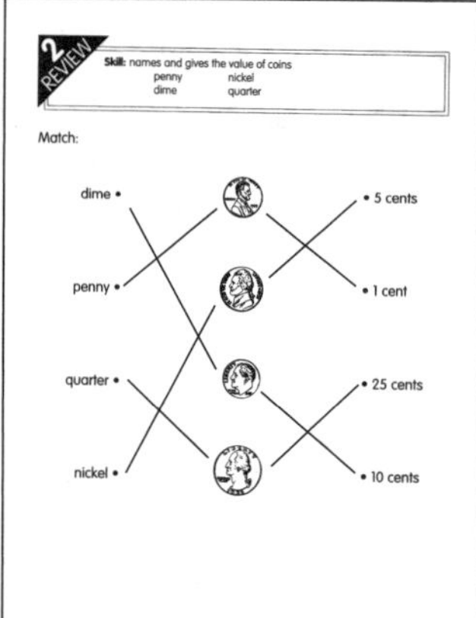

Skill: names and gives the value of coins
penny nickel
dime quarter

Match:

dime • • 5 cents
penny • • 1 cent
quarter • • 25 cents
nickel • • 10 cents

page 309

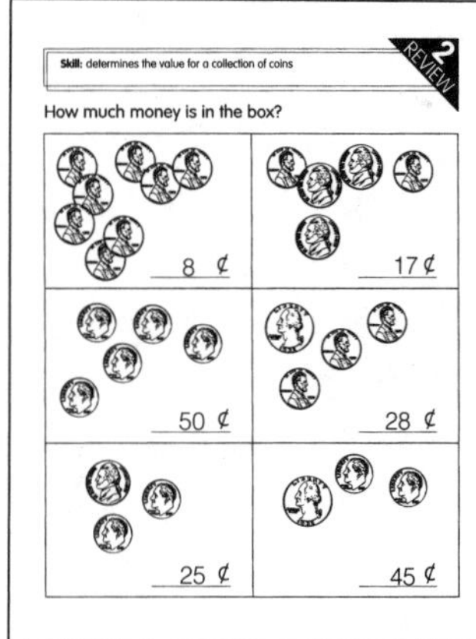

Skill: determines the value for a collection of coins

How much money is in the box?

8 ¢ 17 ¢
50 ¢ 28 ¢
25 ¢ 45 ¢

page 310

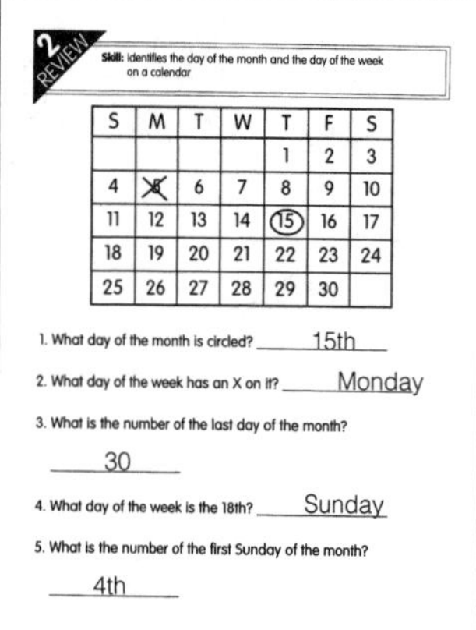

Skill: identifies the day of the month and the day of the week on a calendar

S	M	T	W	T	F	S
				1	2	3
4	X	6	7	8	9	10
11	12	13	14	(15)	16	17
18	19	20	21	22	23	24
25	26	27	28	29	30	

1. What day of the month is circled? 15th
2. What day of the week has an X on it? Monday
3. What is the number of the last day of the month? 30
4. What day of the week is the 18th? Sunday
5. What is the number of the first Sunday of the month? 4th

page 311

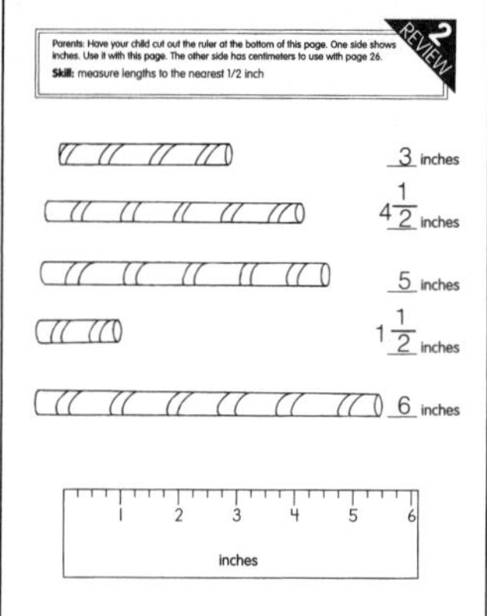

Parents: Have your child cut out the ruler at the bottom of this page. One side shows inches. Use it with this page. The other side has centimeters to use with page 26.

Skill: measure lengths to the nearest 1/2 inch

3 inches
4 1/2 inches
5 inches
1 1/2 inches
6 inches

inches

page 312

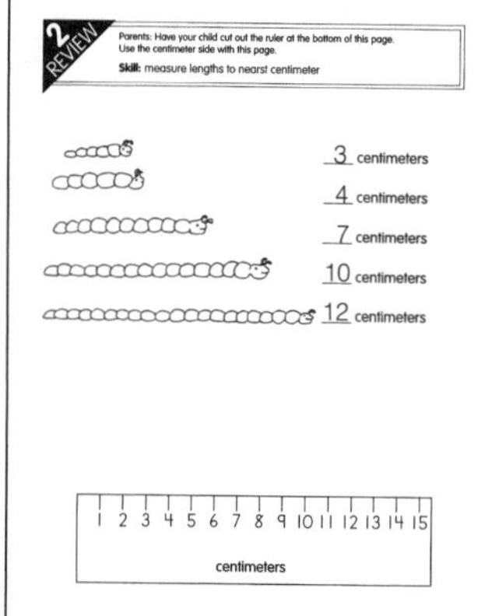

Parents: Have your child cut out the ruler at the bottom of this page. Use the centimeter side with this page.

Skill: measure lengths to nearst centimeter

3 centimeters
4 centimeters
7 centimeters
10 centimeters
12 centimeters

centimeters

page 313

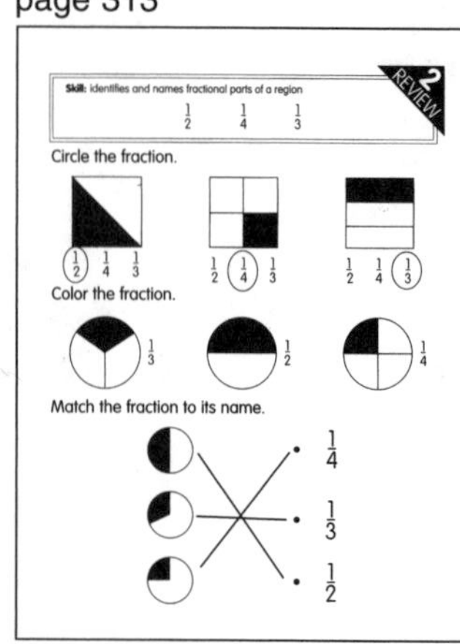

Skill: identifies and names fractional parts of a region
1/2 1/4 1/3

Circle the fraction.

Color the fraction.

Match the fraction to its name.

page 314

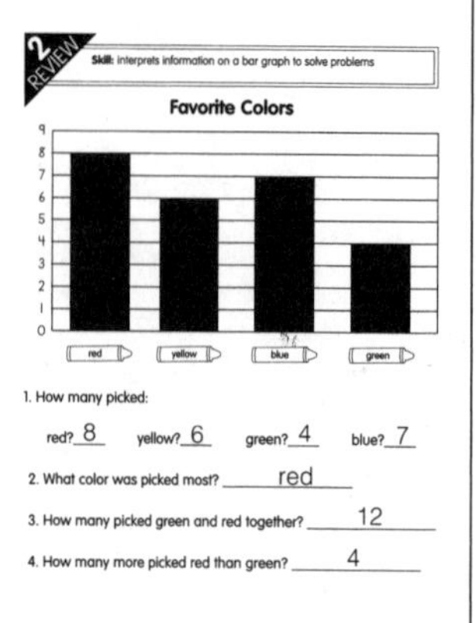

Skill: interprets information on a bar graph to solve problems

Favorite Colors

red yellow blue green

1. How many picked:
red? 8 yellow? 6 green? 4 blue? 7
2. What color was picked most? red
3. How many picked green and red together? 12
4. How many more picked red than green? 4

page 315

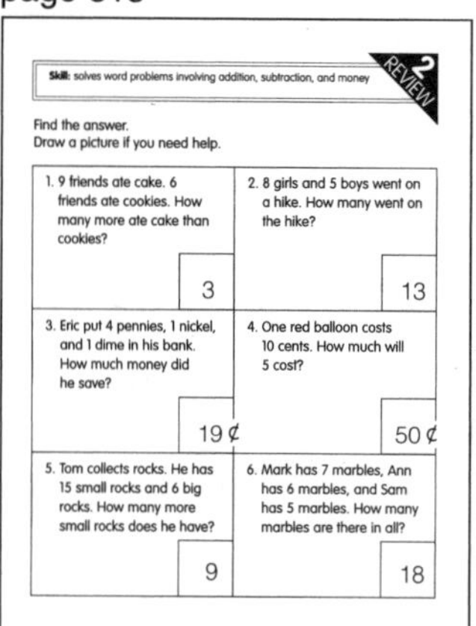

Skill: solves word problems involving addition, subtraction, and money

Find the answer.
Draw a picture if you need help.

1. 9 friends ate cake. 6 friends ate cookies. How many more ate cake than cookies? 3	2. 8 girls and 5 boys went on a hike. How many went on the hike? 13
3. Eric put 4 pennies, 1 nickel, and 1 dime in his bank. How much money did he save? 19 ¢	4. One red balloon costs 10 cents. How much will 5 cost? 50 ¢
5. Tom collects rocks. He has 15 small rocks and 6 big rocks. How many more small rocks does he have? 9	6. Mark has 7 marbles, Ann has 6 marbles, and Sam has 5 marbles. How many marbles are there in all? 18

page 316

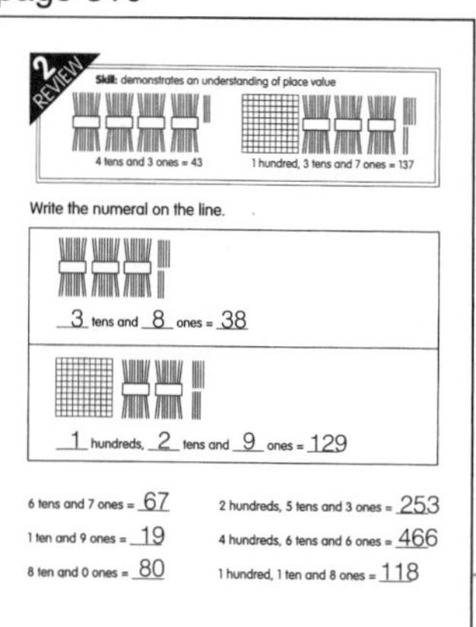

Skill: demonstrates an understanding of place value

4 tens and 3 ones = 43 1 hundred, 3 tens and 7 ones = 137

Write the numeral on the line.

3 tens and 8 ones = 38

1 hundreds, 2 tens and 9 ones = 129

6 tens and 7 ones = 67 2 hundreds, 5 tens and 3 ones = 253
1 ten and 9 ones = 19 4 hundreds, 6 tens and 6 ones = 466
8 ten and 0 ones = 80 1 hundred, 1 ten and 8 ones = 118